W9-CSL-907

Leaps AND Bounds TOWARD Math Understanding 3/4

Senior Author
Marian Small

Authors
Kathy Kubota-Zarivnij
Amy Lin

Advisory Panelists
Katharine Borgen, BC
Anna D'Armento, ON
Carla Kozak, AB
Gladys Sterenberg, AB
Joyce Tonner, ON

Reviewers

Doug Duff
Thames Valley District
School Board, ON

Kerri Dunford
Peel District School Board, ON

Linda Edwards
Toronto District School Board, ON

Sandra Ferguson
Pembina Trails School Division, MB

Susan Forbes
Catholic District School Board
of Eastern Ontario, ON

Deb McLean
District School Board of Niagara, ON

Selina Millar
School District 36, BC

Kerry Dwyer Mitchell
Hamilton-Wentworth Catholic
District School Board, ON

Meagan Mutchmor
Winnipeg School Division, MB

Jennifer Portelli
Dufferin-Peel Catholic District
School Board, ON

Joseph Romano
Toronto District School Board, ON

Jamie Scott
Upper Canada District
School Board, ON

Joanne Simmons
Toronto District School Board, ON

Lindsay Sirois
Toronto District School Board, ON

Paula Watson
Calgary Catholic District
School Board, AB

NELSON EDUCATION

NELSON EDUCATION

Leaps and Bounds Toward Math Understanding 3/4
Teacher's Resource

Editorial Director
Linda Allison

Publisher, Mathematics K–8
Audrey Wearn

Managing Editor, Development
Erynn Marcus

Product Manager
Linda Krepinsky

Program Manager
Mary Reeve

Developmental Editors
Shirley Barrett
Kathryn Chris
Janice Nixon
Megan Robinson
Alexandra Romic
Jackie Williams

Editorial Assistant
Jessica Reeve

Senior Content Production Manager
Sujata Singh

Content Production Editor
Carolyn Pisani

Copyeditor
Gerry Jenkison

Proofreader
John Green

Senior Production Coordinator
Sharon Latta Paterson

Production Manager
Helen Jager Locsin

Design Director
Ken Phipps

Interior Design
Visutronx

Cover Design
Jennifer Leung

Cover Photo
Rob Jenkins/Getty Images

Asset Coordinator
Suzanne Peden

Illustrators
Visutronx
Dave Whamond

Compositor
MPS Limited, a Macmillan Company

Printer
Transcontinental Printing

COPYRIGHT © 2011 by
Nelson Education Ltd.

ISBN-13: 978-0-17-615812-5
ISBN-10: 0-17-615812-X

Printed and bound in Canada
3   4   5   6   14   13   12   11

For more information contact
Nelson Education Ltd.,
1120 Birchmount Road, Toronto,
Ontario, M1K 5G4. Or you can
visit our Internet site at
http://www.nelson.com.

ALL RIGHTS RESERVED. No part of
this work covered by the copyright
herein, except for any reproducible
pages included in this work, may
be reproduced, transcribed, or
used in any form or by any means—
graphic, electronic, or mechanical,
including photocopying, recording,
taping, Web distribution, or
information storage and retrieval
systems—without the written
permission of the publisher.

For permission to use material
from this text or product, submit
a request online at
www.cengage.com/permissions
Further questions about
permissions can be e-mailed to
permissionrequest@cengage.com.

Every effort has been made to
trace ownership of all copyrighted
material and to secure permission
from copyright holders. In the
event of any question arising as
to the use of any material, we will
be pleased to make the necessary
corrections in future printings.

Reproduction of BLMs is permitted
for classroom/instruction purposes
only and only to the purchaser of
this product.

Note:
Solutions for the
Student Resource
questions can be found at
www.nelson.com/leapsandbounds
User name: leapsandbounds34
Password: SRsolutions34

Contents

Strand: Patterns and Algebra

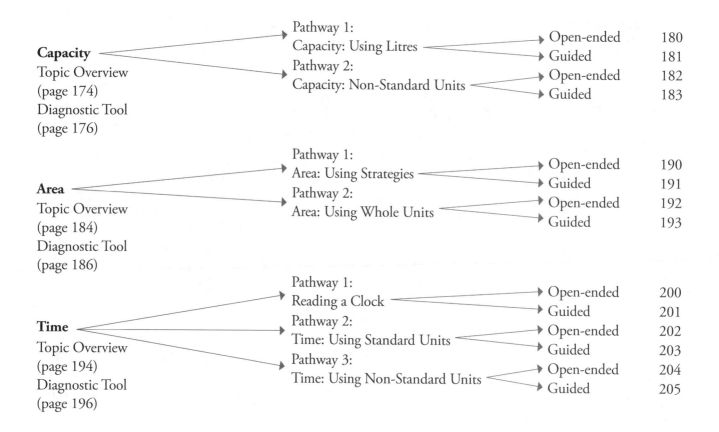
Strand: Data Management

Blackline Masters

Student Resource Solutions

www.nelson.com/leapsandbounds
User name: leapsandbounds34
Password: SRsolutions34

What Is *Leaps and Bounds*?

Leaps and Bounds Toward Math Understanding is a supplementary resource for students struggling in mathematics, Grades 3 to 8. Often these students are not struggling in other areas. This resource is designed to assist teachers in providing precise, targeted remediation for these students—as a whole class, in small groups, or individually. With *Leaps and Bounds*, teachers can help students better understand the prerequisite math so they can be successful in meeting the curriculum requirements for their grade. *Leaps and Bounds* materials determine gaps in understanding and then provide tailored interventions that target the missing knowledge, rather than simply repeating all curriculum expectations and outcomes from previous grades.

For each topic in each strand, a short diagnostic assessment provides a snapshot of what students understand and what they do not. Each diagnostic leads to tailored intervention materials that provide differentiated instruction for each student or group of students. These materials are organized into pathways with open-ended and guided interventions. Both approaches to intervention are developmentally appropriate and based on knowledge gaps identified through the diagnostic tools in conjunction with the other assessment processes used in the classroom.

> There is a belief that students, especially students struggling in mathematics, want and need you to model each new concept or skill. However, what we are learning is that students can figure out many mathematical ideas on their own and in their own way. Some can also benefit from clearly explained, conceptually based, development of mathematical ideas. *Leaps and Bounds* recognizes that many students will not be able to make a substantial leap if the learning is overly structured; they become too dependent on someone else doing too much of the thinking for them. If we want leaps forward, and not just baby steps, we need to provide accessible, conceptually based interventions with lots of visual support.
>
> **—Marian Small**

Who Is *Leaps and Bounds* Designed For?

Leaps and Bounds is designed for students experiencing difficulty in mathematics in situations such as the following:

- an age-appropriate classroom program
- an individualized educational program either in a regular classroom or in a separate instructional setting
- a formal after-school tutoring program
- additional help sessions

The resource may be used by a classroom teacher, special education teacher, or tutor.

Leaps and Bounds addresses the need for differentiated instruction based on how children learn. *Leaps and Bounds* has a solid research foundation that reflects

- developmental learning of mathematics, as determined from specific research (described below)
- current research literature about how to support students who are struggling in mathematics.

Before considering how to best support these students, it is important to understand how students learn mathematics in stages, and what the key concepts are.

Developmental Learning of Math

Marian Small conducted Canadian research on the developmental learning of mathematics from 2002 to 2004 with 12 000 students from junior kindergarten to Grade 7 in seven provinces. This research was the foundation of developmental maps published in *PRIME* (*Professional Resources and Instruction for Math Educators,* Nelson Education, 2005–2010). *PRIME* is a Canadian research-based professional learning initiative designed to assist teachers, administrators, and district personnel with elementary school mathematics instruction and learning.

Dr. Small's research led to the creation of developmental maps to describe stages, or phases, of mathematical learning in each of 5 strands. Each phase is characterized by sets of behaviours that cluster together and typically describe a level of mathematical sophistication. Although younger students tend to be in earlier phases and older students in later phases, an individual student's phase is not based on his or her grade level.

Dr. Small organized the mathematical content in each strand using key concepts and skills (or big ideas) to help teachers make better connections in their teaching and to help students focus on the key ideas of mathematics. The *PRIME* key concepts and skills relate many seemingly disparate outcomes and expectations over the whole elementary spectrum. This clustering helps students make conceptual connections, which means there are fewer isolated concepts to learn. The key concepts also facilitate using consistent language throughout the elementary school program. This can help students internalize the concepts and skills more readily.

The *PRIME* research also allowed for the creation of diagnostic tools that teachers can use to confirm their assessment of the phase a student is working in. The *PRIME* resource kit includes common errors and misconceptions that arose from the research.

Leaps and Bounds uses the findings of *PRIME* research as well as other educational research to identify common errors and misconceptions in a section of the *Leaps and Bounds* Teacher's Resource called "Why might students struggle with …" in each of the 19 topics at the Grade 3/4 level. For example:

Why might students struggle with equality?

Students might struggle with equality because they might

- incorrectly interpret an equal sign as meaning "here comes the answer" on the right side of the equal sign, such as when you press the equal sign on a calculator (e.g., They would think $\blacksquare = 8$ in the equation $5 + 3 = \blacksquare + 2$.)
- use equal signs to incorrectly link a string of calculations for an expression to a number (e.g., For $27 + 38 = 65$, students might write $20 + 30 = 50 + 7 = 57 + 8 = 65$.)
- have little familiarity with determining equality using strategies that focus on number relationships rather than on computation (e.g., If you add [or take away] the same amount on both sides of the equation, then the equation is still balanced.)

Based on this background knowledge of misconceptions and errors, *Leaps and Bounds* provides ways for teachers to diagnose a student's gaps in knowledge. *Leaps and Bounds* then presents carefully sequenced intervention pathways to remediate those gaps.

Current Research: Supporting Students Who Are Struggling with Math

Educational research literature on the subject of supporting students who are struggling in mathematics suggests the need for differentiating instruction through individualization of content and strategies, conceptually based explicit instruction and questioning, visual representations, meaningful practice, scaffolding, and math discussions. *Leaps and Bounds* addresses each of these aspects of differentiated instruction.

For more information on the research foundation for *Leaps and Bounds* and a list of resources, see www.nelson.com/leapsandbounds.

Leaps and Bounds provides intervention for various topics in each of the 5 strands of mathematics. Each intervention can be used in a variety of instructional groupings—whole class, small group, or individual. The plan below outlines how a classroom teacher might use *Leaps and Bounds* in conjunction with core math resources such as *Nelson Mathematics* or *Nelson Math Focus*.

Step 1 Diagnostic Assessment

When you start a new topic in the core resource, use the review questions at the beginning of a chapter (e.g., Getting Started) to identify students who may be struggling. Have these students complete the diagnostic tool for that topic in the *Leaps and Bounds* Teacher's Resource to get a more detailed picture of their understanding. You may have students complete the questions independently in writing, or you may want to read the questions and have students respond orally.

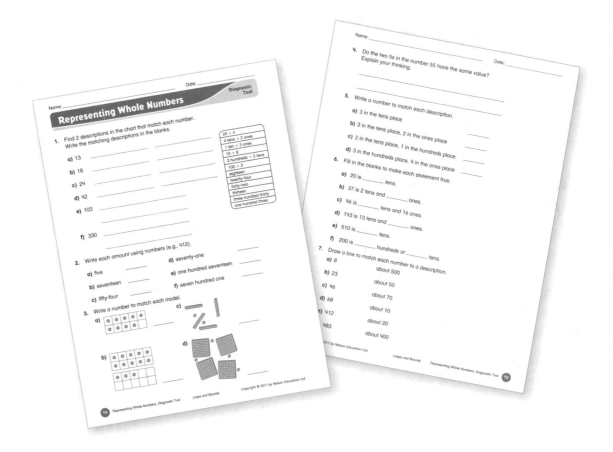

Step 2 Pathway

Use the results of the diagnostic tool to choose an appropriate pathway for each student. Solutions are provided in this Teacher's Resource with a key to pathways.

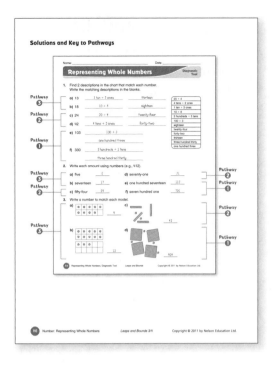

Step 3 Intervention

Choose either the open-ended intervention or the guided intervention for the pathway. The remainder of the class could be working on an exploration lesson from the core resource.

Use the "Before Using the Intervention" section of the Teacher's Resource to get students ready. Then introduce the Student Resource pages. Read through the open-ended tasks or work through the guided instruction with students. While students then continue their work on either the open-ended or guided task in pairs, you could return to the core resource with the rest of the class.

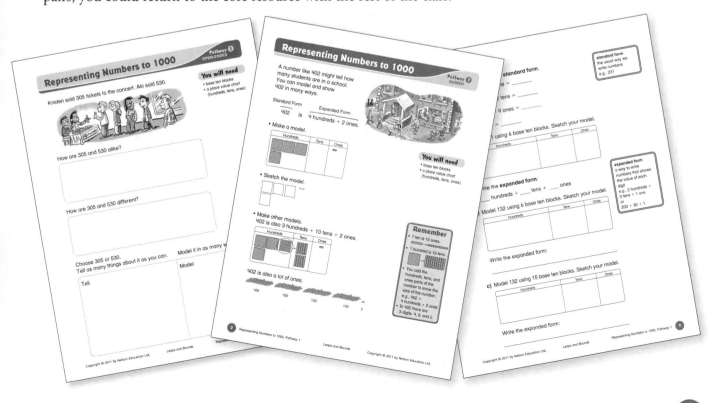

Step 4 Consolidation

When students have completed their work with the Student Resource pages, bring out and consolidate the key ideas from the intervention. Use the questions in the "Consolidating and Reflecting" section of the Teacher's Resource, adapted with examples from students' work.

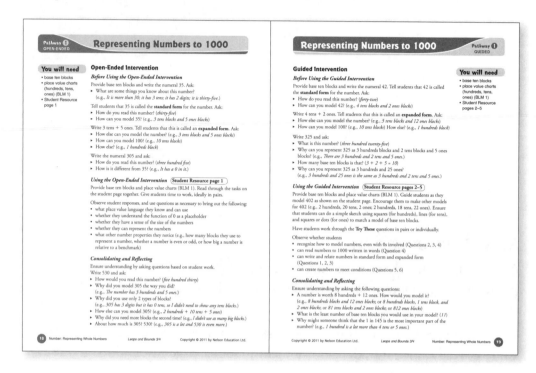

Frequently Asked Questions

How were *Leaps and Bounds* topics chosen?

Leaps and Bounds includes materials for intervention in all 5 strands of mathematics. The topics for each strand were selected based on 2 factors. The first involved an analysis of Grade 3 and 4 curricula across the country. No topics new to Grade 4 were included since a Grade 4 student could not yet be significantly behind in those topics. The second factor was an examination of the research literature—what we know about what aspects of each topic students struggle with. Prerequisite concepts and skills needed for success in Grade 3 or 4 mathematics were determined from curriculum documents, *PRIME* developmental maps (Small, Nelson Education, 2005–2010), and other educational research. The prerequisites determine the topics, which are in turn divided into levels, called pathways.

How were the pathways determined?

To determine the pathways for each topic, an analysis of the prerequisites was undertaken. Attention was given to the curriculum outcomes and expectations, but the decision about which pathways to choose was based on a deep analysis of the mathematics. We pinpoint the missing knowledge and provide an intervention to fill that gap. By being this precise, we ensure students do not waste valuable learning time on unnecessary material.

Some of the pathways for a topic vary in the complexity addressed. For example, one pathway might focus on much smaller numbers than another within the same overall topic. But the pathways are treated in a parallel manner so that students at different levels of readiness can be taught the same fundamental concept at the same time.

Generally, Pathway 3 knowledge is prerequisite to Pathway 2 knowledge and Pathway 2 knowledge is prerequisite to Pathway 1 knowledge. However, there are exceptions. Sometimes there are only 2 pathways to cover all necessary prerequisites. At other times, there might be pathways where one is not a prerequisite to the other: both contribute critical knowledge for the student to meet success in the regular grade-level outcomes or expectations.

Each pathway has 2 types of structure to choose from: open-ended or guided.

Why open-ended and guided interventions?

Two types of structure are provided so that you may choose the intervention that is most suitable for the student's needs or style and most appropriate for the specific classroom learning situation. Either the guided intervention or the open-ended intervention or both can be used. If both are used, either order is acceptable.

Why is Pathway 1 for the stronger student and not the weaker student?

Pathway 1 is the pathway closest to the ultimate desired behaviour. This ensures that no student is required to cover more material than necessary. A student farther behind would usually benefit from using Pathway 2 or 3.

The nature and extent of a student's area of struggle in a topic will be determined through use of the diagnostic tool in addition to other classroom assessments and observations. Therefore, each student will engage in only the appropriate pathway activities, rather than work through all of them.

Must a student do all pathways consecutively?

A student who completes Pathway 2 or 3 may or may not still require the support of the materials in higher-level pathways. If the underlying problem is resolved, the student can bypass pathways between the one successfully completed and the normal grade-level work. To decide if work in additional pathways is required, the relevant items on the diagnostic for the higher pathway(s) can be re-administered; if students still struggle, the additional pathway(s) might be beneficial.

Alternatively, you might decide to ask students to complete a limited version of the open-ended intervention or one or two items in the guided intervention in the higher pathway to determine if more work in that pathway is needed.

To find out whether student work is at an acceptable level once he or she has completed a pathway, you can re-administer the diagnostic tool or use other assessment items relevant for that topic.

How were the diagnostic questions developed?

The diagnostic questions were created to address what we know from the literature about common misconceptions as well as what we know from the *PRIME* research about developmental growth. For example, in the fractions topic, some diagnostic questions present pictures of fractions with non-adjacent sections shaded. Many students do not understand that the fractional sections being named do not have to be touching. Also, parts of wholes are presented separately from parts of sets, because student performance with these domains can be very different.

Concepts in each topic are broken down so that precise misconceptions can be identified. At the same time, the diagnostic sections are short enough to be practical and not overwhelming.

Leaps and Bounds is designed to address all 5 math strands by diagnosing areas of weakness and filling in knowledge gaps to allow students to meet success at grade level. It provides instructional support to allow students who are struggling to grow—by leaps and bounds.

The 2 format options for the Teacher's Resource are
- a book
- an online version or a DVD-ROM including SMART Notebook files

The 3 format options for the Student Resource are
- a bound softcover
- blackline masters
- a CD-ROM with student pages in MS Word or PDF

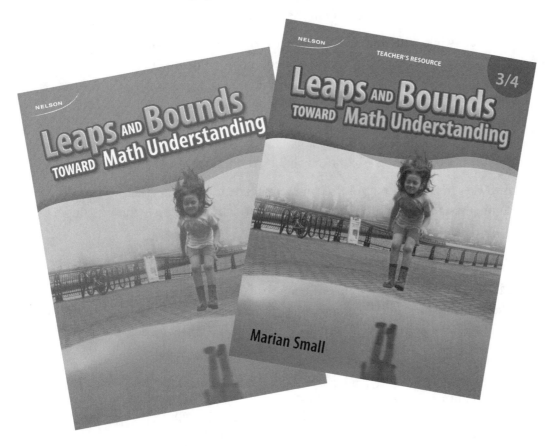

The pedagogy of *Leaps and Bounds* is based on the teacher diagnosing a student's areas of weakness and then providing instruction and guidance to move that student forward, with a focus on conceptual understanding. *Leaps and Bounds* supports multiple strategies to meet individual needs. Both the Teacher's Resource and the Student Resource are necessary for implementation.

Number Strand Overview

How were the number topics chosen?

This resource provides materials for assisting students with 7 number topics. These topics were drawn from curriculum outcomes across the country for Grades 1 to 3. Topic selections are also based on research about particular aspects of each topic that students struggle with. Topics are divided into distinct levels, called pathways, that address gaps in students' prerequisite skills and knowledge.

What number topics were omitted?

The number topics for this grade band do not include multiplication, division, or decimals. These are relatively new to students at this level, so it would be too early to target a student as struggling in these areas.

There are slight differences in curricula about the grade level for introducing fraction concepts. The interventions here include introductory fraction topics.

How were the pathways determined?

The pathways for representing whole numbers, skip counting, comparing whole numbers, and adding and subtracting whole numbers are distinguished primarily by the sizes of numbers used, from single-digit to three-digit numbers.

Pathways for mental math focus on the complexity of strategies used, including: compensation, regrouping (or adding or subtracting in parts), and relating to 5 and 10.

Materials

Materials for assisting students who are struggling with number topics will likely already be in the classroom or easily accessible. These materials are listed below. Blackline masters are also listed below and are provided at the back of this resource.

base ten blocks
linking cubes
counters
play coins
100 bead chains
coloured pencils, markers
stickers
pattern blocks
square tiles
fraction circles
fraction rectangles

BLM 1: Place Value Chart (Hundreds, Tens, Ones)
BLM 2: Place Value Chart (Tens, Ones)
BLM 3: 10-frames
BLM 4: Number Lines
BLM 5: 100 Charts
BLM 6: 1 cm Square Grid Paper
BLM 7: 2 cm Square Grid Paper
BLM 8: Fraction Circles
BLM 9: Fraction Rectangles

Number Topics and Pathways

Topics and pathways in this strand are shown below.
Each pathway has an open-ended intervention and a guided intervention.

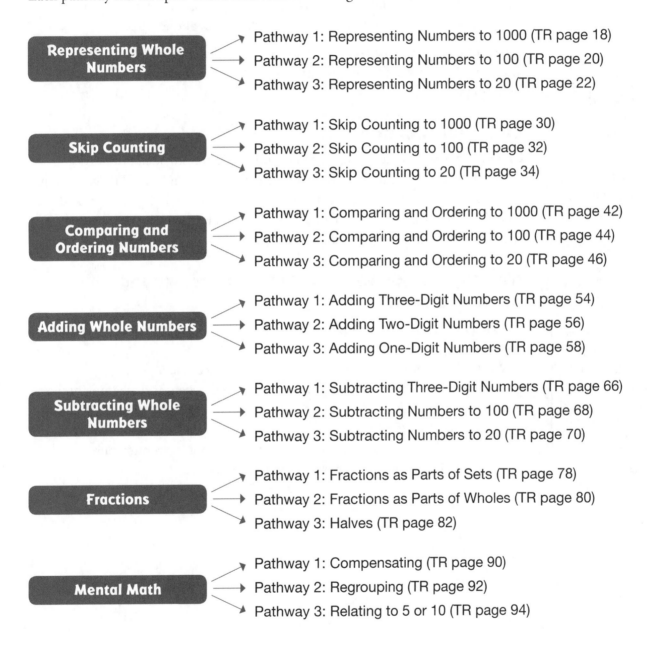

Representing Whole Numbers
- Pathway 1: Representing Numbers to 1000 (TR page 18)
- Pathway 2: Representing Numbers to 100 (TR page 20)
- Pathway 3: Representing Numbers to 20 (TR page 22)

Skip Counting
- Pathway 1: Skip Counting to 1000 (TR page 30)
- Pathway 2: Skip Counting to 100 (TR page 32)
- Pathway 3: Skip Counting to 20 (TR page 34)

Comparing and Ordering Numbers
- Pathway 1: Comparing and Ordering to 1000 (TR page 42)
- Pathway 2: Comparing and Ordering to 100 (TR page 44)
- Pathway 3: Comparing and Ordering to 20 (TR page 46)

Adding Whole Numbers
- Pathway 1: Adding Three-Digit Numbers (TR page 54)
- Pathway 2: Adding Two-Digit Numbers (TR page 56)
- Pathway 3: Adding One-Digit Numbers (TR page 58)

Subtracting Whole Numbers
- Pathway 1: Subtracting Three-Digit Numbers (TR page 66)
- Pathway 2: Subtracting Numbers to 100 (TR page 68)
- Pathway 3: Subtracting Numbers to 20 (TR page 70)

Fractions
- Pathway 1: Fractions as Parts of Sets (TR page 78)
- Pathway 2: Fractions as Parts of Wholes (TR page 80)
- Pathway 3: Halves (TR page 82)

Mental Math
- Pathway 1: Compensating (TR page 90)
- Pathway 2: Regrouping (TR page 92)
- Pathway 3: Relating to 5 or 10 (TR page 94)

Representing Whole Numbers

Planning For This Topic

Materials for assisting students with representing whole numbers consist of a diagnostic tool and 3 intervention pathways. The pathways differ in the sizes of the numbers being represented: numbers to 1000, to 100, and to 20.

Each pathway has an open-ended option and a guided option. Choose the type of intervention most suitable for your students' needs and your particular teaching circumstances.

Curriculum Connections

Grades 1 to 4 curriculum connections for this topic are provided online. See www.nelson.com/leapsandbounds. The curriculum outcomes are fairly consistent in covering representing numbers to 100 in Grade 2, to 1000 in Grade 3, and to 10 000 in Grade 4. For Grade 1, the WNCP covers representing numbers to 20 and Ontario includes representing to 50.

Why might students struggle with Representing whole numbers?

Students might struggle with representing whole numbers for any of the following reasons:

- Written conventions for numbers are based on place value.
- It is not intuitively obvious why the value of a digit changes depending on its place in a numeral. For example, the value of the 3 in 302 is different from the value of the 3 in 203.
- The digit 0 has no value but can be used as a placeholder in numerals.
- A variety of representations may have the same value.

Professional Learning Connections

PRIME: Number and Operations, Background and Strategies (Nelson Education, 2005), pages 63–66

Making Math Meaningful to Canadian Students K–8 (Nelson Education Ltd., 2008), pages 137–143

Big Ideas from Dr. Small Grades K–3 (Nelson Education Ltd., 2010), pages 22, 27–32

Good Questions (dist. by Nelson Education Ltd., 2009), pages 21–22, 25, 27–28

Diagnostic Tool: Representing Whole Numbers

Use the diagnostic tool to determine the most suitable intervention for representing numbers. Provide Diagnostic Tool: Representing Whole Numbers, Teacher's Resource pages 14 and 15, and have students complete it in writing or orally. Have place value materials available for students to use (e.g., base ten blocks, 10-frames, place value charts).

See solutions on Teacher's Resource pages 16 and 17.

Intervention Pathways

The purpose of the intervention pathways is to help students represent two-digit or three-digit numbers in a variety of ways so that ultimately they can do the same with four-digit numbers.

There are 3 pathways:
- Pathway 1: Representing Numbers to 1000
- Pathway 2: Representing Numbers to 100
- Pathway 3: Representing Numbers to 20

Use the chart below (or the Key to Pathways on Teacher's Resource pages 16 and 17) to determine which pathway is most suitable for each student or group of students.

Diagnostic Tool Results	Intervention Pathway
If students struggle with Questions 1e–f, 2e–f, 3d, 5c–d, 6d–f, 7e–f	use Pathway 1: Representing Numbers to 1000 *Teacher's Resource pages 18–19* *Student Resource pages 1–5*
If students struggle with Questions 1c–d, 2c–d, 3c, 4, 5a–b, 6b–c, 7c–d	use Pathway 2: Representing Numbers to 100 *Teacher's Resource pages 20–21* *Student Resource pages 6–9*
If students struggle with Questions 1a–b, 2a–b, 3a–b, 6a, 7a–b	use Pathway 3: Representing Numbers to 20 *Teacher's Resource pages 22–23* *Student Resource pages 10–13*

Representing Whole Numbers

1. Find 2 descriptions in the chart that match each number.
Write the matching descriptions in the blanks.

20 + 4
4 tens + 2 ones
1 ten + 3 ones
10 + 8
3 hundreds + 3 tens
100 + 3
eighteen
twenty-four
forty-two
thirteen
three hundred thirty
one hundred three

a) 13 _____ _____

b) 18 _____ _____

c) 24 _____ _____

d) 42 _____ _____

e) 103 _____

_____

f) 330 _____

_____

2. Write each amount using numbers (e.g., 412).

a) five _____   **d)** seventy-one _____

b) seventeen _____   **e)** one hundred seventeen _____

c) fifty-four _____   **f)** seven hundred one _____

3. Write a number to match each model.

a) 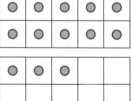 _____

c) 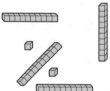 _____

b) _____

d) 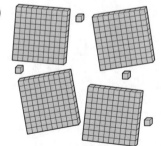 _____

Leaps and Bounds Copyright © 2011 by Nelson Education Ltd.

4. Do the two 5s in the number 55 have the same value?
Explain your thinking.

_____

_____

5. Write a number to match each description.

a) 3 in the tens place   _____

b) 3 in the tens place, 2 in the ones place   _____

c) 2 in the tens place, 1 in the hundreds place   _____

d) 3 in the hundreds place, 4 in the ones place   _____

6. Fill in the blanks to make each statement true.

a) 20 is _____ tens.

b) 37 is 2 tens and _____ ones.

c) 46 is _____ tens and 16 ones.

d) 143 is 13 tens and _____ ones.

e) 510 is _____ tens.

f) 200 is _____ hundreds or _____ tens.

7. Draw a line to match each number to a description.

a) 8   about 500

b) 23   about 50

c) 46   about 70

d) 68   about 10

e) 412   about 20

f) 483   about 400

Copyright © 2011 by Nelson Education Ltd.   *Leaps and Bounds*   Representing Whole Numbers, Diagnostic Tool

Solutions and Key to Pathways

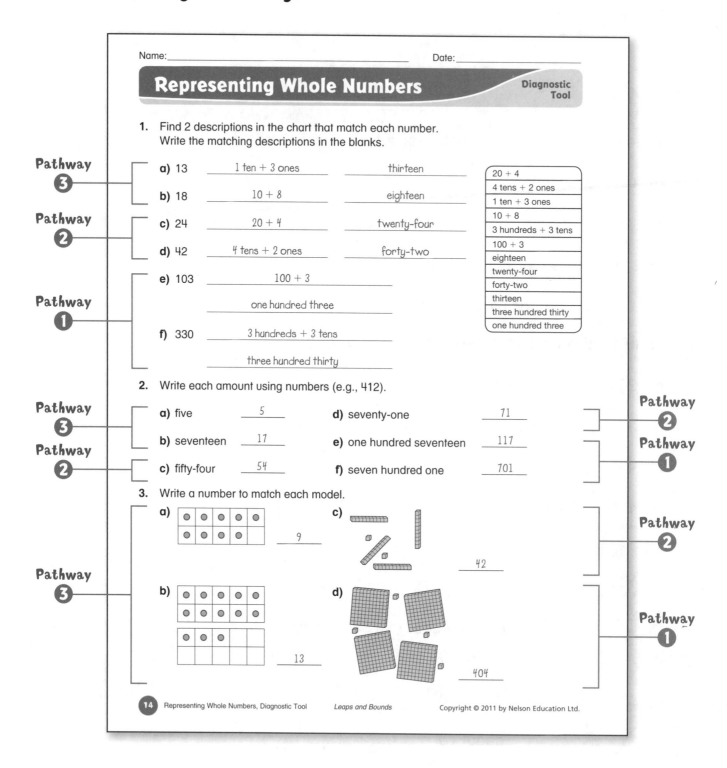

Name: _____ Date: _____

Representing Whole Numbers

Diagnostic Tool

Pathway 3
Pathway 2
Pathway 1

1. Find 2 descriptions in the chart that match each number.
   Write the matching descriptions in the blanks.

a) 13 ___1 ten + 3 ones___ ___thirteen___

b) 18 ___10 + 8___ ___eighteen___

c) 24 ___20 + 4___ ___twenty-four___

d) 42 ___4 tens + 2 ones___ ___forty-two___

e) 103 ___100 + 3___
___one hundred three___

f) 330 ___3 hundreds + 3 tens___
___three hundred thirty___

20 + 4
4 tens + 2 ones
1 ten + 3 ones
10 + 8
3 hundreds + 3 tens
100 + 3
eighteen
twenty-four
forty-two
thirteen
three hundred thirty
one hundred three

2. Write each amount using numbers (e.g., 412).

Pathway 3
Pathway 2

a) five ___5___
b) seventeen ___17___
c) fifty-four ___54___

d) seventy-one ___71___
e) one hundred seventeen ___117___
f) seven hundred one ___701___

Pathway 2
Pathway 1

3. Write a number to match each model.

Pathway 3

a) ___9___

b) ___13___

c) ___42___

d) ___404___

Pathway 2
Pathway 1

Solutions and Key to Pathways

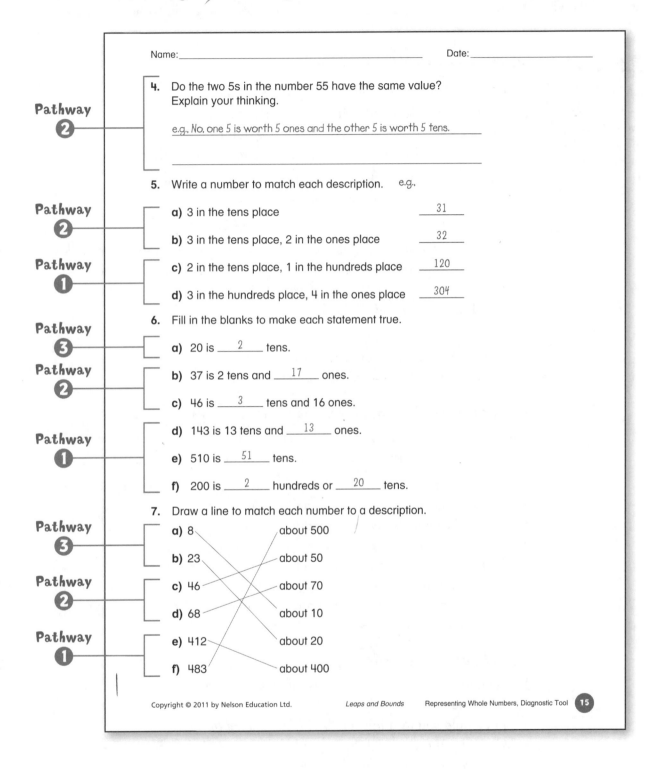

Name:_____ Date:_____

Pathway 2

4. Do the two 5s in the number 55 have the same value? Explain your thinking.

   e.g., No, one 5 is worth 5 ones and the other 5 is worth 5 tens._____

   _____

5. Write a number to match each description.   e.g.,

Pathway 2

   a) 3 in the tens place   _31_

   b) 3 in the tens place, 2 in the ones place   _32_

Pathway 1

   c) 2 in the tens place, 1 in the hundreds place   _120_

   d) 3 in the hundreds place, 4 in the ones place   _304_

6. Fill in the blanks to make each statement true.

Pathway 3

   a) 20 is __2__ tens.

Pathway 2

   b) 37 is 2 tens and __17__ ones.

   c) 46 is __3__ tens and 16 ones.

Pathway 1

   d) 143 is 13 tens and __13__ ones.

   e) 510 is __51__ tens.

   f) 200 is __2__ hundreds or __20__ tens.

7. Draw a line to match each number to a description.

Pathway 3

   a) 8   about 500

   b) 23   about 50

Pathway 2

   c) 46   about 70

   d) 68   about 10

Pathway 1

   e) 412   about 20

   f) 483   about 400

Copyright © 2011 by Nelson Education Ltd.   *Leaps and Bounds*   Representing Whole Numbers, Diagnostic Tool **15**

Copyright © 2011 by Nelson Education Ltd.   *Leaps and Bounds 3/4*   Number: Representing Whole Numbers **17**

Representing Numbers to 1000

You will need

- base ten blocks
- place value charts (hundreds, tens, ones) (BLM 1)
- Student Resource page 1

Open-Ended Intervention

Before Using the Open-Ended Intervention

Provide base ten blocks and write the numeral 35. Ask:

▸ What are some things you know about this number?
(e.g., *It is more than 30; it has 3 tens; it has 2 digits; it is thirty-five.*)

Tell students that 35 is called the **standard form** for the number. Ask:

▸ How do you read this number? (*thirty-five*)
▸ How can you model 35? (e.g., *3 tens blocks and 5 ones blocks*)

Write 3 tens + 5 ones. Tell students that this is called an **expanded form**. Ask:

▸ How else can you model the number? (e.g., *3 tens blocks and 5 ones blocks*)
▸ How can you model 100? (e.g., *10 tens blocks*)
▸ How else? (e.g., *1 hundreds block*)

Write the numeral 305 and ask:

▸ How do you read this number? (*three hundred five*)
▸ How is it different from 35? (e.g., *It has a 0 in it.*)

Using the Open-Ended Intervention   (Student Resource page 1)

Provide base ten blocks and place value charts (BLM 1). Read through the tasks on the student page together. Give students time to work, ideally in pairs.

Observe student responses, and use questions as necessary to bring out the following:
- what place value language they know and can use
- whether they understand the function of 0 as a placeholder
- whether they have a sense of the size of the numbers
- whether they can represent the numbers
- what other number properties they notice (e.g., how many blocks they use to represent a number, whether a number is even or odd, or how big a number is relative to a benchmark)

Consolidating and Reflecting

Ensure understanding by asking questions based on student work.
Write 530 and ask:

▸ How would you read this number? (*five hundred thirty*)
▸ Why did you model 305 the way you did?
(e.g., *The number has 3 hundreds and 5 ones.*)
▸ Why did you use only 2 types of blocks?
(e.g., *305 has 3 digits but it has 0 tens, so I didn't need to show any tens blocks.*)
▸ How else can you model 305? (e.g., *2 hundreds + 10 tens + 5 ones*)
▸ Why did you need more blocks the second time? (e.g., *I didn't use as many big blocks.*)
▸ About how much is 305? 530? (e.g., *305 is a lot and 530 is even more.*)

Guided Intervention

Before Using the Guided Intervention

Provide base ten blocks and write the numeral 42. Tell students that 42 is called the **standard form** for the number. Ask:

▸ How do you read this number? (*forty-two*)
▸ How can you model 42? (e.g., *4 tens blocks and 2 ones blocks*)

Write 4 tens + 2 ones. Tell students that this is called an **expanded form**. Ask:

▸ How else can you model the number? (e.g., *3 tens blocks and 12 ones blocks*)
▸ How can you model 100? (e.g., *10 tens blocks*) How else? (e.g., *1 hundreds block*)

Write 325 and ask:

▸ What is this number? (*three hundred twenty-five*)
▸ Why can you represent 325 as 3 hundreds blocks and 2 tens blocks and 5 ones blocks? (e.g., *There are 3 hundreds and 2 tens and 5 ones.*)
▸ How many base ten blocks is that? ($3 + 2 + 5 = 10$)
▸ Why can you represent 325 as 3 hundreds and 25 ones?
  (e.g., *3 hundreds and 25 ones is the same as 3 hundreds and 2 tens and 5 ones.*)

Using the Guided Intervention   (Student Resource pages 2–5)

Provide base ten blocks and place value charts (BLM 1). Guide students as they model 402 as shown on the student page. Encourage them to make other models for 402 (e.g., 2 hundreds, 20 tens, 2 ones; 2 hundreds, 18 tens, 22 ones). Ensure that students can do a simple sketch using squares (for hundreds), lines (for tens), and squares or dots (for ones) to match a model of base ten blocks.

Have students work through the **Try These** questions in pairs or individually.

Observe whether students

• recognize how to model numbers, even with 0s involved (Questions 2, 3, 4)
• can read numbers to 1000 written in words (Question 4)
• can write and relate numbers in standard form and expanded form (Questions 1, 2, 3)
• can create numbers to meet conditions (Questions 5, 6)

Consolidating and Reflecting

Ensure understanding by asking the following questions:

▸ A number is worth 8 hundreds + 12 ones. How would you model it?
  (e.g., *8 hundreds blocks and 12 ones blocks*; or *8 hundreds blocks, 1 tens block, and 2 ones blocks*; or *81 tens blocks and 2 ones blocks*; or *812 ones blocks*)
▸ What is the least number of base ten blocks you would use in your model? (*11*)
▸ Why might someone think that the 1 in 145 is the most important part of the number? (e.g., *1 hundred is a lot more than 4 tens or 5 ones.*)

You will need

• base ten blocks
• place value charts (hundreds, tens, ones) (BLM 1)
• Student Resource pages 2–5

Representing Numbers to 100

You will need

- base ten blocks
- place value charts (tens, ones) (BLM 2)
- linking cubes
- Student Resource page 6

Open-Ended Intervention

Before Using the Open-Ended Intervention

Provide either base ten blocks or linking cubes in groups of ten and singles. Write the number 12. Tell students that 12 is called the **standard form** for the number. Ask:

▸ How do you read this number? (*twelve*)
▸ How can you model 12? (e.g., *1 stick of 10 cubes and 2 single cubes*)

Write 1 ten + 2 ones. Tell students that this is called an **expanded form** for the number. Ask:

▸ How else can you model the number? (e.g., *12 loose cubes*)
▸ How can you model 20? (e.g., *2 tens blocks*)
▸ How else? (e.g., *1 tens block and 10 loose cubes*)

Using the Open-Ended Intervention   (Student Resource page 6)

Provide base ten blocks or linking cubes (in tens and ones) and place value charts (BLM 2). Read through the task on the student page together. Give students time to work, ideally in pairs. Encourage students to think of different ways to model the numbers, think of their sizes, and consider where they might meet these numbers in real situations.

Observe student responses and use questions as necessary to bring out the following:

- what place value language they know and can use
- whether they have a sense of the size of the numbers
- whether they can represent the numbers in several ways
- what other number properties they notice (e.g., how many blocks they use to represent a number, whether a number is even or odd, or how big a number is relative to a benchmark)

Consolidating and Reflecting

Ensure understanding by asking the following questions. Start by writing the number 24.

▸ How would you read this number? (*twenty-four*)
▸ Why did you model 24 the way you did?
  (e.g., *The number has 2 tens and 4 ones.*)
▸ Why did you use 2 types of blocks?
  (e.g., *The first digit means tens and the second digit means ones.*)
▸ How else could you represent 24?
  (e.g., *with 1 tens block and 14 ones blocks*)
▸ Did you use more blocks that time?
  (e.g., *yes, since I didn't use as many big ones*)
▸ About how much is 42? 24?
  (e.g., *42 is a lot if it's money, and 24 is less.*)

Representing Numbers to 100

Guided Intervention

Before Using the Guided Intervention

Provide either base ten blocks or linking cubes made into groups of ten and singles. Write the number 17. Tell students that 17 is the **standard form** for the number. Ask:

- How do you read this number? (*seventeen*)
- How would you model 17? (e.g., *1 stick of 10 cubes and 7 single cubes*)

Write 1 ten + 7 ones. Tell students that this is an **expanded form** for the number. Ask:
- How else could you model the number? (e.g., *17 loose cubes*)
- How can you model 40? (e.g., *4 tens blocks*)
- How else? (e.g., *3 tens blocks and 10 loose cubes*)

Using the Guided Intervention (Student Resource pages 7–9)

Provide base ten blocks or linking cubes (in tens and ones), and place value charts (BLM 2). Guide students as they represent 42 in various ways, as shown on the student page. Ensure that they know how to do a quick sketch of base ten blocks using rectangles or simple lines and dots.

Have students work through the **Try These** questions in pairs or individually.

Observe whether students
- recognize how to model numbers, even with 0s involved (Questions 2, 3, 4)
- can read numbers to 100 written in words (Question 4)
- can write and relate numbers in standard form and expanded form (Questions 1, 2, 3)
- can create numbers to meet conditions (Questions 5, 6)

Consolidating and Reflecting

Ensure understanding by asking the following questions:
- A number is worth 8 tens + 12 ones. How would you model it? (e.g., *8 tens blocks and 12 ones*, or *9 tens blocks and 2 ones*, or *7 tens blocks and 22 ones*)
- What is the least number of base ten blocks you would use in your model? (*11*)
- Why might someone think that the 1 in 15 is the most important part of the number? (e.g., *1 ten is a lot more than 5 ones.*)

You will need

- base ten blocks
- place value charts (tens, ones) (BLM 2)
- linking cubes
- Student Resource pages 7–9

You will need

- counters
- 10-frames (BLM 3)
- Student Resource page 10

Open-Ended Intervention

Before Using the Open-Ended Intervention

Provide counters and 10-frames (BLM 3) and write the numeral 8. Ask:

▸ How do you read this number? (*eight*)

▸ How would you model 8 using a 10-frame?
  (e.g., *Fill one row and 3 of the next row.*)

▸ How does the model show that 8 is less than 10, but close?
  (e.g., *It almost fills a 10-frame, but not quite.*)

▸ What else do you know about the number 8?
  (e.g., *It's even; it's 4 and 4; it's curvy; it's the number of hot dogs in a pack.*)

Show a full 10-frame to the left of the 10-frame that shows 8, so that the model shows 18. Ask:

▸ How is the model for 18 different from the model for 8?
  (e.g., *You need another 10-frame that's full plus the one that you did for 8.*)

Using the Open-Ended Intervention   (Student Resource page 10)

Provide counters and 10-frames (BLM 3) and present the task on the student page. Give students time to work, ideally in pairs. Encourage students to consider how to model the number using 10-frames (or alternative ways). Have them talk about how big the number is and where they might see that number in the real world.

Observe student responses and use questions as necessary to bring out the following:

- whether they have a sense of the size of the numbers
- whether they can represent the numbers
- what other number properties they notice (e.g., how many blocks they use to represent a number, whether a number is even or odd, or how big a number is relative to a benchmark)

Consolidating and Reflecting

Ensure understanding by asking questions based on students' work:

▸ How did you model 18?
  (e.g., *I used two 10-frames, one that's full and one with 8.*)

▸ How is the model for 18 different from the model for 8?
  (e.g., *18 has another 10-frame that's full.*)

▸ Is 18 a lot more than 12 or just a little? How can you tell?
  (e.g., *18 is a little more than 12 because they both use two 10-frames.*)

Guided Intervention

You will need
- counters
- 10-frames (BLM 3)
- Student Resource pages 11–13

Before Using the Guided Intervention

Provide two 10-frames (BLM 3) and 20 counters. Ask:

▶ How can you make 15 using 10-frames and counters?
(e.g., *one full 10-frame and one full row of another 10-frame*)

▶ How do you know this shows 15? (e.g., *It shows 10 and 5.*)

▶ What numbers would need two 10-frames to model them?
(*numbers from 11 to 20*)

Write the numeral 12. Ask:

▶ How do you read this number? (*twelve*)

Using the Guided Intervention   (Student Resource pages 11–13)

Provide counters and 10-frames (BLM 3). Have students model 12 and 6, as shown on the student page. Note the standard and expanded forms for the numbers.

Have students work through the **Try These** questions in pairs or individually.

Observe whether students
- recognize how to model numbers (Questions 1, 2, 3, 4)
- can write and relate numbers in standard form and expanded form (Questions 1, 2, 3)
- can create numbers to meet conditions (Question 4)

Consolidating and Reflecting

Ensure understanding by asking the following questions:

▶ When did you need more than one 10-frame?
(*when the number was more than 10*)

▶ How could you have looked at the number to tell?
(*Numbers with 2 digits except for 10 need more than one 10-frame.*)

▶ How easy is it to tell how much more or less than 10 a number is, using a 10-frame?
(e.g., *Easy; you just count how many counters are in the second 10-frame or how many are missing from the first one.*)

▶ How do the models for 15 and 5 look alike? How do they look different?
(e.g., *Both fill whole rows of 10-frames, but 15 fills three rows and 5 fills one row.*)

Skip Counting

Planning For This Topic

Materials for assisting students with skip counting consist of a diagnostic tool and 3 intervention pathways. The pathways differ in the sizes of the numbers being counted: numbers to 1000, to 100, and to 20.

Each pathway has an open-ended option and a guided option. Choose the type of intervention most suitable for your students' needs and your particular circumstances.

Curriculum Connections

Grades 1 to 4 curriculum connections for this topic are provided online. See www.nelson.com/leapsandbounds. The curriculum outcomes are consistent in requiring skip counting by 2s, 5s, 10s, 25s, and 100s before Grade 4.

Why might a student struggle with skip counting?

Skip counting is fundamental to representing numbers and comparing them, particularly on number lines. Many students struggle with skip counting because it requires attention to patterns in the place value system that are not always clear to students.

- Students may struggle over transitions, where more than one digit changes (e.g., going from 108 to 110, or 95 to 100, or 375 to 400).
- Students may have difficulty when not beginning at the start (e.g., starting at 35 instead of starting at 5 when skip counting by 5s).
- Students might struggle when counting backwards.

Sometimes these problems are alleviated with experience. Frequently students are exposed to only limited types of skip-counting situations.

Professional Learning Connections

PRIME: Number and Operations, Background and Strategies (Nelson Education Ltd., 2005), pages 37, 40, 67

Making Math Meaningful to Canadian Students K–8 (Nelson Education Ltd., 2008), pages 140–141, 144

Big Ideas from Dr. Small Grades K–3 (Nelson Education Ltd., 2010), pages 18, 30, 33

Leaps and Bounds 3/4 Copyright © 2011 by Nelson Education Ltd.

Diagnostic Tool: Skip Counting

Use the diagnostic tool to determine the most suitable intervention for skip counting. Provide Diagnostic Tool: Skip Counting, Teacher's Resource pages 26 and 27, and have students complete it in writing or orally. It may be useful to observe how students skip count—whether they use their fingers or say all the numbers between—to help them improve their ability.

See solutions on Teacher's Resource pages 28 and 29.

Intervention Pathways

The purpose of the intervention pathways is to help students count and skip count both forwards and backwards, particularly over transition points, depending on students' needs. The focus is to prepare them for skip counting using a broader range of intervals and to count to greater numbers.

There are 3 pathways:
- Pathway 1: Skip Counting to 1000
- Pathway 2: Skip Counting to 100
- Pathway 3: Skip Counting to 20

Use the chart below (or the Key to Pathways on Teacher's Resource pages 28 and 29) to determine which pathway is most suitable for each student or group of students.

Diagnostic Tool Results	Intervention Pathway
If students struggle with Questions 1d, 3e–h, 4c, 6e–h	use Pathway 1: Skip Counting to 1000 *Teacher's Resource pages 30–31* *Student Resource pages 14–18*
If students struggle with Questions 1c, 2a–b, 3b–d, 4b, 5b, 6b–d	use Pathway 2: Skip Counting to 100 *Teacher's Resource pages 32–33* *Student Resource pages 19–23*
If students struggle with Questions 1a–b, 3a, 4a, 5a, 6a	use Pathway 3: Skip Counting to 20 *Teacher's Resource pages 34–35* *Student Resource pages 24–27*

Name:_____ Date:_____

Skip Counting

1. Fill in the next 3 numbers in the counting pattern.

a)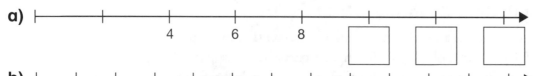
4   6   8

b)
7 8 9

c)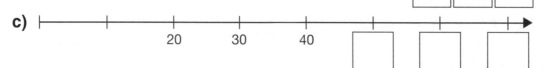
20   30   40

d)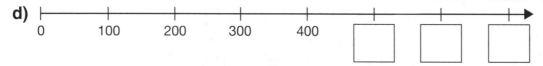
0 100 200 300 400

2. Fill in the numbers in the grey boxes to continue each pattern for counting on a 100 chart.

a)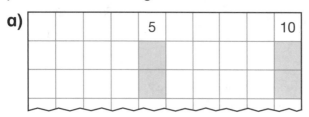

b)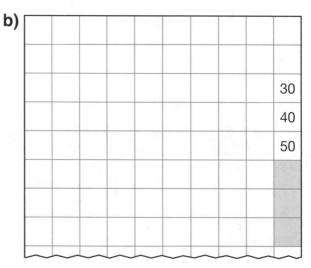

3. Count forwards to continue the pattern for 3 more numbers.

a) 8, 10, 12, _____, _____, _____

b) 5, 10, 15, _____, _____, _____

c) 60, 70, 80, _____, _____, _____

d) 9, 19, 29, _____, _____, _____

e) 125, 150, 175, _____, _____, _____

f) 194, 196, 198, _____, _____, _____

g) 220, 320, 420, _____, _____, _____

h) 403, 503, 603, _____, _____, _____

Leaps and Bounds Copyright © 2011 by Nelson Education Ltd.

4. Fill in the missing numbers in the counting pattern.

a)
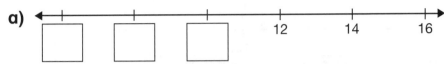

b)

c)
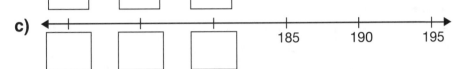

5. Fill in the numbers in the grey boxes to continue
the pattern for counting on a 100 chart.

a)
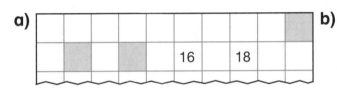

b)
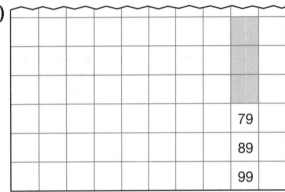

6. Count backwards to continue the pattern for 3 more numbers.

a) 20, 18, 16, _____, _____, _____

b) 35, 30, 25, _____, _____, _____

c) 100, 90, 80, _____, _____, _____

d) 200, 175, 150, _____, _____, _____

e) 304, 302, 300, _____, _____, _____

f) 210, 205, 200, _____, _____, _____

g) 902, 802, 702, _____, _____, _____

Solutions and Key to Pathways

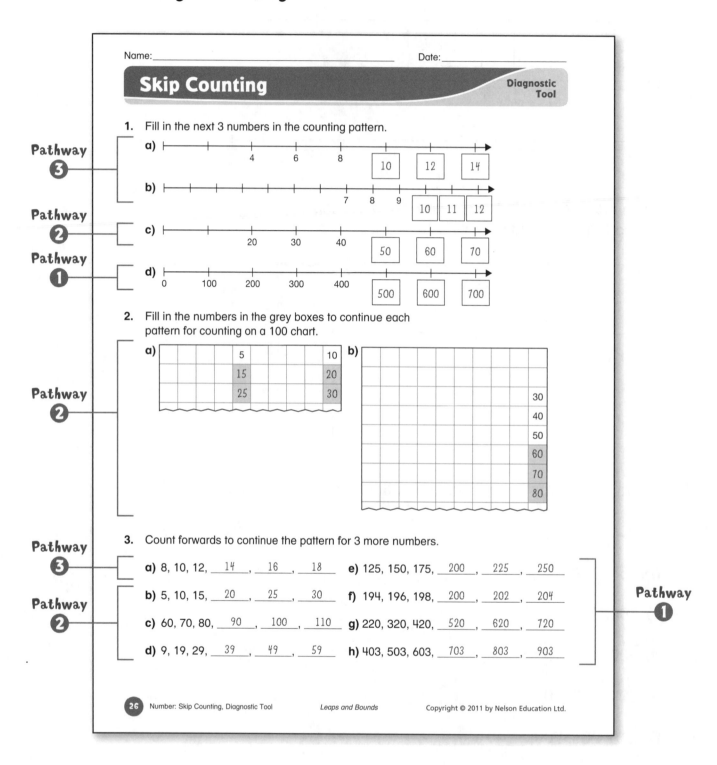

Name: _____ **Date:** _____

Skip Counting

1. Fill in the next 3 numbers in the counting pattern.

Pathway **3**

a) 4   6   8 | 10 | 12 | 14 |

b) 7   8   9 | 10 | 11 | 12 |

Pathway **2**

c) 20   30   40 | 50 | 60 | 70 |

Pathway **1**

d) 0   100   200   300   400 | 500 | 600 | 700 |

2. Fill in the numbers in the grey boxes to continue each pattern for counting on a 100 chart.

Pathway **2**

a)
				5					10
				15					20
				25					30

b)
									30
									40
									50
									60
									70
									80

3. Count forwards to continue the pattern for 3 more numbers.

Pathway **3**

a) 8, 10, 12, __14__, __16__, __18__   e) 125, 150, 175, __200__, __225__, __250__

Pathway **2**

b) 5, 10, 15, __20__, __25__, __30__   f) 194, 196, 198, __200__, __202__, __204__

c) 60, 70, 80, __90__, __100__, __110__   g) 220, 320, 420, __520__, __620__, __720__

d) 9, 19, 29, __39__, __49__, __59__   h) 403, 503, 603, __703__, __803__, __903__

Pathway **1**

Solutions and Key to Pathways

Name:_____ Date:_____

4. Fill in the missing numbers in the counting pattern.

Pathway **3**

a) ⟵—┼——┼——┼——┼——┼——┼——┼——⟶ 12 14 16
   [6] [8] [10]

Pathway **2**

b) ⟵—┼——┼——┼——┼——┼——┼——┼——⟶ 50 60 70
   [20] [30] [40]

Pathway **1**

c) ⟵—┼——┼——┼——┼——┼——┼——┼——⟶ 185 190 195
   [170] [175] [180]

5. Fill in the numbers in the grey boxes to continue the pattern for counting on a 100 chart.

Pathway **3**

a)

					10
	12	14	16	18	

b)

Pathway **2**

						49
						59
						69
						79
						89
						99

6. Count backwards to continue the pattern for 3 more numbers.

Pathway **3**

a) 20, 18, 16, ___14___, ___12___, ___10___

Pathway **2**

b) 35, 30, 25, ___20___, ___15___, ___10___

c) 100, 90, 80, ___70___, ___60___, ___50___

Pathway **1**

d) 200, 175, 150, ___125___, ___100___, ___75___

e) 304, 302, 300, ___298___, ___296___, ___294___

f) 210, 205, 200, ___195___, ___190___, ___185___

g) 902, 802, 702, ___602___, ___502___, ___402___

Copyright © 2011 by Nelson Education Ltd.   *Leaps and Bounds*   Number: Skip Counting, Diagnostic Tool   **27**

Skip Counting to 1000

You will need

- base ten blocks (optional)
- number lines (BLM 4, optional)
- Student Resource page 14

Open-Ended Intervention

Before Using the Open-Ended Intervention

Sketch a number line like this one and ask the following questions:

70   75

▸ Suppose you were skip counting forwards by 5s from 70 on the number line. What numbers would you put on the line? (e.g., *70, 75, 80, 85, 90, 95*)

▸ What comes after 95? (*100*) Why?
(e.g., *95 is 9 tens and 5; if you go up by 5, you'll have 10 tens, and that's 100.*)

▸ Would you ever write 104 as part of skip counting by 5s from 80? Why or why not? (*No; the numbers at the ticks are all numbers that end in 5 or 0.*)

▸ Suppose you were skip counting forwards by 25s starting at 150. What numbers would you say next? (*175 and 200*)

▸ Could you skip count backwards by the same numbers? What would be the same and what would be different?
(e.g., *You would say the same numbers but in the opposite order.*)

Using the Open-Ended Intervention   (Student Resource page 14)

Read through the tasks on the student page together. Students may want to count using base ten blocks (hundreds, tens, and ones) to help them over the transitions where more than one digit changes. Then they can record the counting numbers on the number lines. Provide more number lines if necessary (BLM 4). Give students time to work, ideally in pairs.

Observe student responses and use questions as necessary to see whether they
- are able to count up and down by various skip-counting factors both in simple situations and over transitions (where more than one digit changes)
- recognize which digits are affected by various skip-counting factors

Consolidating and Reflecting

Ensure understanding by asking the following questions:

▸ Which type of skip counting did you find easiest?
(e.g., *up by 100s, since you just change one digit*)

▸ What happens to the number 299 when you skip count by 10s? Why does it happen? (e.g., *You have to change the hundreds and the tens, since once you have an extra ten, you really have an extra hundred.*)

▸ How is skip counting backwards by 100s like skip counting backwards by 10s? How is it different? (e.g., *Both times it's usually just one digit that changes, either the hundreds or the ones. Both times, you don't really have to subtract; you just change a digit. But you can't say as many numbers when you are counting down by 100.*)

Leaps and Bounds 3/4

Copyright © 2011 by Nelson Education Ltd.

Skip Counting to 1000

Guided Intervention

Before Using the Guided Intervention

Sketch a number line like this one and ask the following questions:

You will need

- number lines (BLM 4)
- base ten blocks
- play coins (quarters)
- Student Resource pages 15–18

▸ Suppose you were skip counting forwards by 5s from 80 on the number line. What numbers would you put on the line? (e.g., *80, 85, 90, 95*)
▸ What comes after 95? Why?
(*100*; e.g., *95 is 9 tens and 5; if you go up by 5, you'll have 10 tens, and that's 100.*)
▸ If you were skip counting backwards by 10s from 150, what would happen?
(e.g., *You would say a lot of the same numbers as if you were skip counting up from 80.*)

Using the Guided Intervention   (**Student Resource pages 15–18**)

Work through the instructional section of student pages 15 and 16 together. Provide blank number lines (BLM 4) and base ten blocks (hundreds, tens, ones) and guide students as they count forwards from 462 by 100s and by 10s, backwards from 663 by 100s and by 10s, forwards from 325 by 25s, and backwards from 875 by 25s. Have students model counting forwards and backwards by 25s using quarters.

Have students work through the **Try These** questions in pairs or individually.

Observe whether students
- recognize which digits change and why, when counting forwards and backwards by 10s or 100s (Questions 1, 2, 3, 4, 6)
- understand when the hundreds digit changes as they cycle through the endings of 25, 50, 75, and 00 when counting by 25s (Questions 1, 2, 4)
- relate skip counting to adding and subtracting (Question 5)

Consolidating and Reflecting

Ensure understanding by asking the following prompts and questions:
▸ Show how to skip count forwards from 175 by 100s, 10s, and 25s.
(for 100s: *175, 275, 375, ...*; for 10s: *175, 185, 195, 205, 215, ...*; for 25s: *175, 200, 225, ...*)
▸ Show how to skip count backwards from 725 by 100s, 10s, and 25s.
(for 100s: *725, 625, 525, ...*; for 10s: *725, 715, 705, 695, ...*; for 25s: *725, 700, 675, ...*)
▸ How do you decide if the skip counting is by 100s, 10s, or 25s?
(e.g., *I looked to see what digits changed each time. If the hundreds digit changed, then it was by 100s; if the endings were 25, 50, 75, 00, then it was by 25s; if the tens digit changed, it was by 10s.*)

Skip Counting to 100

You will need

- base ten blocks
- 100 charts (BLM 5, optional)
- 100-bead chains (optional)
- number lines (BLM 4, optional)
- Student Resource page 19

Open-Ended Intervention

Before Using the Open-Ended Intervention

Sketch a number line like this one and ask the following questions:

▶ Suppose you were skip counting forwards by 2s from 8 to label points on the number line. What numbers would you put on the number line? (e.g., *8, 10, 12, 14, …*)

▶ Would you ever write 23 as part of this skip-counting pattern? Why or why not? (*No, since all the numbers are even.*)

▶ What skip-counting patterns might include the number 25? (e.g., *5 or 10 or 25*)

▶ Suppose you were skip counting forwards by 5s. What would you say next if you started at 15? (*20*)

▶ Could you skip count backwards by the same numbers? How would that be different? (*Yes, you would say the same numbers, but in the opposite order.*)

Using the Open-Ended Intervention   (Student Resource page 19)

Read through the tasks on the student page together. Students may want to count using base ten blocks (tens and ones), 100 charts (BLM 5), or 100-bead chains to help them over the transitions where more than one digit changes. Then they can record the counting numbers on the number lines. Provide more number lines if necessary (BLM 4). Give students time to work, ideally in pairs.

Observe student responses and use questions as necessary to see whether they
- are able to count forwards and backwards by various skip-counting values both in simple situations and over transitions (where more than one digit changes)
- recognize which digits are affected by various skip-counting values

Consolidating and Reflecting

Ensure understanding by asking the following questions:

▶ Which type of skip counting did you find easiest? (e.g., *up by 10s, since you just change one digit*)

▶ Why is it easier to skip count backwards by 2s or 10s from 88 than by 5s? (e.g., *To skip down by 10s, you just change the tens place one at a time, and to skip count down by 2s, you just use the even digits. To count back by 5s, you'd have to figure out what 88 – 5 is.*)

▶ Why does it take longer to get to a higher number when you skip count by 5s than by 10s? (*5 is less than 10, so it takes longer to add up by 5s than by 10s.*)

▶ When might you skip count? (e.g., *to count a lot of objects quickly; to figure out what numbers to write on a number line*)

Skip Counting to 100

Guided Intervention

Before Using the Guided Intervention

Sketch a number line like this one and ask:

You will need
• number lines
  (BLM 4)
• 100 charts (BLM 5,
  optional)
• Student Resource
  pages 20–23

10   20   30

- ▸ How do you know that 40 comes next on the number line?
  (e.g., *It shows counting up by 10s.*)
- ▸ How would the skip counting continue? (*50, 60, 70*)
- ▸ Which digits change when you skip count forwards by 10s? (*the tens digit*)
- ▸ Why does that make sense? (*If you add 10, only the number of tens changes.*)

Sketch a number line like this one and ask the following questions:

60   70   80

- ▸ What number goes before 60 on this number line? (*50*)
- ▸ How do you know? (*It shows counting back by 10s.*)

Using the Guided Intervention (Student Resource pages 20–23)

Work through the instructional section of the student pages together. Provide
blank number lines (BLM 4), and guide students as they count forwards by 10s
from 32, forwards by 5s from 45, forwards by 2s from 82, and backwards by 5s
from 75. Have 100 charts (BLM 5) available for students.

Have students work through the **Try These** questions in pairs or individually.

Observe whether students
- • recognize which digits change and why, when counting forwards and backwards
  by 10s, 5s, or 2s (Questions 1, 2, 3, 4, 6)
- • relate skip counting to adding and subtracting (Question 5)

Consolidating and Reflecting

Ensure understanding by asking the following questions:
- ▸ Start with 40. Show how to skip count forwards by 10s, 5s, and 2s. (for 10s:
  40, 50, 60, …; for 5s: *40, 45, 50, 55, …*; for 2s: *40, 42, 44, 46, …*)
- ▸ Start with 70. Show how to skip count backwards by 10s, 5s and 2s. (for 10s:
  70, 60, 50, …; for 5s: *70, 65, 60, 55, …*; for 2s: *70, 68, 66, 64, …*)
- ▸ How do you decide if the skip counting is by 10s, 5s, or 2s?
  (e.g., *I looked to see which digits changed every time. If it was the tens digit, then
  it was by 10s; if the endings were 5 or 0, then it was by 5s; if the ones digits were a
  pattern of digits like 0, 2, 4, 6, 8, then it was by 2s.*)
- ▸ Why doesn't the ones digit change if you're skip counting by 10?
  (*In the place value chart, the column for ones is not changed if you put something
  extra or take something away from the tens.*)

Skip Counting to 20

- counters
- 10-frames (BLM 3)
- Student Resource page 24

Open-Ended Intervention

Before Using the Open-Ended Intervention

Sketch an arrangement of counters like this:

Row 1 ●●

Row 2 ●●●●

Row 3 ●●●●●●

Ask:

▸ What pattern do you notice?
(*There are 2 more counters each time.*)

▸ What numbers would you say to tell how many counters are in each row?
(*2, 4, 6*)

▸ What would come next? (*8*)

▸ Why didn't you say 7?
(e.g., *because it goes up by 2 and not 1*)

Using the Open-Ended Intervention   (Student Resource page 24)

Read through the tasks on the student page together. Give students time to work, ideally in pairs. Have counters and 10-frames (BLM 3) available for students to use.

Observe student responses and use questions as necessary to see whether they are able to count forwards and backwards by 1s, 2s, and 5s.

Consolidating and Reflecting

Ensure understanding by asking the following questions:

▸ I'm going to cover 6 of the 20 counters. Can you still figure out how many there are altogether by counting?
(*Yes, just start counting after 6.*)

▸ Why does it take longer to count by 2s than by 5s?
(*2 is less than 5, so it takes longer to get to an amount by adding by 2s than by 5s.*)

▸ What patterns do you see when you skip count by 2s?
(e.g., *The numbers go up or down by 2 and they are all even.*)

▸ What patterns do you see when you skip count by 5s?
(e.g., *You always end with a 5 or 0.*)

▸ Why does it make more sense to skip count than to count by 1s when there are a lot of things to count?
(e.g., *to make it go faster; it's fast enough to count by 1s if there are only a few things*)

Copyright © 2011 by Nelson Education Ltd.

Skip Counting to 20

Guided Intervention

Before Using the Guided Intervention

Display 4 nickels and ask:

▶ What numbers could you say to count how much these coins are worth?
(*5, 10, 15, 20*)

▶ Why did you say only those numbers?
(e.g., *You don't need to say the other numbers since nickels are worth 5¢ each.*)

Display 6 pairs of counters. Start counting by moving 2 at a time, saying 2, 4, 6, …

▶ How can I continue counting to figure out the number of counters? (*8, 10, 12*)

Sketch a number line like this one and ask the following questions:

▶ When skip counting backwards by 2s, what number goes before 12? (*10*)

▶ How do you know? (*You just go down by 2s.*)

Using the Guided Intervention (Student Resource pages 25–27)

Work through the instructional section of the student pages together. Provide
counters and 10-frames (BLM 3), and guide students as they count forwards by
2s from 4 and by 5s from 0. Then count backwards together from 16 by 2s. Talk
about the patterns for 2s and 5s.

Have students work through the **Try These** questions in pairs or individually.
Provide pennies for Question 8.

Observe whether students notice the patterns when they skip count forwards and
backwards.

Consolidating and Reflecting

Ensure understanding by asking the following questions:

▶ Start with 10. Show how to skip count up by 5s and by 2s.
(for 5s: *10, 15, 20, …*; for 2s: *10, 12, 14, 16, …*)

▶ Start with 20. Show how to skip count backwards by 5s and by 2s.
(for 5s: *20, 15, 10, 5, …*; for 2s: *20, 18, 16, 14, …*)

▶ Why would you count tally marks by 5s and not by 2s?
(*because they come in 5s*)

▶ What would you do if there were a few extra tallies but not 5?
(*Count by 5s and then start counting by 1s.*)

▶ What numbers are in both of your skip-counting patterns for 2s and for 5s?
(*10, 20*)

▶ What patterns do you notice when you count by 2s?
(e.g., *the 2, 4, 6, 8, 0 pattern*)

- play coins (pennies and nickels)
- counters
- 10-frames (BLM 3)
- Student Resource pages 25–27

Planning For This Topic

Materials for assisting students with comparing and ordering whole numbers consists of a diagnostic tool and 3 intervention pathways. The pathways differ in the sizes of numbers being compared: numbers to 1000, to 100, and to 20.

Each pathway has an open-ended option and a guided option. Choose the type of intervention most suitable for your students' needs and your particular circumstances.

Curriculum Connections

Grades 1 to 4 curriculum connections for this topic are provided online. See www.nelson.com/leapsandbounds. The curriculum outcomes are fairly consistent in covering comparing and ordering numbers to 100 in Grade 2, to 1000 in Grade 3, and to 10 000 in Grade 4. For Grade 1, some aspects of comparing numbers cover numbers to 50 in Ontario, whereas most other aspects go to 20 in Ontario and WNCP.

Why might students struggle with comparing and ordering numbers?

Students might struggle with comparing and ordering whole numbers for any of the following reasons:

- Students might focus on individual digits when comparing numbers.
- Students might misuse the symbols for greater than and less than, forgetting which is which.
- Students might be comfortable comparing familiar numbers or friendly numbers like 100 and 200, but not less-familiar numbers.
- Students might focus only on the leftmost digits (e.g., thinking that 93 > 123 since 9 > 1).

Professional Learning Connections

PRIME: Number and Operations, Background and Strategies (Nelson Education Ltd., 2005), pages 37, 65–66

Making Math Meaningful to Canadian Students K–8 (Nelson Education Ltd., 2008), pages 87–89, 143–144

Big Ideas from Dr. Small Grades K–3 (Nelson Education Ltd., 2010), pages 19, 32

Good Questions (dist. by Nelson Education Ltd., 2009), pages 20, 26–27

Copyright © 2011 by Nelson Education Ltd.

Diagnostic Tool: Comparing and Ordering Numbers

Use the diagnostic tool to determine the most suitable intervention for comparing and ordering numbers. Provide Diagnostic Tool: Comparing and Ordering Numbers, Teacher's Resource pages 38 and 39, and have students complete it in writing or orally. Have available place value materials for students to use.

See solutions on Teacher's Resource pages 40 and 41.

Intervention Pathways

The purpose of the intervention pathways is to help students compare and order two-digit or three-digit numbers in a variety of ways so that ultimately they can do the same with four-digit numbers.

There are 3 pathways:
- Pathway 1: Comparing and Ordering to 1000
- Pathway 2: Comparing and Ordering to 100
- Pathway 3: Comparing and Ordering to 20

Use the chart below (or the Key to Pathways on Teacher's Resource pages 40 and 41) to determine which pathway is most suitable for each student or group of students.

Diagnostic Tool Results	Intervention Pathway
If students struggle with Questions 1f–g, 2e–f, 4e–f	use Pathway 1: Comparing and Ordering to 1000 *Teacher's Resource pages 42–43* *Student Resource pages 28–31*
If students struggle with Questions 1d–e, 2c–d, 4c–d	use Pathway 2: Comparing and Ordering to 100 *Teacher's Resource pages 44–45* *Student Resource pages 32–35*
If students struggle with Questions 1a–c, 2a–b, 3, 4a–b	use Pathway 3: Comparing and Ordering to 20 *Teacher's Resource pages 46–47* *Student Resource pages 36–38*

Comparing and Ordering Numbers

1. Circle the greater number in each pair.

a)

or

b) 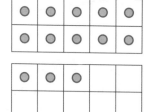   or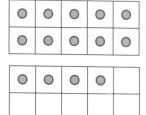

c)   or

d)    or

e)    or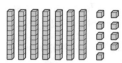

f) 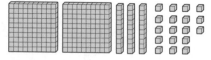   or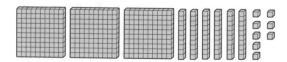

g)    or

2. Write the numbers where they belong on the number line.

a) 3, 11, 9, 14

0 1 2   18

b) 8, 11, 5, 18

0   2   4   20

c) 35, 75, 20, 90

0 5 10   100

d) 29, 82, 22, 88

20   100

e) 700, 400, 600, 300

0   100   200   1000

f) 325, 175, 250, 475

100   500

3. Draw a circle around the 4th square.
Draw a triangle around the 18th square.

■ ■ ■ ■ ■ ■ ■ ■ ■ ■ ■ ■ ■ ■ ■ ■ ■ ■ ■ ■

4. Write the 4 numbers in order from least to greatest.

a) 7, 10, 2, 5   _____ , _____ , _____ , _____

b) 18, 12, 9, 10   _____ , _____ , _____ , _____

c) 33, 38, 29, 91   _____ , _____ , _____ , _____

d) 14, 41, 19, 40   _____ , _____ , _____ , _____

e) 32, 230, 23, 320   _____ , _____ , _____ , _____

f) 705, 507, 750, 570 _____ , _____ , _____ , _____

Copyright © 2011 by Nelson Education Ltd.   *Leaps and Bounds*   Comparing and Ordering Numbers, Diagnostic Tool

Solutions and Key to Pathways

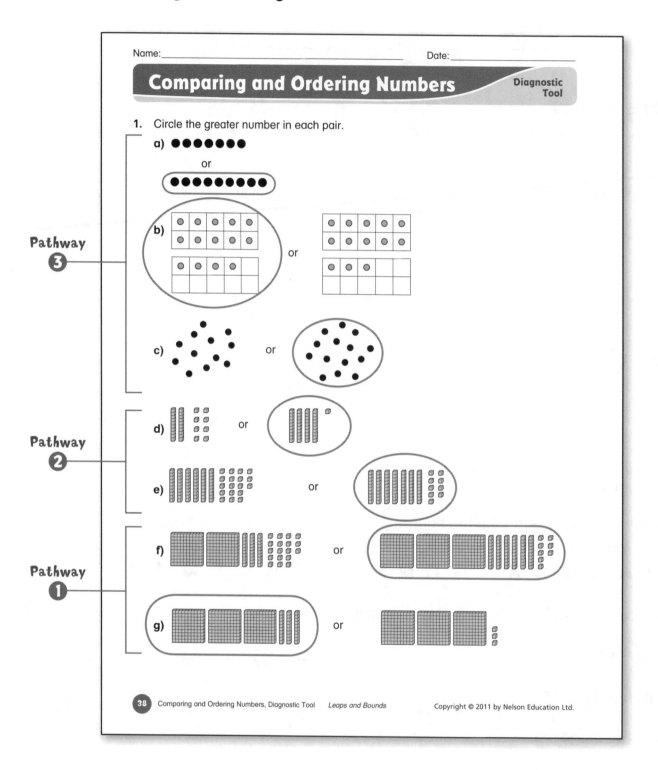

Name:_____ Date:_____

Comparing and Ordering Numbers

Diagnostic Tool

1. Circle the greater number in each pair.

Pathway 3

a) ●●●●●●● or ●●●●●●●●●

b) _(circled left group)_ or

c) or _(circled right group)_

Pathway 2

d) or _(circled right group)_

e) or _(circled right group)_

Pathway 1

f) or _(circled right group)_

g) _(circled left group)_ or

Name:_____ Date:_____

2. Write the numbers where they belong on the number line.

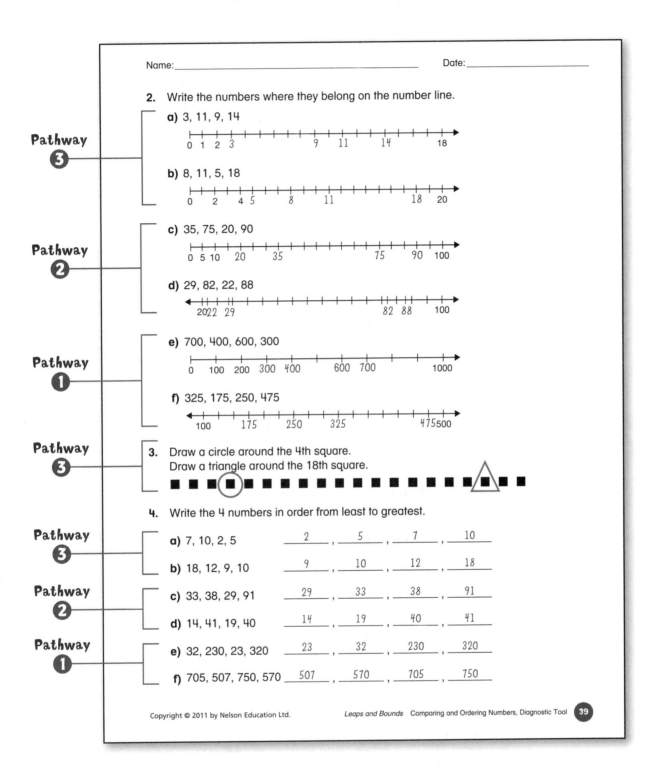

Pathway 3

a) 3, 11, 9, 14

0 1 2 3   9   11   14   18

b) 8, 11, 5, 18

0   2   4 5   8   11   18   20

Pathway 2

c) 35, 75, 20, 90

0 5 10   20   35   75   90   100

d) 29, 82, 22, 88

2022   29   82 88   100

Pathway 1

e) 700, 400, 600, 300

0   100 200 300 400   600 700   1000

f) 325, 175, 250, 475

100   175   250   325   475 500

Pathway 3

3. Draw a circle around the 4th square.
Draw a triangle around the 18th square.

■ ■ ■ Ⓘ ■ ■ ■ ■ ■ ■ ■ ■ ■ ■ ■ ■ ■ △ ■ ■

4. Write the 4 numbers in order from least to greatest.

Pathway 3

a) 7, 10, 2, 5   _2_ , _5_ , _7_ , _10_

b) 18, 12, 9, 10   _9_ , _10_ , _12_ , _18_

Pathway 2

c) 33, 38, 29, 91   _29_ , _33_ , _38_ , _91_

d) 14, 41, 19, 40   _14_ , _19_ , _40_ , _41_

Pathway 1

e) 32, 230, 23, 320   _23_ , _32_ , _230_ , _320_

f) 705, 507, 750, 570   _507_ , _570_ , _705_ , _750_

Copyright © 2011 by Nelson Education Ltd.   *Leaps and Bounds* Comparing and Ordering Numbers, Diagnostic Tool **39**

Comparing and Ordering to 1000

You will need

- base ten blocks
- place value charts (hundreds, tens, ones) (BLM 3)
- number lines (BLM 4)
- Student Resource page 28

Open-Ended Intervention

Before Using the Open-Ended Intervention

Write 24 and 28 and ask the following questions:

▶ Suppose you were comparing 24 and 28. Which is greater? Why?
(*28, e.g., It comes after 24 when you count.*)

▶ Suppose you were comparing 28 and 41. Which is greater? Why?
(*41, e.g., It has more tens.*)

▶ But 41 has fewer ones. Why doesn't that matter?
(e.g., *8 ones isn't even 1 ten, and 41 is more than 1 ten more than 28.*)

▶ What rule would you give for comparing two-digit numbers?
(e.g., *I would say that the one that has more tens is greater. But if the tens are the same, the number with more ones is greater.*)

Write the number 414. Ask:

▶ How much is the first 4 in this three-digit number worth? (*400*) How much is the last 4 worth? (*4*) Why isn't it 400?
(*The 4 is in the ones place and not the hundreds place.*)

▶ What is another number with the same digits as 414? (e.g., *441*)

▶ Is your number greater or less than 414? How do you know?
(e.g., *Greater; the numbers have the same number of hundreds, but 441 has more tens.*)

Remind students how to write statements with "greater than" or "less than" symbols, for example, 441 > 414 or 144 < 414.

Using the Open-Ended Intervention (Student Resource page 28)

Provide base ten blocks, place value charts (BLM 1), and number lines (BLM 4). Read through the tasks on the student pages together. Give students time to work, ideally in pairs.

Observe students as they work to see

- whether they focus on the entire number or just digits to decide which number is greater
- what comparison strategies they use (e.g., skip counting to mark number lines, one-to-one correspondence with base ten blocks, or a more abstract comparison to benchmarks)

Consolidating and Reflecting

Ensure understanding by asking the following questions:

▶ How did you choose the digits to create the numbers? (e.g., *I chose 1, 5, and 9 so that I could move around digits that were worth different amounts.*)

▶ How did you create your numbers so that one was much greater than the other?
(e.g., *I put the greatest digit in the greatest place value for one number, and I put the least digit in the greatest place value for the other number.*)

Comparing and Ordering to 1000

Guided Intervention

Before Using the Guided Intervention

Provide base ten blocks and place value charts (BLM 1) and ask:

▶ Suppose you were comparing 24 and 42. Which number is greater? Why?
(*42, e.g., It comes after 24 when you count.*)

▶ How do you write "42 is greater than 24" with symbols? (*42 > 24*)

▶ But 42 has fewer ones. Why doesn't that matter?
(e.g., *4 ones isn't even 1 ten, and 42 is more than 1 ten more than 24.*)

▶ How do you know that 24 is less? (*because 42 is greater*)

▶ What rule would you give for comparing two-digit numbers?
(e.g., *I would say that the number that has more tens is greater. But if the tens are the same, the number with more ones is greater.*)

Write the number 414. Ask:

▶ How much is the first 4 in this three-digit number worth? (*400*)
How much is the last 4 worth? (*4*)

Using the Guided Intervention (Student Resource pages 29–31)

Provide base ten blocks, place value charts (BLM 1), and number lines (BLM 4). Work through the instructional section of the student pages together. Guide students as they represent 512 and 378 in various ways and use the representations to compare the numbers.

Have them work through the **Try These** questions in pairs or individually.

Observe whether students

- have a variety of strategies for comparing numbers (Questions 1–8)
- recognize which digits matter the most when considering the size of a number (Questions 1, 3, 4, 7)
- recognize that numbers to the left on a number line are less than numbers to the right (Question 6)

Consolidating and Reflecting

Ensure understanding by asking the following questions:

▶ Is a three-digit number always more than a two-digit number? Why or why not?
(*Yes; a three-digit number is at least 100, but a two-digit number is less than 100.*)

▶ A three-digit number is greater than 617. Do you know any of the digits in the number for sure? Explain your thinking.
(e.g., *Not for sure, but I know the first digit is 6 or more.*)

▶ Alyson says that 317 is greater than 308, since 31 is greater than 30. Do you agree? Explain your thinking. (e.g., *Yes, since 31 tens is more than 30 tens, 317 is greater.*)

▶ How can you use a number line to compare numbers?
(e.g., *You see which number is farther to the right.*)

You will need

- base ten blocks
- place value charts (hundreds, tens, ones) (BLM 1)
- number lines (BLM 4, optional))
- Student Resource pages 29–31

Comparing and Ordering to 100

You will need

- base ten blocks (optional)
- place value charts (tens, ones) (BLM 2, optional)
- number lines (BLM 4, optional)
- Student Resource page 32

Open-Ended Intervention

Before Using the Open-Ended Intervention

Write the numeral 35 and ask:

▶ How do you read this number?
(*thirty-five*)

▶ Give an example of a number that is greater than 35.
(e.g., *36*)

▶ How do you know that your number is greater?
(e.g., *36 has one more than 35.*)

▶ What do the digits in 35 represent?
(e.g., *3 tells the number of tens and 5 tells the number of ones.*)

Using the Open-Ended Intervention   (Student Resource page 32)

Read through the task on the student page together. Provide base ten blocks, place value charts (BLM 2), and number lines (BLM 4) for students to use as they wish. Give students time to work, ideally in pairs.

Students should list two-digit numbers with 3s and 9s in them and discover many numbers with 3 in them that are greater than numbers with 9 in them.

Observe students as they work to see

- whether they focus on the entire number or just digits to decide which number is greater
- how systematic they are in listing and comparing numbers that contain 3s and 9s
- what comparison strategies they use (e.g., skip counting to mark number lines, one-to-one correspondence with base ten blocks, or a more abstract comparison to benchmarks)

Consolidating and Reflecting

Ensure understanding by asking the following questions:

▶ When you were looking for a number with a 3 that was greater than a number with a 9, what did you look for?
(e.g., *I looked mostly at the ones digits, because I knew any number with 3 in the tens was less than a number with 9 in the tens.*)

▶ What are some two-digit numbers that have 3 in them that are greater than 29?
(e.g., *any numbers in the 30s*)

▶ Are there numbers with a 3 in them that are greater than 79?
(*yes, e.g., 83 or 93*)

Comparing and Ordering to 100

Guided Intervention

Before Using the Guided Intervention

Ask the following questions:

▸ How do you know that 27 is greater than 14?
(e.g., *27 is more than 20, but 14 is less than 20.*)

▸ How do you write "27 is greater than 14" with symbols? (*27 > 14*)

▸ How do you know that 38 is less than 39?
(e.g., *You say 39 after 38 when you count.*)

▸ Name 2 numbers that are greater than 39. How you know they are greater?
(e.g., *40 and 41; You say them after 39 when you count by ones.*)

▸ How do you know that if 18 is less than 19, then 19 is greater than 18?
(e.g., *Being greater is just the reverse of being less. If one number is less than another, the other is automatically greater.*)

▸ How would you model 51 with base ten blocks? (e.g., *5 tens and 1 one*)

▸ Where would 51 be on a number line? (e.g., *just a little past 50*)

Using the Guided Intervention (Student Resource pages 33–35)

Provide base ten blocks, place value charts (BLM 2), and number lines (BLM 4). Work through the instructional section of the student pages together. Guide students as they represent 51 and 37 and use the representations to compare the numbers. Have them work through the **Try These** questions in pairs or individually.

Observe whether students
• have a variety of strategies for comparing numbers (Questions 1–8)
• recognize which digits matter the most when considering the size of a number (Questions 1, 3, 5, 7)
• recognize that numbers to the left on a number line are less than numbers to the right (Question 6)

Consolidating and Reflecting

Ensure understanding by asking the following questions:

▸ Is a two-digit number always more than a one-digit number? Why or why not?
(*Yes.* e.g., *A two-digit number is always at least 10, but a one-digit number is always less than 10.*)

▸ A number is greater than 67. Do you know any of the digits in the number for sure? Explain your thinking.
(e.g., *Not for sure, but I know the tens digit is at least 6.*)

▸ Alyson says that 63 is greater than 57, since 6 is greater than 5. Do you agree? Explain your thinking. (e.g., *yes, since 6 tens is more than 5 tens*)

▸ How can you use a number line to compare numbers?
(e.g., *You see which number is farther to the right.*)

You will need
• base ten blocks
• place value charts (BLM 2, optional)
• number lines (BLM 4, optional)
• Student Resource pages 33–35

Comparing and Ordering to 20

Open-Ended Intervention

Before Using the Open-Ended Intervention

Ask the following questions:

▸ Which is more, 7 or 10? How do you know?
(e.g., *10 is more, since you say it after 7 when you count.*)

▸ How do you write "10 is greater than 7" with symbols? (*10 > 7*)

Provide two 10-frames and counters. Ask:

▸ Put 7 counters in one 10-frame and 10 in the other one. How does that help you see which number is greater? (e.g., *The frame is fuller with 10.*)

Use a number line with ticks but no numbers. Put a dot on a tick in the middle of the line. Ask:

▸ The dot is at 7. Would 10 be far from 7 on the line? (*not too far*)

Ask a student to put a mark where 7 would go on the number line.

▸ What other numbers are not too far apart and not too close together on the number line? (e.g., *6 and 9, 8 and 12*)

▸ How would the 10-frame models for each pair of numbers look different?
(e.g., *The greater number uses a few more counters than the other number, but not a whole lot more.*)

Using the Open-Ended Intervention   (Student Resource page 36)

Provide counters, 10-frames (BLM 3), and blank number lines (BLM 4). Read the task on the student page. Give students time to work, ideally in pairs.

Observe
- whether students realize that one of the numbers is almost 10 more than the other
- what comparison strategies they use (e.g., counting to mark number lines, one-to-one correspondence, or a more abstract comparison to benchmarks)

Consolidating and Reflecting

Ensure understanding by asking the following questions:

▸ How far apart are 1 and 9? How do you know?
(*They are 8 apart.* e.g., *I counted on a number line.*)

▸ Suppose the first number is less than 10; what could the second number be?
(e.g., *It could be 10 if the first number is 0, but otherwise it is between 10 and 20.*)

▸ Could the greater number be less than 10? more than 10?
(*Yes.* e.g., *The numbers could be 0 and 9 or 9 and 17.*)

▸ How do you know that there are a lot of answers?
(e.g., *because if I get one answer I could just make the second number higher and it would be an answer too*)

Guided Intervention

Before Using the Guided Intervention

Ask the following questions:

You will need
- counters
- 10-frames (BLM 3)
- number lines
  (BLM 4, optional)
- Student Resource
  pages 37–38

▶ How do you know that 8 is greater than 6?
  (e.g., *8 is more than 7, but 6 is less than 7.*)

▶ How do you know that 8 is less than 9?
  (e.g., *You say 9 after 8 when you count.*)

▶ Name 2 numbers that are more than 10. How do you know they are more?
  (e.g., *11 and 14; you say them after 10 when you count.*)

▶ How do you know that if 18 is less than 19, then 19 is greater than 18?
  (e.g., *Being greater is just the reverse of being less; if one number is less than another, the other is automatically greater.*)

▶ How would you model 13 with counters and 10-frames?
  (e.g., *one full 10-frame and three in the other frame*)

▶ Where would 13 be on a number line?
  (e.g., *between 10 and 15*)

Using the Guided Intervention ⟮Student Resource pages 37–38⟯

Provide counters, 10-frames (BLM 3), and blank number lines (BLM 4). Work through the instructional section of the student pages together. Guide students as they represent 11 and 9 in various ways and use the representations to compare the numbers.

Have students work through the **Try These** questions in pairs or individually. Note that for Question 5, students may choose numbers greater than 20. This is fine and will give you an opportunity to assess their knowledge.

Observe whether students
- have a variety of strategies for comparing numbers (Questions 1 to 7)
- recognize that numbers to the left on a number line are less than numbers to the right (Question 6)

Consolidating and Reflecting

Ensure understanding by asking the following questions:

▶ Is a two-digit number always more than a one-digit number?
  (*Yes.* e.g., *A two-digit number is at least 10 but a one-digit number is less than 10.*)

▶ A number is greater than 7. Could it have a 4 in it? Explain your thinking.
  (e.g., *Yes, it could be 14.*)

▶ Alyson says that 13 is less than 9 since 3 is less than 9. Do you agree? Explain.
  (*No.* e.g., *13 is more than 10 and 9 is less than 10.*)

▶ How could you use a number line to compare numbers?
  (e.g., *You can see which number is to the right. That number is greater.*)

Adding Whole Numbers

Planning For This Topic

Materials for assisting students with adding whole numbers consist of a diagnostic tool and 3 intervention pathways. The pathways for this topic differ in the sizes of numbers being added: three-digit, two-digit, and one-digit numbers.

Each pathway has an open-ended option and a guided option. Choose the type of intervention most suitable for your students' needs and your particular circumstances.

Curriculum Connections

Grades 1 to 4 curriculum connections for this topic are provided online. See www.nelson.com/leapsandbounds. The WNCP curriculum outcomes include adding two-digit numbers with sums to 100 for Grade 2 and adding three-digit numbers with sums to 1000 for Grade 3. The pathways here generally have the same limits, but also offer open-ended opportunities for students to create their own sums. Their selections will tell you about their understanding of adding numbers with greater sums.

Why might students struggle with adding whole numbers?

Students might struggle with adding whole numbers for any of the following reasons:

- They have not yet mastered many addition facts and find it difficult to use the many facts often required to perform a single calculation with greater numbers.
- They may not have fully grasped procedures required to perform the task. For example, they might add in columns correctly when the numbers have the same number of digits but add incorrectly when the numbers have different numbers of digits.
- Some students have misunderstandings about place value that interfere with their understanding of addition. For example, they might have difficulty when 0 is used as a placeholder.
- Some students may struggle when the total number of ones or tens is greater than 10. For example, they might think that $43 + 59 = 912$.
- Some students might not recognize situations that call for addition or might not be able to create situations to match particular addition expressions.
- Some students might be unfamiliar with greater numbers, so adding those numbers would not be meaningful.

Professional Learning Connections

PRIME: Number and Operations, Background and Strategies (Nelson Education, 2005), pages 41–48, 69–81

Making Math Meaningful to Canadian Students K–8 (Nelson Education Ltd., 2008), pages 104–117, 160–167, 171–172

Big Ideas from Dr. Small Grades K–3 (Nelson Education Ltd., 2010), pages 35–37, 39–44, 48–55

Good Questions (dist. by Nelson Education Ltd., 2009), pages 22–24, 39

Diagnostic Tool: Adding Whole Numbers

Use the diagnostic tool to determine the most suitable intervention pathway for adding whole numbers. Provide Diagnostic Tool: Adding Whole Numbers, Teacher's Resource pages 50 and 51, and have students complete it in writing or orally.

See solutions on Teacher's Resource pages 52 and 53.

Intervention Pathways

Use the intervention pathways to help students add using a variety of strategies in different number ranges. The focus is to prepare them for adding when numbers are greater.

There are 3 pathways:
- Pathway 1: Adding Three-Digit Numbers
- Pathway 2: Adding Two-Digit Numbers
- Pathway 3: Adding One-Digit Numbers

Use the chart below (or the Key to Pathways on Teacher's Resource pages 52 and 53) to determine which pathway is most suitable for each student or group of students.

Diagnostic Tool Results	Intervention Pathway
If students struggle with Questions 3d–e, 4c–d, 5c–d, 6b–c, 7c, 8c	use Pathway 1: Adding Three-Digit Numbers *Teacher's Resource pages 54–55* *Student Resource pages 39–43*
If students struggle with Questions 3b–c, 4a–b, 5a–b, 6a, 7b, 8b	use Pathway 2: Adding Two-Digit Numbers *Teacher's Resource pages 56–57* *Student Resource pages 44–48*
If students struggle with Questions 1, 2, 3a, 7a, 8a	use Pathway 3: Adding One-Digit Numbers *Teacher's Resource pages 58–59* *Student Resource pages 49–53*

Adding Whole Numbers

Diagnostic Tool

1. Calculate each sum.

a) 7 + 5 = _____   **c)** 6 + 6 = _____

b) 7 + 9 = _____   **d)** 5 + 8 = _____

2. How much more is 6 + 9 than 5 + 5? _____

How do you know? _____

3. Complete each equation and write the number.
For example, 6 ones + 8 ones = 14 ones, or 14

a) 9 ones + 7 ones = _____

b) 2 tens + 7 tens = _____

c) 3 tens + 6 tens = _____

d) 14 tens + 16 ones = _____

e) 2 hundreds + 30 tens = _____

4. Calculate each sum.

a) 7 + 10 = _____   **c)** 100 + 24 = _____

b) 53 + 30 = _____   **d)** 200 + 359 = _____

5. Calculate each sum.

a) 18 + 8 = _____   **c)** 526 + 18 = _____

b) 14 + 85 = _____   **d)** 389 + 275 = _____

6. Circle the best estimate for each sum.

a) 19 + 6   about 20   about 25   about 70

b) 84 + 75   about 120   about 140   about 160

c) 462 + 78   about 500   about 650   about 700

7. Show 2 ways to figure out each sum.

a) 9 + 8

b) 33 + 64

c) 183 + 568

8. Write a story problem that could be solved with each calculation.

a) 7 + 6

b) 28 + 7

c) 348 + 25

Copyright © 2011 by Nelson Education Ltd.   *Leaps and Bounds*

Solutions and Key to Pathways

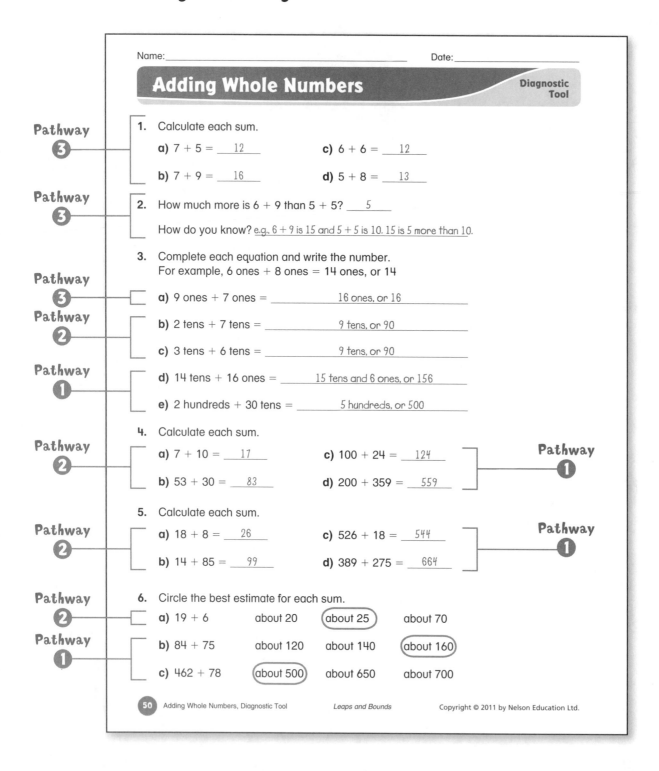

Name: _____   Date: _____

Adding Whole Numbers

Diagnostic Tool

Pathway 3

1. Calculate each sum.

   a) 7 + 5 = ___12___   c) 6 + 6 = ___12___

   b) 7 + 9 = ___16___   d) 5 + 8 = ___13___

Pathway 3

2. How much more is 6 + 9 than 5 + 5? ___5___

   How do you know? _e.g., 6 + 9 is 15 and 5 + 5 is 10. 15 is 5 more than 10._

3. Complete each equation and write the number.
   For example, 6 ones + 8 ones = 14 ones, or 14

Pathway 3

   a) 9 ones + 7 ones = _____16 ones, or 16_____

Pathway 2

   b) 2 tens + 7 tens = _____9 tens, or 90_____

   c) 3 tens + 6 tens = _____9 tens, or 90_____

Pathway 1

   d) 14 tens + 16 ones = _____15 tens and 6 ones, or 156_____

   e) 2 hundreds + 30 tens = _____5 hundreds, or 500_____

4. Calculate each sum.

Pathway 2

   a) 7 + 10 = ___17___   c) 100 + 24 = ___124___   **Pathway 1**

   b) 53 + 30 = ___83___   d) 200 + 359 = ___559___

5. Calculate each sum.

Pathway 2

   a) 18 + 8 = ___26___   c) 526 + 18 = ___544___   **Pathway 1**

   b) 14 + 85 = ___99___   d) 389 + 275 = ___664___

6. Circle the best estimate for each sum.

Pathway 2

   a) 19 + 6   about 20   (about 25)   about 70

Pathway 1

   b) 84 + 75   about 120   about 140   (about 160)

   c) 462 + 78   (about 500)   about 650   about 700

Name:_____ Date:_____

7. Show 2 ways to figure out each sum.

Pathway 3

a) 9 + 8   *For example:*

$9 + 9 = 18$ $18 - 1 = 17$ $9 + 8 = 17$	$9 + 1 + 7 = 10 + 7$ $9 + 8 = 17$

Pathway 2

b) 33 + 64

$30 + 3 + 60 + 4$ $= 90 + 7$ $= 97$	$\begin{array}{r} 60 \\ + 33 \\ \hline 90 \\ + 7 \\ \hline 97 \end{array}$

Pathway 1

c) 183 + 568

$100 + 500 + 80 + 60 + 3 + 8$ $= 600 + 140 + 11$ $= 751$	$183 + 17 + (568 - 17)$ $= 200 + 551$ $= 751$

8. Write a story problem that could be solved with each calculation.

Pathway 3

a) 7 + 6

e.g., Britney has made 2 piles of socks. She has 7 socks for her left foot and 6 socks for her right foot. How many socks does she have in total? Is she missing a sock?

Pathway 2

b) 28 + 7

e.g., Ragan has 28 stickers and Kathy has 7 stickers. They want to put all their stickers in a sticker book and start a collection. How many stickers do they have together?

Pathway 1

c) 348 + 25

e.g., Phillip scored 348 points in a video game. He needs 25 more points to win the game. How many points does he need altogether to win?

Copyright © 2011 by Nelson Education Ltd.   *Leaps and Bounds*   Adding Whole Numbers, Diagnostic Tool   **51**

Copyright © 2011 by Nelson Education Ltd.   *Leaps and Bounds 3/4*   Number: Adding Whole Numbers   **53**

Adding Three-Digit Numbers

You will need

- base ten blocks
- place value charts (hundreds, tens, ones) (BLM 1)
- number lines (BLM 4)
- Student Resource page 39

Open-Ended Intervention

Before Using the Open-Ended Intervention

Ask the following questions:

▶ How would you add 488 + 2?

(e.g., *I would count up 2 to say 489, 490.*)

▶ How would you add 488 + 20?

(e.g., *I would add 10 to get 498, then add 2 to get to 500, and then 8 to get 508.*)

▶ How would you add 488 + 200?

(e.g., *There are 2 more hundreds, so that's 688.*)

▶ Which did you find easiest? Why?

(e.g., *Adding 2 or 200 was easier than adding 20 because I didn't really have to think of a lot of parts to do.*)

Using the Open-Ended Intervention   (Student Resource page 39)

Provide base ten blocks, place value charts (BLM 1), and number lines (BLM 4). Read through the tasks on the student page together. Give students time to work, ideally in pairs. If students choose numbers that result in a sum over 1000, you might want to encourage them to choose lower numbers to make the task more manageable.

Observe whether students

- are able to add using more than one strategy
- see the value of combinations like 8 + 2
- recognize how a story relates to addition
- recognize how to relate one addition to another

Consolidating and Reflecting

Ensure understanding by asking questions such as the following, drawing examples from students' work:

▶ How could you have estimated your sum?

(e.g., *by thinking about the hundreds digits*)

▶ How are your 2 ways of adding alike?

(e.g., *Each time, I added 700 and 80 and 2; I just did it different ways.*)

▶ How did you know that 519 + 290 would have the same sum as 520 + 289?

(e.g., *I just moved 1 from the 520 over to the 289.*)

▶ What about your story problem made it an addition problem?

(e.g., *I was combining things.*)

Adding Three-Digit Numbers

Guided Intervention

Before Using the Guided Intervention

Write 348 + 500 and ask:

▸ If you were adding 500 to 348, which digits of 348 would change and which wouldn't? Why? (*The hundreds changes and not the others, because you have more hundreds but no more tens or ones.*)

Write 348 + 250 and ask:

▸ If you were adding 250 to 348, which digits of 348 would change and which wouldn't? (*There are more hundreds and more tens, so those two would change, but there are no more ones, so that digit wouldn't change.*)

Using the Guided Intervention   (Student Resource pages 40–43)

Provide base ten blocks, place value charts (BLM 1), and number lines (BLM 4). Work through the estimation strategy for 257 + 284 shown, and encourage students to share a variety of estimation strategies. For example, some students might prefer to use other numbers for estimating, such as 250 and 300.

Have students model the numbers with base ten blocks, and guide them as they add and record in a place value chart. Have them compare other recording strategies, some of which are shown. Some students might like to record on grid paper (BLM 6) with one digit in each cell. Work through the strategy of adding in parts, and model it on a number line.

Have students work through the **Try These** questions individually or in pairs.

Observe whether students
- can estimate sums when adding greater numbers (Questions 1, 2, 3, 7, 8)
- have a variety of strategies for adding (Question 5)
- recognize real-life situations that involve adding (Question 4)
- can perform addition (Questions 3 to 9)

Consolidating and Reflecting

Ensure understanding by asking the following questions:

▸ Which digits do you think about when you estimate sums? Which do you ignore? Why? (e.g., *I think about the hundreds digits but not the ones digits, since the ones digits only change the answer a small amount.*)

▸ Why is it easy to get 2 pairs of numbers with the same sum? (e.g., *Just take a bit from one of the numbers and add it to the other, and the sum stays the same.*)

▸ What strategy did you use to figure out whether 800 was possible in Question 6? (e.g., *I added the 2 lowest numbers and the 2 highest numbers and saw if the sum I was supposed to get was between them.*)

You will need
- base ten blocks
- place value charts (hundreds, tens, ones) (BLM 1)
- number lines (BLM 4)
- grid paper (BLM 6, optional)
- Student Resource pages 40–43

Adding Two-Digit Numbers

You will need

- base ten blocks (at least 20 tens and 20 ones)
- place value charts (tens, ones) (BLM 2)
- number lines (BLM 4)
- 100 charts (BLM 5)
- Student Resource page 44

Open-Ended Intervention

Before Using the Open-Ended Intervention

Ask the following questions:

▸ How would you add 48 + 2?
  (e.g., *I would just count up 2 to say 49, 50.*)
▸ How would you add 48 + 20?
  (e.g., *There are 2 more tens, so that's 68.*)
▸ How are the questions alike?
  (e.g., *Both times I added 2, once to the ones and once to the tens.*)

Using the Open-Ended Intervention   (Student Resource page 44)

Provide base ten blocks, place value charts (BLM 2), number lines (BLM 4), and a 100 chart (BLM 5). Read through the tasks on the student page together. Give students time to work, ideally in pairs. If students choose numbers that result in a sum over 100, you might want to encourage them to choose lower numbers to make the task more manageable.

Observe whether students

- are able to add using more than one strategy
- look for combinations that equal 10, such as 9 + 1
- recognize how a story relates to addition
- recognize how to relate one addition to another

Consolidating and Reflecting

Ensure understanding by asking questions such as the following, drawing examples from students' work:

▸ How could you have estimated your sum?
  (e.g., *by thinking about the tens digits*)
▸ How are your 2 ways of adding alike?
  (e.g., *Each time, I am adding 80 and 1; I just did it different ways.*)
▸ How did you know that 58 + 32 would have the same sum as 59 + 31?
  (e.g., *I just moved 1 from the 59 over to the 31.*)
▸ What about your story problem made it an addition problem?
  (e.g., *I was combining things.*)

Guided Intervention

Before Using the Guided Intervention

Write 34 + 50 and ask:

▶ If you were adding 50 to 34, which digits in 34 would change and which wouldn't? Why? (*The tens digit changes and not the ones, because you have more tens but no more ones.*)

Write 34 + 25 and ask:

▶ If you were adding 25 to 34, which digits in 34 would change and which wouldn't? (*There are more tens and more ones, so both digits change.*)

Write 34 + 51 and ask:

▶ How do you know that 34 + 51 is more than 80 but less than 90? (e.g., *34 + 51 is more than 30 + 50, which is 80, but 4 + 1 is less than 10.*)

Using the Guided Intervention (Student Resource pages 45–48)

Provide base ten blocks, place value charts (BLM 2), number lines (BLM 4), and 100 charts (BLM 5). Work through the estimation strategy for 27 + 28 shown on the student pages and encourage students to share a variety of estimation strategies. For example, some students might estimate using 30 + 30 or 25 + 30.

Have students model the numbers with base ten blocks, and guide them as they record in a place value chart. Have them compare other recording strategies. Some students might like to record on grid paper (BLM 6) with one digit in each cell. Work through the strategy of adding in parts and model it on a number line.

Have students work through the **Try These** questions individually or in pairs.

Observe whether students
- can estimate sums (Questions 1, 2, 6, 7)
- have a variety of strategies for adding (Question 5)
- recognize real-life situations that involve adding (Question 4)
- can add 2 quantities (Questions 3, 4, 5, 8)

Consolidating and Reflecting

Ensure understanding by asking the following questions:

▶ Which digits do you think about when you estimate sums? Which do you ignore? Why? (e.g., *I think about the tens digits but not the ones digits, since the ones digits change the answer only a small amount.*)

▶ Why is it easy to get 2 pairs of numbers with the same sum? (e.g., *Just move some from one of the numbers to the other and the sum stays the same.*)

▶ What strategy did you use to figure out whether 82 was possible in Question 6? (e.g., *I added the 2 lowest numbers and the 2 highest numbers and saw if the sum I was supposed to get was between them.*)

You will need

- base ten blocks (at least 20 tens blocks and 20 ones blocks)
- place value charts (tens, ones) (BLM 2)
- number lines (BLM 4)
- 100 charts (BLM 5, optional)
- grid paper (BLM 6)
- Student Resource pages 45–48

Adding One-Digit Numbers

- 10-frames (BLM 3)
- 16 counters
- number lines (BLM 4)
- Student Resource page 49

Open-Ended Intervention

Before Using the Open-Ended Intervention

Provide 10-frames (BLM 3) and counters, and ask:

▸ What pairs of numbers add to make 10?
(*0 + 10, 1 + 9, 2 + 8, 3 + 7, 4 + 6, and 5 + 5*)

▸ How could you use a 10-frame to figure that out?
(*You could fill the 10-frame with 2 colours of counters and count the number of each colour.*)

▸ How would knowing that 3 + 7 = 10 help you figure out 3 + 6?
(*Take away 1.*)

▸ What is 9 + 9? How does knowing that help you figure out 9 + 8?
(*18; subtract 1.*)

Using the Open-Ended Intervention   (Student Resource page 49)

Provide 10-frames (BLM 3), counters, and number lines (BLM 4). Read through the task on the student page together. Make sure students realize they should use different combinations on each line. They should also complete the sum and tell how they added.

They can use additional pages if they have more combinations. Give students time to work, ideally in pairs.

Observe whether students are able to

- add using more than one strategy
- relate one addition to another one

Consolidating and Reflecting

Ensure understanding by asking questions such as the following, drawing examples from students' work:

▸ How did you know that 5 + 4 was too low?
(e.g., *since 5 + 5 = 10 and 5 + 4 is less*)

▸ How did you know that 9 + 8 was too much?
(e.g., *9 + 8 is 1 more than 8 + 8. 8 + 8 = 16, so 9 + 8 is too much.*)

▸ Once you knew that 7 + 7 was a choice, how could you find other combinations?
(e.g., *I took 3 away from the 7s, either all from one 7 or a little from each; I also added 2 to one of the 7s and added 1 to each of the 7s.*)

▸ What strategies did you use to add 7 + 6?
(e.g., *I added 5 + 5 and then added 2 + 1; I also knew that 6 + 6 = 12, so I added 1 to 12.*)

Leaps and Bounds 3/4
Copyright © 2011 by Nelson Education Ltd.

Guided Intervention

Before Using the Guided Intervention

You will need

- 10-frames (BLM 3)
- counters, 20 or more
- number lines (BLM 4)
- Student Resource pages 50–53

Ask the following questions:

▶ How might you figure out 5 + 4 if you didn't already know the answer?
(e.g., *Add 5 + 5 and take away 1. Or add 4 + 4 and then add 1.*)

▶ Would you use similar strategies to add 9 + 5?
(e.g., *Yes, but I would add 10 + 5 and take away 1.*)

▶ How could you use 10-frames to add 9 + 5?
(e.g., *I would put 9 counters in one 10-frame, then I would put 1 of the 5 with it and there would be 4 left in the other 10-frame. That means the sum is 14.*)

Using the Guided Intervention   (Student Resource pages 50–53)

Provide 10-frames (BLM 3), counters, and number lines (BLM 4), and guide students as they add 7 + 8 in different ways. Have them fill 10-frames with counters and then sketch the addition jumps on a number line. Then have them relate 7 + 8 to facts they may know.

Have students work through the **Try These** questions individually or in pairs.

Observe
- whether students know facts for 10 (Question 1)
- whether students relate sums to 5 or 10 (Questions 2, 3, 6)
- what facts students know (Questions 1, 4, 7)
- whether students have a variety of strategies for calculating (Questions 5, 8)
- whether students can relate one addition fact to another (Question 6)

Consolidating and Reflecting

Ensure understanding by asking the following questions:

▶ If you add 4 to 9, how do you know the sum is more than 10, but not a lot more?
(e.g., *If you add 1 to 9 you get 10, and 4 is not that much more than 1.*)

▶ What 2 numbers can you add to make 14? How can you use that pair to think of other numbers that add to 14?
(e.g., *7 + 7; 8 + 6 by moving 1 from one of the 7s to the other; 5 + 9 by moving 2 from one of the 7s to the other 7*)

▶ What other facts can you figure out from 6 + 6 = 12?
(e.g., *7 + 6 = 13 by adding 1; 7 + 7 = 14 by adding 1 to each 6; 5 + 6 = 11 by taking 1 away*)

▶ How does knowing that 8 + 2 = 10 help you figure out 8 + 6?
(e.g., *Take 2 from the 6 to make 10 and then leave the other 4; that makes the sum 14.*)

Subtracting Whole Numbers

Planning For This Topic

Materials for assisting students with subtracting whole numbers consist of a diagnostic tool and 3 intervention pathways. The pathways for this topic differ in the sizes of numbers being subtracted: three-digit numbers, numbers to 100, and numbers to 20.

Each pathway has an open-ended option and a guided option. Choose the type of intervention most suitable for your students' needs and your particular circumstances.

Curriculum Connections

Grades 1 to 4 curriculum connections for this topic are provided online. See www.nelson.com/leapsandbounds.

Why might a student struggle with subtracting whole numbers?

Students might struggle with subtracting whole numbers for any of the following reasons:

- They have not yet mastered subtraction facts to 20.
- They may have learned subtraction facts by rote and may not understand the meanings of subtraction, especially in problem-solving contexts. For example, students may not realize that the same operation can be applied in situations that show different meanings of subtraction (i.e., separation [take away], comparison, or missing addend).
- They might subtract in columns correctly when the numbers do not require regrouping, but subtract incorrectly when the numbers require single or successive regrouping (e.g., $27 - 5$; $334 - 89$).
- They might not be able to subtract when the number of digits is different (e.g., $442 - 28$).
- They might not be comfortable with greater numbers (e.g., three-digit numbers), and therefore not comfortable with subtracting greater numbers.
- They might not recognize that subtracting tens from tens (or hundreds from hundreds) requires only knowing the facts for the numbers of tens (or hundreds) being subtracted.

Professional Learning Connections

PRIME: Number and Operations, Background and Strategies (Nelson Education, 2005), pages 41–48, 69–81

Making Math Meaningful to Canadian Students K–8 (Nelson Education Ltd., 2008), pages 160–173

Big Ideas from Dr. Small Grades K–3 (Nelson Education Ltd., 2010), pages 35–44

Good Questions (dist. by Nelson Education Ltd., 2009), page 30

Diagnostic Tool: Subtracting Whole Numbers

Use the diagnostic tool to determine the most suitable intervention pathway for subtracting whole numbers. Provide Diagnostic Tool: Subtracting Whole Numbers, Teacher's Resource pages 62 and 63, and have students complete it in writing or orally.

See solutions on Teacher's Resource pages 64 and 65.

Intervention Pathways

The purpose of the intervention pathways is to help students subtract in various mathematical situations (i.e., separation, comparison, missing addend) using a variety of strategies and number ranges. The focus is to prepare them for subtracting when numbers are greater.

There are 3 pathways:
- Pathway 1: Subtracting Three-Digit Numbers
- Pathway 2: Subtracting Numbers to 100
- Pathway 3: Subtracting Numbers to 20

Use the chart below (or the Key to Pathways on Teacher's Resource pages 64 and 65) to determine which pathway is most suitable for each student or group of students.

Diagnostic Tool Results	Intervention Pathway
If students struggle with Questions 3c–e, 4c–d, 5c–d, 6c–d, 7c, 8c	use Pathway 1: Subtracting Three-Digit Numbers *Teacher's Resource pages 66–67* *Student Resource pages 54–58*
If students struggle with Questions 3b, 4b, 5a–b, 6b, 7b, 8b	use Pathway 2: Subtracting Numbers to 100 *Teacher's Resource pages 68–69* *Student Resource pages 59–63*
If students struggle with Questions 1, 2, 3a, 4a, 6a, 7a, 8a	use Pathway 3: Subtracting Numbers to 20 *Teacher's Resource pages 70–71* *Student Resource pages 64–67*

Name:________________________ Date:________________

Subtracting Whole Numbers

Diagnostic Tool

1. Calculate each difference.

a) 7 − 2 = ________ **c)** 16 − 9 = ________

b) 12 − 6 = ________ **d)** 17 − 8 = ________

2. How can you use another fact to figure out each difference? For example, to calculate 12 − 3, you can calculate 12 − 2 and subtract 1 more.

a) 13 − 5 ________________________

b) 15 − 6 ________________________

3. Complete each equation and write the number.
For example, 28 tens − 6 tens = 22 tens, or 220

a) 15 ones − 8 ones = ________________

b) 2 tens − 11 ones = ________________

c) 14 tens − 8 ones = ________________

d) 32 tens − 16 tens = ________________

e) 2 hundreds − 12 tens = ________________

4. Calculate each difference.

a) 17 − 10 = ________ **c)** 124 − 100 = ________

b) 53 − 30 = ________ **d)** 609 − 500 = ________

5. Calculate each difference.

a) 43 − 13 = ________ **c)** 102 − 29 = ________

b) 52 − 18 = ________ **d)** 413 − 275 = ________

6. Circle the best estimate for each difference.

a) 15 − 6	about 5	about 10	about 15
b) 84 − 45	about 30	about 40	about 50
c) 462 − 78	about 350	about 400	about 450
d) 644 − 287	about 300	about 350	about 400

 Copyright © 2011 by Nelson Education Ltd.

7. Show 2 ways to complete each subtraction.

a) 14 − 9

b) 84 − 33

c) 568 − 183

8. Write a story problem that could be solved with each calculation.

a) 15 − 6

b) 41 − 18

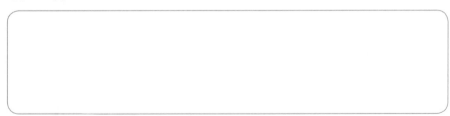

c) 345 − 28

Solutions and Key to Pathways

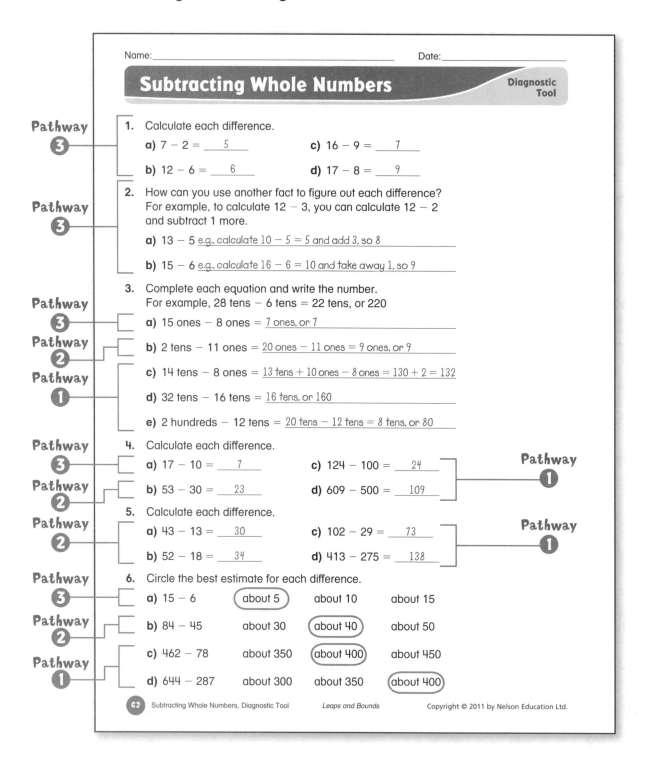

Name: _____ Date: _____

Subtracting Whole Numbers

Pathway 3

1. Calculate each difference.

a) 7 − 2 = ___5___   c) 16 − 9 = ___7___

b) 12 − 6 = ___6___   d) 17 − 8 = ___9___

Pathway 3

2. How can you use another fact to figure out each difference? For example, to calculate 12 − 3, you can calculate 12 − 2 and subtract 1 more.

a) 13 − 5 _e.g., calculate 10 − 5 = 5 and add 3, so 8_

b) 15 − 6 _e.g., calculate 16 − 6 = 10 and take away 1, so 9_

3. Complete each equation and write the number.
For example, 28 tens − 6 tens = 22 tens, or 220

Pathway 3

a) 15 ones − 8 ones = _7 ones, or 7_

Pathway 2

b) 2 tens − 11 ones = _20 ones − 11 ones = 9 ones, or 9_

Pathway 1

c) 14 tens − 8 ones = _13 tens + 10 ones − 8 ones = 130 + 2 = 132_

d) 32 tens − 16 tens = _16 tens, or 160_

e) 2 hundreds − 12 tens = _20 tens − 12 tens = 8 tens, or 80_

Pathway 3

4. Calculate each difference.

a) 17 − 10 = ___7___   c) 124 − 100 = ___24___

Pathway 2

b) 53 − 30 = ___23___   d) 609 − 500 = ___109___

Pathway 1

Pathway 2

5. Calculate each difference.

a) 43 − 13 = ___30___   c) 102 − 29 = ___73___

b) 52 − 18 = ___34___   d) 413 − 275 = ___138___

Pathway 1

Pathway 3

6. Circle the best estimate for each difference.

a) 15 − 6   (about 5)   about 10   about 15

Pathway 2

b) 84 − 45   about 30   (about 40)   about 50

c) 462 − 78   about 350   (about 400)   about 450

Pathway 1

d) 644 − 287   about 300   about 350   (about 400)

Name:_____ Date:_____

7. Show 2 ways to complete each subtraction.

Pathway ❸

a) $14 - 9$

e.g., $14 - 4 = 10$ $10 - 5 = 5$ so $14 - 9 = 5$	e.g., $14 - 10 = 4$ so $14 - 9 = 5$

Pathway ❷

b) $84 - 33$

e.g., $84 - 30 = 54$ $54 - 3 = 51$ so $84 - 33 = 51$	e.g., $\begin{array}{r} 84 \\ -\ 33 \\ \hline 51 \end{array}$

Pathway ❶

c) $568 - 183$

e.g., $568 - 100 = 468$ $468 - 80 = 368 + 20 = 388$ $388 - 3 = 385$ so $568 - 183 = 385$	e.g., $\begin{array}{r} {}^{4\ 16} \\ 568 \\ -\ 183 \\ \hline 385 \end{array}$

8. Write a story problem that could be solved with each calculation.

Pathway ❸

a) $15 - 6$

e.g., Thomas gave me 15 comic books. I gave 6 to Aneela. How many do I have left? $15 - 6 = 9$ I have 9 comic books left.

Pathway ❷

b) $41 - 18$

e.g., The reds got 41 points to win the game. The blues got 18 points. How many more points did the reds get? $41 - 18 = 23$ The reds won by 23 points.

Pathway ❶

c) $345 - 28$

e.g., Philip had $345. He spent $28. How much money did he have left? $345 - $28 = $317 He has $317 left.

Subtracting Three-Digit Numbers

You will need
- base ten blocks
- place value charts (hundreds, tens, ones) (BLM 1)
- number lines (BLM 4)
- Student Resource page 54

Open-Ended Intervention

Before Using the Open-Ended Intervention

Ask the following questions:

▸ How would you calculate $355 - 3$?
(e.g., *I would count down 3 to say 354, 353, 352.*)

▸ How would you calculate $355 - 30$?
(e.g., *I just have to take away 3 tens from 5 tens, so there are still 3 hundreds, 2 ten and 5 ones. That's 325.*)

▸ How would you calculate $355 - 300$?
(e.g., *There are 3 hundreds to start with in 355 and you are taking them away.*)

▸ Which did you find easiest? Why?
(e.g., *Subtracting 300 was easiest since I knew I had 300 + 55 so I just got rid of the 300.*)

Using the Open-Ended Intervention (Student Resource page 54)

Provide base ten blocks, place value charts (BLM 1), and number lines (BLM 4). Read through the task on the student page together. Give students time to work, ideally in pairs.

Observe whether students
- are able to subtract using more than one strategy
- recognize how a story relates to subtraction
- recognize how to relate addition to subtraction

Consolidating and Reflecting

Ensure understanding by asking questions based on students' work:

▸ How did you estimate the difference between the 2 numbers?
(e.g., *I rounded the numbers to tens and subtracted tens and hundreds.*)

▸ How are your 2 ways of subtracting alike?
(e.g., *The subtraction uses the same numbers.*)

▸ How are your 2 ways of subtracting different?
(e.g., *I used different materials: base ten blocks, a number line.*)

▸ How did you know that $790 - 519$ would have the same difference as $791 - 520$ or $789 - 518$?
(e.g., *I increased both numbers by 1 or decreased both numbers by 1. The difference doesn't change, but the numbers are easier to use.*)

▸ What made your story problem a subtraction problem?
(e.g., *I was taking things away; I was comparing things to see how much larger one number is than another number.*)

Subtracting Three-Digit Numbers

Guided Intervention

Before Using the Guided Intervention

Write 550 − 300 and ask:

▸ Why is this subtraction fairly easy?
(e.g., *If you are taking away only hundreds you just get rid of 3 of the 5 hundreds in 550 and use what's left.*)

▸ How could you model 100 − 35 on a number line?
(e.g., *You could start at 100 and go back 35.*)

▸ How else could you model it?
(e.g., *Start at 35 and see how much to add to get to 100.*)

Using the Guided Intervention (Student Resource pages 55–58)

Provide base ten blocks, place value charts (hundreds, tens, ones: BLM 1), and number lines (BLM 4) for students to use in calculating 543 − 157. Have students estimate first and share their strategies. Then have them work through the subtraction strategies shown on the student pages by modelling the numbers with materials as shown and working through the recording options.

Have students work through the **Try These** questions in pairs or individually.

Observe whether students

• can estimate differences (Questions 1, 2, 5, 6, 8)
• use a variety of strategies for subtracting (Questions 4, 5, 7)
• recognize real-life situations that involve subtracting (Question 3)

Consolidating and Reflecting

Ensure understanding by asking questions such as the following:

▸ Which digits do you ignore when you estimate differences?
(e.g., *I ignore the ones digits, since the ones digits change the answer only a small amount.*)

▸ Which way of subtracting do you prefer to use? Why?
(e.g., *I like to subtract in parts: first the hundreds, then the tens, and then the ones, because it helps me to make sure that I didn't miss a part of the number.*)

▸ How do you choose 2 pairs of numbers with the same difference?
(e.g., *To keep the difference the same, I add 2 to both numbers to make a new pair.*)

▸ What strategy did you use to look for errors in Question 7?
(e.g., *I tried it myself first; then I tried to figure out how they got the numbers.*)

▸ How did you figure out the missing numbers in Question 8?
(e.g., *I used addition; I guessed and checked until I got close to the difference I needed.*)

You will need

• base ten blocks
• place value charts (hundreds, tens, ones) (BLM 1)
• number lines (BLM 4)
• Student Resource pages 55–58

Subtracting Numbers to 100

You will need

- base ten blocks
- place value charts (tens, ones) (BLM 2)
- number lines (BLM 4)
- 100 charts (BLM 5)
- Student Resource page 59

Open-Ended Intervention

Before Using the Open-Ended Intervention

Write 48 − 3 and ask:

▸ How would you calculate 48 − 3?
(e.g., *Count down 3 to say 47, 46, 45.*)

Write 48 − 30 and ask:

▸ How would you calculate 48 − 30?
(e.g., *3 tens, so that's 38, 28, 18*)

▸ How are the questions alike?
(e.g., *They start with the same number, 48. Both times I subtracted 3: 3 ones or 3 tens.*)

Using the Open-Ended Intervention (Student Resource page 59)

Provide base ten blocks, place value charts (BLM 2), number lines (BLM 4), and a 100 chart (BLM 5). Read the task together. Have students work through the prompts in pairs.

Observe the various strategies that students use to subtract, such as

- regrouping to make 5s and 10s
- relating subtraction to addition
- constant difference (e.g., calculating 50 − 32 using 48 − 30)

Consolidating and Reflecting

Ensure understanding by asking questions such as the following, based on students' work:

▸ How did you estimate your difference?
(e.g., *by rounding to tens*)

▸ How are your 2 ways of subtracting alike?
(e.g., *Each time, I subtracted by taking away; I did it different ways.*)

▸ How did you know that 82 − 58 would have the same difference as 81 − 57?
(e.g., *Both numbers are decreased by 1, so the difference stays the same.*)

▸ What about your story problem made it a subtraction problem?
(e.g., *I was taking away things.*)

Guided Intervention

Before Using the Guided Intervention

Write $50 - 34$ and ask:

▸ How do you know that $50 - 30 = 20$?
(e.g., *You have 5 tens and if you take away 3 of them, there are 2 of them left.*)

▸ How do you know that $50 - 34$ is less than 20?
(e.g., *since you're taking away more than 30*)

Write $51 - 34$ and ask:

▸ How do you know that $51 - 34$ is more than 10 but less than 20?
(e.g., *$51 - 34$ is about $50 - 35 = 15$.*)

Using the Guided Intervention   (Student Resource pages 60–63)

Provide base ten blocks, place value charts (BLM 2), 100 charts (BLM 5), and number lines (BLM 4) for students to use as they calculate $37 - 18$ in different ways. Have them estimate first and share their strategies. Then have them work through the subtraction strategies shown on the student page by modelling the numbers with materials as shown and working through the recording options.

Have students work through the **Try These** questions in pairs or individually.

Observe whether and how students

• can estimate differences (Questions 1, 2, 6, 7, 9)
• use a variety of strategies for subtracting (Questions 3, 4, 5, 6, 8)
• recognize real-life situations that involve subtracting (Question 4)

Consolidating and Reflecting

Ensure understanding by asking questions based on students' work:

▸ Which digits do you ignore when you estimate differences?
(e.g., *I ignore the ones digits, since the ones digits change the answer only a small amount.*)

▸ Which way of subtracting do you find easiest?
(e.g., *I like to subtract in parts: first the tens and then the ones, so I don't miss a part of the number.*)

▸ How do you get 2 pairs of numbers that have the same difference?
(e.g., *To keep the difference the same, I subtract 3 from the whole and 3 from the other number to make a new pair.*)

▸ What strategy did you use to figure out whether a difference was possible in Question 7?
(e.g., *I chose the largest and smallest numbers to subtract to see how close I got to the difference I needed.*)

▸ How did you figure out the difference? (e.g., *I used addition.*)

You will need

• base ten blocks
• place value charts (tens, ones) (BLM 2)
• number lines (BLM 4)
• 100 charts (BLM 5)
• Student Resource pages 60–63

Subtracting Numbers to 20

You will need

- 10-frames (BLM 3)
- counters
- base ten blocks
- place value charts (tens, ones) (BLM 2)
- number lines (BLM 4)
- Student Resource page 64

Open-Ended Intervention

Before Using the Open-Ended Intervention

Provide 10-frames and counters, and ask the following questions:

▶ $20 - 10 = 10$. What other pairs of numbers between 1 and 20 have a difference of 10? How could you use 10-frames to figure that out? (e.g., *19 − 9, 18 − 8, 17 − 7, 16 − 6; You could fill 10-frames with 11 to 20 counters and subtract 10 counters.*)

▶ How does knowing that $10 - 3 = 7$ help you figure out $9 - 3$? (*Because 9 is 1 less than 10, 9 − 3 will be 1 less than 10 − 3.*)

▶ What is $18 - 9$? How does knowing that help you figure out $18 - 8$? (*9; 18 − 8 is one more than 18 − 9 because I subtracted 1 less.*)

Using the Open-Ended Intervention   (Student Resource page 64)

Provide 10-frames (BLM 3), counters, base ten blocks, place value charts (BLM 2), and number lines (BLM 4). Read through the task on the student page together. Provide time for students to work through the task in pairs.

Observe whether students

- realize that one number must be greater than 10 and the other less than 10
- find differences for 11 or 16 and then adjust the number being subtracted (e.g., start with $15 - 4 = 11$ and change to $15 - 3$)
- find differences for 11 or 16 and then adjust the number being subtracted from (e.g., start with $15 - 4 = 11$ and change to $16 - 4$)
- add or subtract the same amount to the values for one answer to get another (e.g., use $19 - 7$ to get $18 - 6$)

Consolidating and Reflecting

Ensure understanding by asking questions, based on students' work:

▶ Will the difference for $19 - 9$ be less than 11 or more than 11? How do you know? (e.g., *If you take 9 ones from 1 ten and 9 ones, the difference is 10, not 11.*)

▶ Does $19 - 7$ have a difference greater than 11? How do you know? (e.g., *greater than 11, since the ones digits have a difference of 2*)

▶ Once you knew that $20 - 9 = 11$ was a choice, how could you find other combinations? (e.g., *I subtracted 1 from both numbers to keep the difference the same, like 19 − 8, 18 − 7, 17 − 6. ... The ones digits have a difference of 1.*)

▶ How did you choose other numbers to get a difference of 12, 13, 14, 15, and 16? (e.g., *I started with 20 − 12 = 8; then I used that subtraction equation to get others with a difference of 1 in the ones digit, like 19 − 7, 18 − 6, 17 − 5.*)

Guided Intervention

Before Using the Guided Intervention

Ask the following questions:

▶ If you were calculating $11 - 6$, what strategies might you use if you forgot the answer? (e.g., *I know $12 - 6$ is 6, and I would subtract 1 because 11 is 1 less than 12; $10 - 6$ is 4, and 11 is 1 more than 10, so add 1 to get 5.*)

▶ How could you use 10-frames to calculate $11 - 6$? (e.g., *I would put 10 counters in one 10-frame and 1 in another 10-frame. Then I would take out 6 counters and count how many are left.*)

Using the Guided Intervention ⟮Student Resource pages 65–67⟯

Provide 10-frames (BLM 3), counters, and number lines (BLM 4) for students to use to calculate $12 - 5$ in various ways. Have them model and work through the strategies shown on the student page.

Have students work through the **Try These** questions individually or in pairs.

Observe
- what facts they relate a given fact to (Questions 1, 4, 5)
- what facts they know (Question 2)
- whether they relate subtraction to real-world situations (Question 3)
- what strategies they use to subtract (Questions 4, 6, 7)
- the use of addition facts (Questions 1, 2, 4, 5, 7)

Consolidating and Reflecting

Ensure understanding by asking questions based on students' work:

▶ If you calculate $12 - 5$, how do you know the difference is more than 5, but not a lot more? (e.g., *I think of $10 - 5 = 5$, and $12 - 5$ is 2 more in the whole so it is 2 more in the difference.*)

▶ What other subtraction facts can you figure out from $12 - 5 = 7$? (e.g., *$13 - 5 = 8$; $14 - 5 = 9$; $13 - 4 = 9$; $14 - 4 = 10$*)

▶ How does knowing that $12 - 7 = 5$ help you figure out $14 - 7 = 7$? (e.g., *The whole is 2 more, so the difference is 2 more.*)

▶ How do you get 2 pairs of numbers that have the same difference of 8? (e.g., *I think of a number to add to 8, like $5 + 8 = 13$, and make a subtraction: $13 - 5 = 8$. Then I add or subtract 1 from both numbers: $14 - 6 = 8$, $15 - 7 = 8$, $13 - 5 = 8$, $12 - 4 = 8$.*)

▶ What strategy did you use to figure out whether a difference was possible in Question 5? (e.g., *I chose the largest and smallest numbers to subtract to see how close I got to the difference I needed.*)

▶ What strategy did you use to look for errors in Question 6? (e.g., *I tried it myself first; then I tried to figure out how they got the numbers.*)

You will need

- base ten blocks
- counters
- 10-frames (BLM 3)
- number lines (BLM 4)
- Student Resource pages 65–67

Fractions

Planning For This Topic

Materials for assisting students with fractions consist of a diagnostic tool and 3 intervention pathways. You can use the pathways to focus on the problem area identified by the diagnostic tool: fractions as parts of a set, parts of a whole, or a beginning understanding of fractions focusing on halves.

Each pathway has an open-ended option and a guided option. Choose the type of intervention most suitable for your students' needs and your particular circumstances.

Curriculum Connections

Grades 1 to 4 curriculum connections for this topic are provided online. See www.nelson.com/leapsandbounds. Note that standard fraction notation is not introduced in most curricula until Grade 4, so many students will have encountered only the word form of fractions. Some students will have encountered standard fraction notation (symbolic form) and will find this easier to read. In these materials, the word form is used primarily, but the symbolic form often appears with the word form. Be sure that students do not think of the numerator and denominator as 2 separate numbers rather than as a relationship. Fractions as parts of sets is introduced in the WNCP curriculum in Grade 4, so those students can omit Pathway 1.

Why might students struggle with fractions?

Although still early in Grades 3 and 4 in a student's exposure to fractions, it is important to ensure there is a firm foundation for subsequent study of fractions.

Students might struggle with fractions for any of the following reasons:

- Even though fractions are numbers, the relationship between the 2 numbers—the numerator and denominator—is the focus of fraction work. Looking at a relationship instead of a single number is always more challenging.
- Sometimes students mix up the roles of the numerator and denominator.
- Sometimes students forget that the parts of the whole must be equal in area, but do not have to be identical, to use a fraction to describe them.
- Sometimes students do not realize that the part of the whole being considered can be anywhere within the whole. (e.g., $\frac{1}{5}$ might be shaded as the middle of 5 sections of a rectangle).
- When fractions are parts of sets, it matters only that the number of elements in the subgroups are equal; we do not consider the relative sizes of the actual objects. However, when fractions are parts of wholes (whether area or linear measures), the parts must be equal in measure.
- Students may not realize we can describe fractions of any measure, whether area, length, volume, capacity, time, mass, or number.

Professional Learning Connections

PRIME: Number and Operations, Background and Strategies (Nelson Education, 2005), pages 103–106, 111–116

Making Math Meaningful to Canadian Students K–8 (Nelson Education Ltd., 2008), pages 196–201, 206–209

Big Ideas from Dr. Small Grades K–3 (Nelson Education Ltd., 2010), pages 58–60

Leaps and Bounds 3/4 Copyright © 2011 by Nelson Education Ltd.

Diagnostic Tool: Fractions

Use the diagnostic tool to determine the most suitable intervention pathway for fractions. Provide Diagnostic Tool: Fractions, Teacher's Resource pages 74 and 75, and have students complete it in writing or orally.

See solutions on Teacher's Resource pages 76 and 77.

Intervention Pathways

The purpose of the intervention pathways is to help students work with proper fractions (fractions less than 1) as parts of sets *and* as parts of wholes. The focus is to prepare them for working with a broader range of fractions.

There are 3 pathways:
- Pathway 1: Fractions as Parts of Sets
- Pathway 2: Fractions as Parts of Wholes
- Pathway 3: Halves

Use the chart below (or the Key to Pathways on Teacher's Resource pages 76 and 77) to determine which pathway is most suitable for each student or group of students.

Diagnostic Tool Results	Intervention Pathway
If students struggle with Questions 1d–f, 2c–d, 5, 6	use Pathway 1: Fractions as Parts of Sets (*Teacher's Resource pages 78–79 Student Resource pages 68–72*)
If students struggle with Questions 2a–b, 3, 4	use Pathway 2: Fractions as Parts of Wholes (*Teacher's Resource pages 80–81 Student Resource pages 73–77*)
If students struggle with Question 1	use Pathway 3: Halves (*Teacher's Resource pages 82–83 Student Resource pages 78–81*)

Fractions

1. Circle the pictures that show one half.

   a)

   b)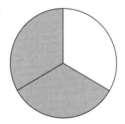

   c)

   d)

   e)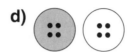

   f)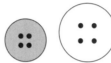

2. Circle the name of the shaded fraction.

   a)

   two thirds $\left(\frac{2}{3}\right)$ or one half $\left(\frac{1}{2}\right)$

   b)

   one third $\left(\frac{1}{3}\right)$ or one quarter $\left(\frac{1}{4}\right)$

   c)

   one half $\left(\frac{1}{2}\right)$ or one third $\left(\frac{1}{3}\right)$

   d)

   two eighths $\left(\frac{2}{8}\right)$ or two tenths $\left(\frac{2}{10}\right)$

3. Colour or shade the shape to show the fraction.

   a)

   one third $\left(\frac{1}{3}\right)$

   b)

   three quarters $\left(\frac{3}{4}\right)$

Leaps and Bounds
Copyright © 2011 by Nelson Education Ltd.

Name:_____ Date:_____

4. Colour or shade the shape to show the fraction.

a)

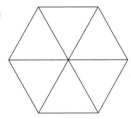

five sixths $\left(\frac{5}{6}\right)$

b)

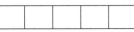

two fifths $\left(\frac{2}{5}\right)$

c)

two fourths $\left(\frac{2}{4}\right)$

d)

one eighth $\left(\frac{1}{8}\right)$

5. What fraction of the balloons is shaded?

a)

_____

b)

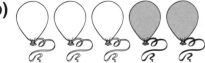

_____

c)

_____

6. Draw buttons to show the fraction.
You can draw buttons like these:

 or

a) one fifth $\left(\frac{1}{5}\right)$

b) two sixths $\left(\frac{2}{6}\right)$

Copyright © 2011 by Nelson Education Ltd.   *Leaps and Bounds*

Solutions and Key to Pathways

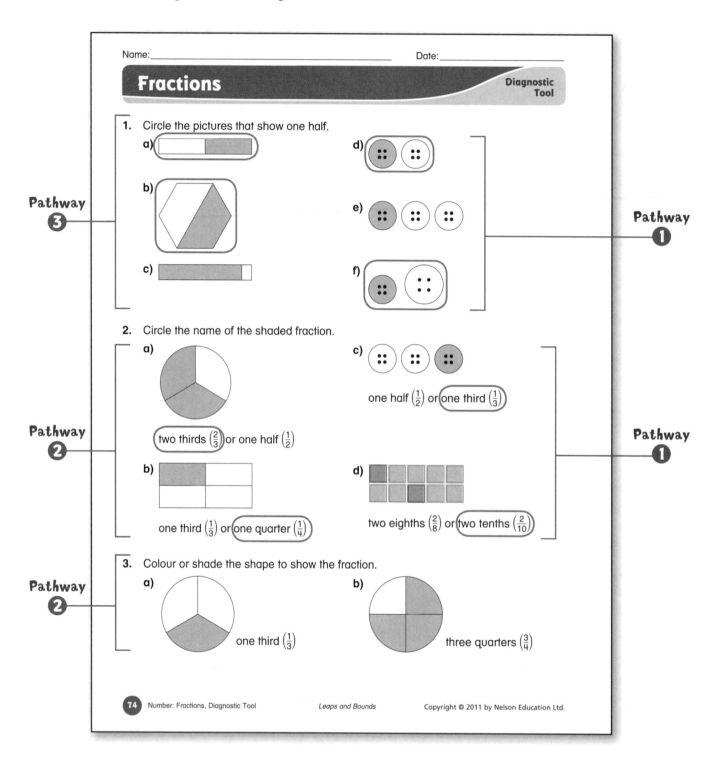

Name:_____ Date:_____

Fractions

Diagnostic Tool

Pathway 3

1. Circle the pictures that show one half.

a)

b)

c)

Pathway 1

d)

e)

f)

Pathway 2

2. Circle the name of the shaded fraction.

a)

two thirds $\left(\frac{2}{3}\right)$ or one half $\left(\frac{1}{2}\right)$

b)

one third $\left(\frac{1}{3}\right)$ or one quarter $\left(\frac{1}{4}\right)$

c)

one half $\left(\frac{1}{2}\right)$ or one third $\left(\frac{1}{3}\right)$

d)

two eighths $\left(\frac{2}{8}\right)$ or two tenths $\left(\frac{2}{10}\right)$

Pathway 1

Pathway 2

3. Colour or shade the shape to show the fraction.

a)

one third $\left(\frac{1}{3}\right)$

b)

three quarters $\left(\frac{3}{4}\right)$

74 Number: Fractions, Diagnostic Tool   *Leaps and Bounds*   Copyright © 2011 by Nelson Education Ltd.

76 Number: Fractions   *Leaps and Bounds 3/4*   Copyright © 2011 by Nelson Education Ltd.

Name: _____ Date: _____

4. Colour or shade the shape to show the fraction.

a)

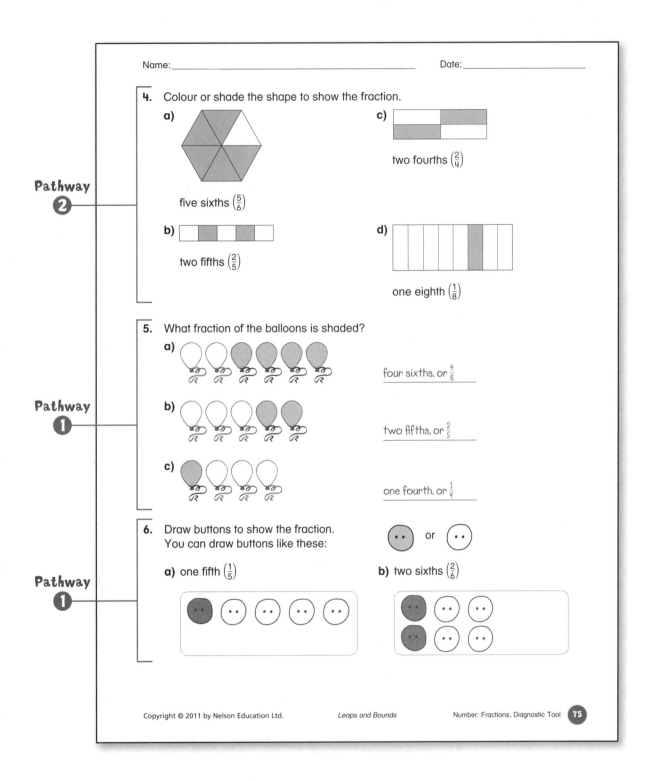

five sixths $\left(\frac{5}{6}\right)$

b)

two fifths $\left(\frac{2}{5}\right)$

c)

two fourths $\left(\frac{2}{4}\right)$

d)

one eighth $\left(\frac{1}{8}\right)$

Pathway 2

5. What fraction of the balloons is shaded?

a)

four sixths, or $\frac{4}{6}$

b)

two fifths, or $\frac{2}{5}$

c)

one fourth, or $\frac{1}{4}$

Pathway 1

6. Draw buttons to show the fraction.
You can draw buttons like these: •• or ••

a) one fifth $\left(\frac{1}{5}\right)$

b) two sixths $\left(\frac{2}{6}\right)$

Pathway 1

Copyright © 2011 by Nelson Education Ltd. *Leaps and Bounds* Number: Fractions, Diagnostic Tool **75**

Copyright © 2011 by Nelson Education Ltd. *Leaps and Bounds 3/4* Number: Fractions **77**

Fractions as Parts of Sets

You will need

- 10–12 counters
- chart paper and drawing materials, such as markers or coloured pencils or stickers
- Student Resource page 68

Open-Ended Intervention

Before Using the Open-Ended Intervention

Ask the following questions.

▶ What is a fraction? (e.g., *It's a number that tells about a part of something.*)

▶ What is one quarter?
(e.g., *It means there are 4 equal parts, and you are only interested in one of them.*)

Provide counters and ask the following questions:

▶ Would you say "three four," "three fourths," or "third four" to describe the boys in a picture where there are 3 boys and 1 girl? Explain.
(*Three fourths; the "three" is the part that are boys, and the "fourths" is the whole group.*)

▶ How can you show two thirds using counters? (e.g., *You can use 3 counters, and 2 of them could be red and 1 yellow. Then two thirds is red.*)

Using the Open-Ended Intervention   (Student Resource page 68)

Provide chart paper and drawing materials and/or stickers. Draw students' attention to the picture on the student page and read through the tasks and the **Remember** box together.

Observe whether students

- realize that every fraction picture shows at least 2 fractions—the part being considered and the rest of the set
- show a number of different fractions in their pictures
- use parts of sets, not parts of wholes, in their pictures
- identify and name their fractions correctly
- use fractions that have a numerator other than 1
- recognize which fractions represent a large part of a whole and which represent a small part
- recognize that the first word in the fraction tells the number of parts being considered, and the second word indicates the number of equal parts in total

Consolidating and Reflecting

Have students summarize their thinking by naming their fractions and creating their pictures. Ask these questions to consolidate their learning:

▶ Why is there more than one fraction describing the animals?
(e.g., *One fraction talks about the dogs, but another one talks about the rabbits.*)

▶ One of your pictures shows 8 trees. What does that mean about the fractions describing the trees? (e.g., *They will all be eighths.*)

▶ Which of your fractions do you think is big?
(e.g., *I think eight eighths is big, since it's everything.*)

▶ What part of your picture tells about the first word in the name of your fraction? (e.g., *the part that I want to describe*)

Fractions as Parts of Sets

Guided Intervention

Before Using the Guided Intervention

Show 2 red counters. Ask the following questions:

▸ What is a fraction? (e.g., *It's a number that tells about a part of something.*)

▸ What do you think one half of the group of counters would be? Why?
  (e.g., *one of them; because there is one of the two*)

▸ What is one quarter?
  (e.g., *It means there are 4 equal parts, and you are interested in only one of them.*)

Show how four quarters make a dollar, to make the link to the other meaning of quarter. Mention that the word *fourth* is interchangeable with the word *quarter*.

Using the Guided Intervention (Student Resource pages 69–72)

Provide counters and work through the instructional section about thirds with students. Have them model the two thirds and one third as they work through the description of the family.

To ensure that students understand, ask them to use counters to model *three fourths*. Encourage them to describe how they know their model fits the fraction.

Have students work through the **Try These** questions in pairs or individually.

Observe whether students

• recognize the name associated with a pictorial representation of a fraction of a set (Question 1)

• can apply a name to a pictorial representation of a fraction of a set (Question 2)

• can create fractions of set models to fit criteria (Questions 3, 6)

• recognize when a fraction is the greater amount of a whole and when it is not (Question 4)

• realize what must be counted when describing the name for a fraction (Question 5)

Consolidating and Reflecting

Ask students to reflect on 1 or 2 of their responses and talk about them. Then ask these questions to consolidate their learning:

▸ 6 children are wearing hats in Question 1 part c). Why wasn't the fraction *sixths*?
  (e.g., *The second word tells how many in all, not how many in one part.*)

▸ Suppose you are asked to model a fraction that is described as *eighths*. What do you know about the model? (e.g., *There must be 8 things altogether.*)

▸ Suppose almost all of a set of fruits is bananas. What fractions might describe the bananas? (e.g., *maybe seven eighths*)

▸ How did you choose the fraction for Question 6 part b)?
  (e.g., *I knew I wanted a lot of people not wearing shoes so that the word "most" made sense, so I used five sixths.*)

Fractions as Parts of Wholes

You will need

- drawing materials
- pattern blocks or square tiles
- Fraction Circles (BLM 8)
- Fraction Rectangles (BLM 9)
- Student Resource page 73

Open-Ended Intervention

Before Using the Open-Ended Intervention

Show a circle divided into 2 equal pieces and a rectangle made up of 6 square tiles. Ask:

▸ What is a fraction? (e.g., *It's a number that tells about a part of something.*)

▸ What does one quarter of a circle look like? (e.g., *It looks like a circle divided into 4 equal parts, and you are talking about one of them.*)

Mention that the word *quarter* is interchangeable with the word *fourth*.

▸ Here is a rectangle made up of 6 square tiles. What fractions can you show? (e.g., *one sixth, two sixths, one half*)

Using the Open-Ended Intervention   (Student Resource page 73)

Provide drawing materials, Fraction Circles (BLM 8), and Fraction Rectangles (BLM 9), as well as either pattern blocks or square tiles. Draw students' attention to the picture on the student page and read through the tasks together.

Make sure that students realize they can use the circles and rectangles on the blackline masters as objects in their pictures, or they can create their own shapes using square tiles or pattern blocks or by drawing.

Observe whether students

- are comfortable with fractions when more than one part is being described
- realize that every fraction picture shows at least 2 fractions—the part being considered and the rest of the whole
- show a number of different fractions in their pictures
- correctly identify and name their fractions
- recognize which fractions represent a large part of a whole
- recognize that the first word in the fraction tells the number of parts being considered, and the second word the number of equal parts in the whole object

Consolidating and Reflecting

Have students summarize their thinking by naming their fractions and creating their pictures. Ask these questions to consolidate their learning:

▸ Why is there more than one fraction describing each pizza? (e.g., *You could talk about the pieces that are there or the pieces that are gone.*)

▸ One of your pictures shows a garden with 8 sections. What does that mean about the fractions describing the garden? (e.g., *They will all be eighths.*)

Name a fraction such as five sixths and point out that 2 words are used to say the fraction. Ask:

▸ What part of your picture tells about the first word in the name of your fraction? (e.g., *the part that I want to describe*)

Fractions as Parts of Wholes

Guided Intervention

Before Using the Guided Intervention

Have available the Fraction Circles and Fraction Rectangles (BLMs 8–9) and ask:

▸ What is a fraction? (e.g., *It's a number that tells about a part of something.*)

Show a circle divided into 2 equal pieces. Point to 1 piece. Ask:

▸ What fraction describes this piece? (*one half*)

▸ How would you show half the square? (e.g., *I would fold it in half and show one side.*)

▸ What does one third of a circle look like? (e.g., *It looks like a circle divided into 3 equal parts, and you care about only one of them.*)

Using the Guided Intervention (Student Resource pages 74–77)

Provide Fraction Circles and Rectangles (BLMs 8–9) and a red pencil or marker for students. Work through the instructional section about thirds together. Have them model the two thirds and one third as they read the description of the flag. Make sure they realize that one third describes the white section and that three thirds describes all 3 sections of the flag.

To ensure that students understand, ask them to choose which of the circles from Fraction Circles (BLM 8) they would use to show four fifths. Have students work through the **Try These** questions in pairs or individually.

Observe whether students

- recognize the name associated with a pictorial representation of a fraction of a whole (Question 1)
- can apply a name to a pictorial representation of a fraction of a whole (Question 2)
- can create fractions of whole models to fit criteria (Questions 3, 6)
- recognize that the parts of a fraction must be equal (Question 4)
- can identify fractions that are close to a whole and fractions that are close to 0 (Question 5)

Consolidating and Reflecting

Ask students to reflect on 1 or 2 of their responses and talk about them. Then ask these questions to consolidate their learning:

▸ Why did you not use part d) in Question 1 to match six sixths, even though it had 6 grey parts?
(e.g., *The second word tells how many in all, not how many shaded parts.*)

▸ Suppose you are asked to model a fraction that is described as *eighths*. What do you know about the model? (e.g., *There have to be 8 equal sections.*)

▸ Two halves is the same as the whole thing. What other fractions describe a whole thing? (e.g., *three thirds, four quarters, six sixths*)

▸ How did you choose the fraction for Question 6 part d)?
(e.g., *I divided the square into a lot of equal parts but made only a few of them red.*)

You will need

- Fraction Circles (BLM 8)
- Fraction Rectangles (BLM 9)
- a red pencil or marker
- Student Resource pages 74–77

Halves

You will need

- 2 pennies
- a circle cut into 2 equal pieces
- a circle cut into 2 unequal pieces
- pattern blocks
- linking cubes
- Fraction Circles (BLM 8)
- drawing materials
- Student Resource page 78

Open-Ended Intervention

Before Using the Open-Ended Intervention

Show 2 pennies and ask:
▸ I am going to give you half of my coins. How many should I give you? (*one*)

Show a circle cut into 2 equal pieces. Ask:
▸ I am going to give you half of my circle. How many pieces should I give you? (*one*)

Give a student one piece of a circle cut into 2 unequal pieces. Ask:
▸ Did I give you half this time? How do you know? (*No, the pieces are not equal.*)

Using the Open-Ended Intervention   (Student Resource page 78)

Draw students' attention to the picture on the student page and read through the tasks together. Make sure students understand that in each part of the picture there are 2 equal sections.

Provide pattern blocks, linking cubes, and several copies of the Fraction Circles (BLM 8). Encourage students to show one half in as many ways as possible.

Observe whether students
- recognize that we use the word *half* when there are 2 equal shares
- ensure that wholes are divided into 2 equal pieces
- realize that halves can also be shown with 2 items, which may or may not be identical
- realize they can show one half with pattern blocks using area (e.g., red is half of yellow) or using parts of sets (e.g., one red block is half of a set of two blocks)
- realize they can show one half with linking cubes using volume (e.g., a structure made of 2 cubes of different colours) or using parts of sets (e.g., 1 cube is half of a set of 2 cubes)

Consolidating and Reflecting

Have students summarize their thinking in creating their halves. Ask these questions to consolidate their learning:
▸ What do all of your pictures and models have in common? (e.g., *They all have two pieces.*)
▸ Are the pieces equal? (e.g., *sometimes—when I had pattern blocks, sometimes one was bigger than the other, but the numbers in each group were equal*)
▸ Was there more than one way to show one half with pattern blocks? (e.g., *Yes, I used green as half of blue and red as half of yellow.*)

Leaps and Bounds 3/4
Copyright © 2011 by Nelson Education Ltd.

Guided Intervention

Before Using the Guided Intervention

Show 2 pennies and ask:

▸ I am going to give you half of my coins. How many should I give you? (*one*)

Show the circle cut into 2 unequal pieces. Ask:

▸ I am going to give you half of my circle. How many pieces should I give you? (*one*)

Show one piece of a circle cut into 2 unequal pieces. Ask:

▸ I am going to give you this piece. Is this half? (*no*) How do you know? (*The pieces are not equal.*)

Using the Guided Intervention (Student Resource pages 79–81)

Work through the instructional section on the student pages about halves together. Have students model the cookie as a circle and fold it in half to show the 2 pieces. Point out that it is critical that the parts be equal. Let students discuss how they know that the parts are equal.

Ensure that students understand that *two halves* refers to the whole and that halves can represent parts of wholes or parts of sets.

Have students work through the **Try These** questions in pairs or individually.

Observe whether students

• recognize that 2 halves must only be equal in number in parts of a set (Questions 1, 4, 6)

• can create halves (Questions 2, 3)

• realize that a whole can be divided in half in more than one way (Question 3)

• realize that two halves make a whole (Question 5)

Consolidating and Reflecting

Ask these questions to consolidate learning:

▸ Why didn't you circle Question 1 part b)?
(e.g., *The parts are not equal—one piece of the bar is a lot bigger.*)

▸ Why did you circle Question 1 part e)?
(e.g., *The dark and light pieces look like the same length.*)

▸ Why was it a little easier to show halves in Question 2 part c) than in Question 2 part b)? (e.g., *If I have to make the pieces, it is hard to be sure the pieces are exactly the same size.*)

▸ The one orange makes up half of the number of fruit and the orange is bigger than the lemon in Question 6. Why isn't the shaded part one half, then, in Question 2? (e.g., *because the halves are equal if you think of 1 fruit = 1 fruit, but the 2 areas are not equal in Question 4*)

You will need

• 2 pennies
• a circle cut into 2 equal pieces
• a circle cut into 2 unequal pieces
• coloured pencils
• Student Resource pages 79–81

Planning For This Topic

Materials for assisting students with mental math consist of a diagnostic tool and 3 intervention pathways. The pathways differ in the nature of the mental math strategy covered for adding or subtracting.

Each pathway has an open-ended option and a guided option. Choose the type of intervention most suitable for your students' learning needs and your particular circumstances.

Curriculum Connections

Grades 1 to 4 curriculum connections for this topic are provided online. See www.nelson.com/leapsandbounds. Note that while various curricula call for mental math strategies, specific strategies are not usually named. The mental math strategies here are for addition and subtraction.

Why might students struggle with mental math?

Students might struggle with using mental math for any of the following reasons:

- Some students struggle with mental math because they are either not encouraged to use it or not given enough opportunities to practise using it.
- Although the use of mental math builds number sense, some students whose number sense is weak struggle with mental math; this is because mental math is premised on the student's knowledge and use of relationships among numbers.
- Some students have either memory problems or simply a discomfort with keeping several pieces of mathematical information in their minds; they are used to writing things down. Often, when doing mental math, students must keep track of several different computations in their heads at once. These students may not have had opportunities to learn to build memory capacity.

The importance of developing competence in mental math is both to build number sense and to develop students who perform proficient and efficient calculations.

Professional Learning Connections

PRIME: Number and Operations, Background and Strategies (Nelson Education, 2005), pages 69–71, 76

Making Math Meaningful to Canadian Students K–8 (Nelson Education Ltd., 2008), pages 162–163, 166

Big Ideas from Dr. Small Grades K–3 (Nelson Education Ltd., 2010), pages 48–50, 54

Good Questions (dist. by Nelson Education Ltd., 2009), page 23

Leaps and Bounds 3/4 Copyright © 2011 by Nelson Education Ltd.

Diagnostic Tool: Mental Math

Use the diagnostic tool to determine the most suitable intervention pathway for mental math. Provide Diagnostic Tool: Mental Math, Teacher's Resource pages 86 and 87, and have students complete it in writing or orally.

Note: You may choose to interview students for this diagnostic to observe their processes.

See solutions on Teacher's Resource pages 88 and 89.

Intervention Pathways

The purpose of the intervention pathways is to help students develop a repertoire of mental math strategies useful when adding or subtracting. The focus is to prepare them for working with larger numbers later on.

There are 3 pathways:
- Pathway 1: Compensating
- Pathway 2: Regrouping
- Pathway 3: Relating to 5 or 10

Use the chart below (or the Key to Pathways on Teacher's Resource pages 88 and 89) to determine which pathway is most suitable for each student or group of students.

Diagnostic Tool Results	Intervention Pathway
If students struggle with Questions 5, 6c–f	use Pathway 1: Compensating *Teacher's Resource pages 90–91* *Student Resource pages 82–87*
If students struggle with Questions 2d–f, 3b–d, 4, 6a–b	use Pathway 2: Regrouping *Teacher's Resource pages 92–93* *Student Resource pages 88–93*
If students struggle with Questions 1, 2a–c, 3a	use Pathway 3: Relating to 5 or 10 *Teacher's Resource pages 94–95* *Student Resource pages 94–99*

Name: _____ Date: _____

Mental Math

Figure out the answers using mental math only.

1. Circle the sum that is more. Then tell how much more.

   a) 4 + 5 or 5 + 5   The sum is _____ more.

   b) 7 + 6 or 5 + 5   The sum is _____ more.

   c) 6 + 7 or 5 + 10   The sum is _____ more.

   d) 9 + 7 or 10 + 5   The sum is _____ more.

2. Calculate each sum using mental math.

   a) 8 + 2 = _____   **d)** 42 + 30 = _____

   b) 7 + 3 = _____   **e)** 57 + 40 = _____

   c) 6 + 4 = _____   **f)** 81 + 60 = _____

3. Calculate each difference using mental math.

   a) 15 − 10 = _____   **c)** 82 − 20 = _____

   b) 60 − 20 = _____   **d)** 94 − 40 = _____

4. Complete the sentence like the example.
   Tell whether to add or subtract and how much.
   Example: For 26 + 5, use 26 + 4 and ___add 1___.

   a) For 37 + 8, use 37 + 3 and _____.

   b) For 55 + 16, use 55 + 10 and _____.

   c) For 55 + 16, use 50 + 16 and _____.

   d) For 22 − 8, use 22 − 2 and _____.

   e) For 73 − 9, use 69 − 9 and _____.

   f) For 82 − 35, use 82 − 30 and _____.

Leaps and Bounds Copyright © 2011 by Nelson Education Ltd.

Name: _____   Date: _____

5. Complete the sentence like the example.
    Tell whether to add or subtract and how much.
    Example: For 28 + 5, use 30 + 5 and ___subtract 2___ .

    a) For 47 + 7, use 50 + 7 and _____ .

    b) For 67 + 19, use 67 + 20 and _____ .

    c) For 83 + 88, use 83 + 90 and _____ .

    d) For 22 − 8, use 22 − 10 and _____ .

    e) For 41 − 9, use 41 − 10 and _____ .

    f) For 81 − 52, use 81 − 50 and _____ .

6. Show or tell how to calculate using mental math.

    a) 25 + 21

    b) 33 + 46

    c) 52 + 29

    d) 39 + 48

    e) 70 − 28

    f) 63 − 25

Solutions and Key to Pathways

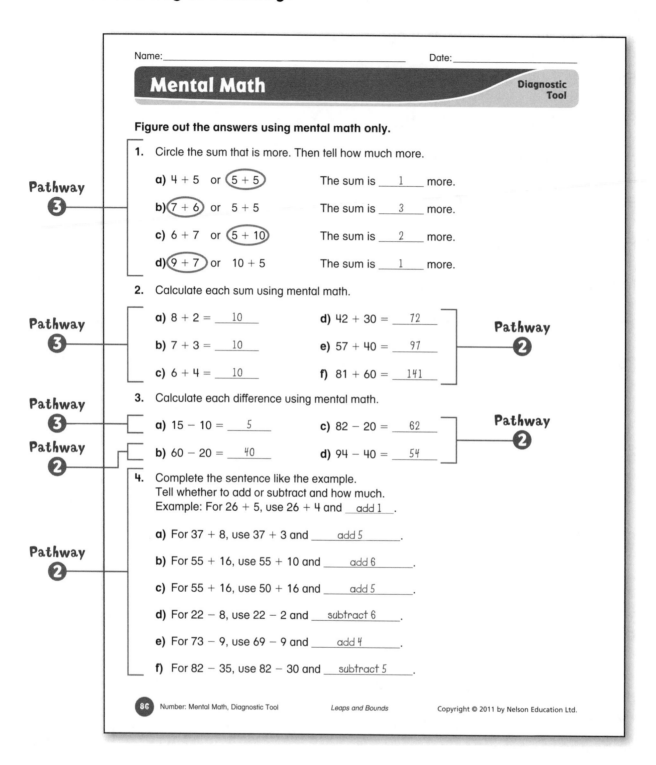

Name: _____   Date: _____

Mental Math

Diagnostic Tool

Figure out the answers using mental math only.

Pathway 3

1. Circle the sum that is more. Then tell how much more.

    a) 4 + 5   or (5 + 5)   The sum is ___1___ more.

    b) (7 + 6) or   5 + 5   The sum is ___3___ more.

    c) 6 + 7   or (5 + 10)   The sum is ___2___ more.

    d) (9 + 7) or   10 + 5   The sum is ___1___ more.

2. Calculate each sum using mental math.

    Pathway 3

    a) 8 + 2 = ___10___   **d)** 42 + 30 = ___72___   **Pathway 2**

    b) 7 + 3 = ___10___   **e)** 57 + 40 = ___97___

    c) 6 + 4 = ___10___   **f)** 81 + 60 = ___141___

3. Calculate each difference using mental math.

    Pathway 3

    a) 15 − 10 = ___5___   **c)** 82 − 20 = ___62___   **Pathway 2**

    Pathway 2

    b) 60 − 20 = ___40___   **d)** 94 − 40 = ___54___

4. Complete the sentence like the example.
    Tell whether to add or subtract and how much.
    Example: For 26 + 5, use 26 + 4 and ___add 1___ .

    Pathway 2

    a) For 37 + 8, use 37 + 3 and _____add 5_____ .

    b) For 55 + 16, use 55 + 10 and _____add 6_____ .

    c) For 55 + 16, use 50 + 16 and _____add 5_____ .

    d) For 22 − 8, use 22 − 2 and ___subtract 6___ .

    e) For 73 − 9, use 69 − 9 and _____add 4_____ .

    f) For 82 − 35, use 82 − 30 and ___subtract 5___ .

86 Number: Mental Math, Diagnostic Tool   *Leaps and Bounds*   Copyright © 2011 by Nelson Education Ltd.

Name:_____ Date:_____

5. Complete the sentence like the example.
Tell whether to add or subtract and how much.
Example: For 28 + 5, use 30 + 5 and ___subtract 2___.

Pathway

1

a) For 47 + 7, use 50 + 7 and ____subtract 3____.

b) For 67 + 19, use 67 + 20 and ____subtract 1____.

c) For 83 + 88, use 83 + 90 and ____subtract 2____.

d) For 22 − 8, use 22 − 10 and _____add 2_____.

e) For 41 − 9, use 41 − 10 and _____add 1_____.

f) For 81 − 52, use 81 − 50 and ____subtract 2____.

6. Show or tell how to calculate using mental math.

Pathway

2

a) 25 + 21

> e.g., Use 25 + 20 and add 1.

b) 33 + 46

> e.g., Use 30 + 46 and add 3.

c) 52 + 29

> e.g., Use 52 + 30 and subtract 1.

d) 39 + 48

> e.g., Use 40 + 48 and subtract 1.

Pathway

1

e) 70 − 28

> e.g., Use 70 − 30 and add 2.

f) 63 − 25

> e.g., Use 65 − 25 and subtract 2.

Copyright © 2011 by Nelson Education Ltd.   *Leaps and Bounds*   Number: Mental Math, Diagnostic Tool **87**

Copyright © 2011 by Nelson Education Ltd.   *Leaps and Bounds 3/4*   Number: Mental Math **89**

Compensating

You will need

• Student Resource pages 82–83

Open-Ended Intervention

Before Using the Open-Ended Intervention

Ask the following questions:

▶ How could you solve 27 + 20 using mental math?
(e.g., *27 has 2 tens and I just put on 2 more tens, so that's 47.*)

▶ How can you solve 27 + 19 if you know 27 + 20?
(e.g., *You just do 27 + 20 and take away 1.*)

▶ How could you solve 37 − 20 using mental math? (e.g., *You take 2 tens away from the 3 tens and you have 1 ten left. There is still 7, so that makes 17.*)

▶ What about 37 − 19? (e.g., *You can do 37 − 20, but you took away too much, so you add it back in your head.*)

Using the Open-Ended Intervention (Student Resource pages 82–83)

Read the tasks on the student pages with students. Ensure they understand that they are to do the calculations in their heads. Encourage them to look for similarities in the strategies they use. Provide time for students to work in pairs, and encourage them to describe their strategies aloud before (or instead of) writing.

Observe whether students

• change one or both of the numbers to a "friendly" number to compute using mental math (e.g., 79 + 49 to 79 + 50 or 80 + 49 or 80 + 50)

• recognize that single-digit multiples of 10 are easy to add

• recognize whether to add or subtract to compensate (e.g., realize that 84 − 46 is 4 more than (not 4 less than) 84 − 50)

• create additional questions involving at least one number close to a multiple of 10

Note that because the problem is open-ended, students might solve the questions in a different way than you might anticipate—that is acceptable.

Consolidating and Reflecting

Ensure understanding by asking questions based on students' work:

▶ Why did you change 32 + 59 to 32 + 60? (e.g., *I knew that 59 is close to 60, and I could do 32 + 60 in my head by putting 6 extra tens with 32. Then I could subtract 1.*)

▶ Would you use the same "friendly" numbers to add 26 + 74 and 32 + 79? Explain your thinking. (e.g., *I wouldn't. I know that 1 quarter and 3 quarters makes a dollar, so I do 26 + 74 as 25 + 75 and then I add 1 and take away 1. But for 32 + 79, I'd probably do 32 + 80 and then take away 1.*)

▶ What was different about calculating 52 − 39 compared with 84 − 46 using mental math? (e.g., *For 52 − 39, I subtracted too much (40) and then added back 1, but for 84 − 46, I subtracted too little (44) and then subtracted 2 more.*)

▶ I noticed you added 47 − 18 to your second group. Why do you think it belonged to that group? (e.g., *because I subtracted a little extra and added some back*)

Compensating

Guided Intervention

Before Using the Guided Intervention

Ask the following questions:

▸ How would you do 27 + 20 using mental math?
(e.g., *27 has 2 tens so I put on 2 more tens, so that makes 47.*)

▸ How can you solve 27 + 19 if you know 27 + 20?
(e.g., *You do 27 + 20 and take away 1.*)

▸ How could you solve 37 − 20 using mental math? (e.g., *You take 2 tens away from the 3 tens and you have 1 ten left. There is still 7, so that makes 17.*)

▸ What about 37 − 19? (e.g., *You can do 37 − 20, but you took away too much, so you add it back in your head.*)

Using the Guided Intervention (Student Resource pages 84–87)

Work through the strategies for calculating 45 + 20 and 83 − 20 with students. Relate the descriptions to the visual models. Have students explain why the suggested solutions for 45 + 19 and 83 − 19 make sense.

To ensure students are ready to proceed more independently, ask them to use mental math to calculate 56 + 18 and 56 − 18. Have them work through the **Try These** questions individually or in pairs.

Observe whether students
• can easily add or subtract single-digit multiples of 10 to two-digit numbers (Question 1)
• can explain their mental math strategies (Questions 2 to 7)
• can describe a simpler related calculation and how much more or less the result is (Questions 4 to 6)
• can describe situations where mental math is useful (Question 8)

Consolidating and Reflecting

Ask students to reflect on one or two of their responses and talk about them. Then ask these questions to consolidate their learning:

▸ What did you notice about the resulting ones digit in each answer in Question 1? Why did that happen? (e.g., *The ones digit was the same as the one in the first number, since you were just putting on or taking away tens and not ones.*)

▸ In Question 4, how did you decide whether 43 −19 was more or less than 43 − 20 and by how much?
(e.g., *I thought about subtraction being take away, and if you take away less, you end up with more. Since 19 is 1 less than 20, the difference is 1 more.*)

▸ I notice that you said that 28 + 10 could also help with 28 + 8 in Question 6. Could you have changed the 28 instead? (e.g., *Yes—it could have been 30 + 8.*)

Copyright © 2011 by Nelson Education Ltd. *Leaps and Bounds 3/4*

Regrouping

You will need

• Student Resource pages 88–89

Open-Ended Intervention

Before Using the Open-Ended Intervention

Ask the following questions:

▶ How could knowing what 8 + 2 is help you figure out 28 + 2? (e.g., *I know that 28 is 20 + 8, so I could put the 8 with the 2 and then add the 20; it is 20 + 10 and that's 30.*)

▶ Suppose you were adding 28 + 8. Why might it be helpful to think of the 8 as 2 + 6? (e.g., *You could add 2 to the 28 to get 30 and then add the other 6.*)

▶ Suppose you were adding 37 + 44. Why might it help to think of this as 30 + 40 + 7 + 4? (e.g., *I can do each of the addition pairs in my head.*)

▶ How much is 62 − 32? How do you know? (*It's 30. e.g., If you add 3 tens to 32, you get to 62.*)

▶ How much is 65 − 32? How do you know? (e.g., *I could take 32 away from 62 to get 30, and then there are still 3 more, so the answer is 33. Instead, I could take 3 tens from 6 tens and 2 ones from 5 ones and do the parts separately.*)

Using the Open-Ended Intervention (Student Resource pages 88–89)

Read the tasks on the student pages with students. Ensure they understand that they are to do the calculations in their heads. Encourage them to look for similarities in the mental math strategies they use. Provide time for students to work in pairs, and encourage them to describe their strategies aloud before (or instead of) writing.

Observe whether students
• add in parts or subtract a part from a part to simplify the calculations (e.g., 54 + 56 as 54 + 6 + 50, or 53 − 15 as either 45 − 15 + 8 or 55 − 15 − 2)
• use multiples of 10 as "bridges" (e.g., adding 48 + 25 by bridging to 50 by adding 2 and then adding the rest)
• rename numbers to subtract (e.g., renaming 50 − 28 as 50 − 20 − 8)
Note that because the problem is open-ended, students might solve the questions in a different way than you might anticipate—that is acceptable.

Consolidating and Reflecting

Have students summarize their thinking about calculating sums and differences. Ask questions like the following to consolidate their learning:

▶ Why did it help you to think of 43 + 37 as 40 + 3 + 30 + 7? (e.g., *I can do 40 + 30 and 3 + 7 in my head; then I can add the parts.*)

▶ How did you solve 57 + 35 using mental math? (e.g., *I thought 57 + 30 is 87 and, to add the extra 5, I add 3 to get to 90 and then 2 more*)

▶ How did you choose the extra questions you made up? (e.g., *I tried to make the new questions a lot like the old ones. For example, to be like 36 + 4, I would use something like 72 + 8, since 2 + 8 is 10 just like 6 + 4.*)

Regrouping

Guided Intervention

Before Using the Guided Intervention

Ask the following questions:

▶ How could knowing what 6 + 4 is help you figure out 26 + 4?
(e.g., *I know that it is 20 + 10 and that's 30.*)

▶ Suppose you were adding 28 + 38. Why might it be helpful to think of this as
28 + 30 and then + 8?
(e.g., *Adding 38 is the same as adding 30 and 8. You could add 30 in your head to
get 58. Then you could add 2 of the 8 to get 60 and then the other 6 to get 66.*)

▶ What if you were subtracting 43 − 18? Why might it be helpful to subtract
13 and then 5 more? (e.g., *You could think 43 − 13 is 30, and 30 − 5 = 25.*)

Using the Guided Intervention   Student Resource pages 90–93

Work through the strategies for adding and subtracting together. To ensure
students understand, ask them to use the modelled strategies to determine
46 + 35 and 52 − 34. Have students work through the **Try These** questions
individually or in pairs.

Observe whether students
- use pairs that add to 10 to simplify calculations (Question 1, parts a) to c))
- easily subtract two-digit numbers with a common units digit (Question 1,
  parts d) to f))
- can communicate their mental math strategies (Questions 2, 3)
- regroup numbers to simplify addition and subtraction (Questions 5, 7)
- relate a more complex calculation to a simpler one (Questions 4, 6)

Consolidating and Reflecting

Ask students to reflect on one or two of their responses and talk about them. Then
ask questions like these to consolidate their learning:

▶ In Question 1, what made it easy to calculate 68 + 2?
(e.g., *8 + 2 is 10, so it's 60 + 10, which is 70.*)

▶ What are some different ways you could have figured out 44 + 39 using mental
math in Question 5? (e.g., *I could have done 40 + 30 and then added 4 + 9 by
adding 4 + 6 and then 3 more. Or I could have done 40 + 30 and then added 1 of
the 44 to the 9 and then added 3 more from the 44. Or I could have done 44 + 6 is
50 and then added 30 and then 3.*)

▶ What are some different ways you could have figured out 64 − 37 using mental
math in Question 4? (e.g., *I could have subtracted 30 from 64 to get 34; then I
could subtract 4 of the extra 7 to get 30 and then go back 3 more to get to 27. Or I
could have thought of 64 as 57 + 7 so that the 7 in 57 matched the 7 in 37. Then I
would subtract 37 from 57 to get 20 and then add the other 7 to get 27.*)

Copyright © 2011 by Nelson Education Ltd.   *Leaps and Bounds 3/4*

You will need

- Student Resource
  pages 90–93

Relating to 5 or 10

- Student Resource
pages 94–95

Open-Ended Intervention

Before Using the Open-Ended Intervention

Ask the following questions:

▸ How much is 8 + 2? (*10*)

▸ How could that help you figure out 8 + 4?
(e.g., *I know that 8 + 4 is 2 more than 8 + 2, since 4 is 2 more than 2; that's 12.*)

▸ What steps could you use to add 6 + 7 to make it easier? (e.g., *I could add 4 to 6 to get to 10 and then 3 more, or maybe I could add 3 to 7 and then add 3 more.*)

▸ Why might it be helpful to think of 7 + 7 as 5 + 2 + 5 + 2?
(e.g., *since 5 + 5 is 10, and it's easy to add 4 to 10*)

▸ How much is 10 − 4? (*6, since 4 + 6 = 10*)

▸ How would that help you figure out 12 − 4?
(e.g., *It's 2 more than 10 − 4, so it is 2 + 6.*)

Using the Open-Ended Intervention (Student Resource pages 94–95)

Read the tasks on the student page with students. Encourage them to look for similarities in the mental math strategies they use.

Provide time for students to work in pairs, and encourage them to describe their strategies aloud before (or instead of) writing.

Observe whether students

- easily recall the combinations for 10
- use the combinations for 10 to help them determine other sums and differences
- use other strategies, such as doubles, to determine sums or differences

Note that because the problem is open-ended, students might solve the questions in a different way than you might anticipate (e.g., for 14 − 5, they do 15 − 5 and then subtract 1)—that is acceptable.

Consolidating and Reflecting

Have students summarize their thinking about calculating sums and differences. Ask questions like these to consolidate their learning:

▸ What other facts could help you figure out 9 + 4?
(e.g., *I could do 9 + 1 = 10 and 3 more makes 13.*)

▸ What other facts could help you figure out 14 − 5?
(e.g., *I could do 14 − 4 = 10 and then subtract 1 more to get 9. I could think that it takes 5 to get from 5 to 10 and then 4 more to get to 14, so altogether you have to move 9. I could think that 10 − 5 = 5, so 14 − 5 is 4 more, and that's 9.*)

▸ Choose one of your new additions and one of your new subtractions and tell how each belongs in its group. (e.g., *I think 8 + 7 fits, since 8 is close to 10, so I could add 10 and then adjust. I think 11 − 5 fits, since it was easy to relate the answer to the answer to 10 − 5.*)

Leaps and Bounds 3/4
Copyright © 2011 by Nelson Education Ltd.

Guided Intervention

Before Using the Guided Intervention

Ask the following questions:

▶ How could knowing what $7 + 3$ is help you figure out $7 + 5$?
(e.g., *I know that $7 + 5$ is 2 more than $7 + 3$, and that's 12.*)

▶ Suppose you were adding $6 + 7$. How could thinking of 10-frames help you see why the result is $1 + 2$ more than 10?
(e.g., *6 is one row of a 10-frame and 1 more, and 7 is one row of a 10-frame and 2 more, so it's a full 10-frame and 3 more.*)

▶ How does knowing that $10 - 8 = 2$ help you figure out $11 - 8$?
(*You can just add 1, since you start with 1 more.*)

Using the Guided Intervention   (Student Resource pages 96–99)

Work through the strategies for adding and subtracting with students. Have students explain why the modelled solutions make sense. Ensure that students know the combinations for 10; visualizing a 10-frame or using a beaded number line might help.

To ensure that students understand, ask them to use the modelled strategies to determine $7 + 7$ and $14 - 8$. Although the goal is to think mentally, if they need to use the models, allow this as long as needed.

Have students work through the **Try These** questions individually or in pairs.

Observe whether students

- are comfortable with combinations for 5 and 10 (Question 1)
- can relate the results of other single-digit calculations to calculations involving 5 and 10 (Questions 2, 3, 7)
- use 10 as an anchor when calculating sums and differences (Question 4)
- relate more complex calculations to simpler ones (Questions 5, 6)

Consolidating and Reflecting

Ask students to reflect on one or two of their responses and talk about them. Then ask questions like these to consolidate their learning:

▶ For Question 2, how did you know that $5 + 8$ was 3 more than $5 + 5$?
(e.g., *On a 10-frame, 5 is one full row, and 8 is one full row and 3 more. That makes 3 more than $5 + 5$.*)

▶ For Question 4, how did you use what you know about getting to 10 to calculate $7 + 4$? (e.g., *I did $7 + 3 = 10$ and then 1 more.*)

▶ In Question 5, you chose $7 + 3$ as the easier question to help you calculate $7 + 9$. That makes sense. Is there anything else you could have chosen instead?
(e.g., *$1 + 9$*)

You will need

- 10-frames (BLM 3)
- counters
- number lines (BLM 4) or beaded number lines
- Rekenrek (optional)
- Student Resource pages 96–99

Patterns and Algebra Strand Overview

How were the patterns and algebra topics chosen?

This resource provides materials for assisting students with 2 patterns and algebra topics. These topics were drawn from the curriculum outcomes from across the country for Grades 1 to 3. Topic selections are also based on research about what aspects of each topic students struggle with. Topics are divided into distinct levels, called pathways, which address gaps in students' prerequisite skills and knowledge.

How were the pathways determined?

The patterns pathways were selected to focus on identifying, describing, and extending both repeating (single and double attribute) and simple growing patterns, with and without pattern rules. They do not focus specifically on patterns in charts (such as 100 charts, addition tables, etc.).

The equality pathways do not include naming number properties such as the commutative or associative properties for addition or the properties of 0 and 1 in multiplication. The focus is on the broader ideas of patterns and the concept of equality, rather than specific aspects of each.

Materials

The materials needed for assisting students who are struggling with patterns and algebra topics will likely already be in the classroom or easily accessible. These materials are listed below. Blackline masters are also listed below and are provided at the back of this resource.

counters	craft sticks
square tiles	index cards
pattern blocks	a pan balance
toothpicks	linking cubes
attribute blocks	base ten blocks
coloured pencils	BLM 4: Number Lines

Patterns and Algebra Topics and Pathways

Topics and pathways in this strand are shown below.
Each pathway has an open-ended intervention and a guided intervention.

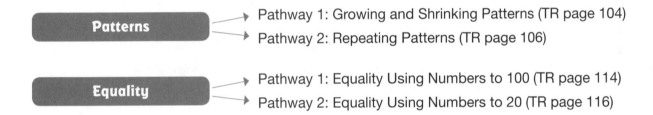

Patterns
→ Pathway 1: Growing and Shrinking Patterns (TR page 104)
→ Pathway 2: Repeating Patterns (TR page 106)

Equality
→ Pathway 1: Equality Using Numbers to 100 (TR page 114)
→ Pathway 2: Equality Using Numbers to 20 (TR page 116)

Patterns

Planning For This Topic

Materials for assisting students with patterns consist of a diagnostic tool and 2 intervention pathways. The pathways for this topic differ in the types of patterns used: growing (increasing) and shrinking (decreasing) patterns, or repeating patterns.

Each pathway has an open-ended option and a guided option. Choose the type of intervention most suitable for your students' needs and your particular circumstances.

Curriculum Connections

Grades 1 to 4 curriculum connections for this topic are provided online. See www.nelson.com/leapsandbounds. Note that the WNCP emphasizes the use of manipulatives, diagrams, sounds, and actions in creating, describing, and extending patterns. Ontario emphasizes the use of number and geometric patterns and the relationship between them.

Because these emphases are not mutually exclusive, they are incorporated into the student learning tasks and teacher prompts, and questions in the interventions.

Why might students struggle with patterns?

Students might struggle with patterns for any of the following reasons:

- They might not recognize that there are different ways to continue a pattern if a pattern rule is not given.
- They might not realize that a pattern results from repeating an action, repeating an operation, changing the orientation, or making some other repeated change to an attribute.
- They might have difficulty representing a pattern in different ways because they do not see the connection between geometric and number representations (e.g., 1 triangle, 3 triangles, 5 triangles, 7 triangles, … can be represented as the number pattern 1, 3, 5, 7, …).
- They might fixate on the particular objects in the pattern rather than on the structure of the pattern (i.e., they might not recognize the core of the pattern).
- They might have difficulty noticing and articulating complete details of a pattern rule because repeating patterns can have multiple attributes (e.g., A student might notice that a geometric pattern changes in size (large triangle, small triangle, large triangle, small triangle, etc.) but not that the triangle also changes orientation in every third element (face up, face up, face down, face up, face up, face down, etc.).
- They may not understand that the function of a pattern rule is for someone else to be able to duplicate the pattern, so they ignore critical features such as the start number.
- Students often have difficulty extending a repeating pattern when the last item given is not the last item of the core (e.g., 1, 3, 5, 1, 3, 5, 1, …).

Professional Learning Connections

PRIME: Patterns and Algebra, Background and Strategies (Nelson Education, 2005), pages 40–49, 58–60

Making Math Meaningful to Canadian Students K–8 (Nelson Education Ltd., 2008), pages 567–573, 579–581

Big Ideas from Dr. Small Grades K–3 (Nelson Education Ltd., 2010), pages 1–6

Good Questions (dist. by Nelson Education Ltd., 2009), pages 123–125, 127

Diagnostic Tool: Patterns

Use the diagnostic tool to determine the most suitable intervention pathway for patterns. Provide Diagnostic Tool: Patterns, Teacher's Resource pages 100 and 101 and have students complete it in writing or orally.

See solutions on Teacher's Resource pages 102 and 103.

Intervention Pathways

The purpose of the intervention pathways is to help students identify, describe, extend, and create number and geometric repeating and growing/shrinking patterns using different materials and models of representation. This will help prepare them for identifying, describing, translating, modelling, and extending growing/shrinking patterns within number and geometric contexts.

There are 2 pathways:
• Pathway 1: Growing and Shrinking Patterns
• Pathway 2: Repeating Patterns

Use the chart below (or the Key to Pathways on Teacher's Resource pages 102 and 103) to determine which pathway is most suitable for each student or group of students.

Diagnostic Tool Results	Intervention Pathway
If students struggle with Questions 5 to 8	use Pathway 1: Growing and Shrinking Patterns *Teacher's Resource pages 104–105* *Student Resource pages 100–105*
If students struggle with Questions 1 to 4	use Pathway 2: Repeating Patterns *Teacher's Resource pages 106–107* *Student Resource pages 106–110*

Patterns

1. Circle the smallest part of the pattern that repeats. Describe each pattern.

a)

_____

b) 34, 24, 44, 34, 24, 44, 34, 24, 44, 34, …

_____

2. How are these patterns the same? How are they different?

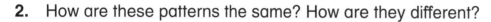

same: _____

_____

different: _____

_____

3. Draw a pattern to fit this pattern rule:
Start with a small shape and then make it bigger. Repeat.

4. Extend each pattern until there are a *total* of 5 repeats.

a) 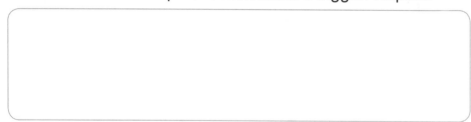 _____

b) 100, 50, 0, 100, 50, 0, 100, 50, 0, _____

c) M, N, O, P, M, N, O, P, M, N, O, P, M, N, _____

5. Describe how the pattern grows or shrinks.

    a) 100, 90, 80, 70, …

_____

    b)

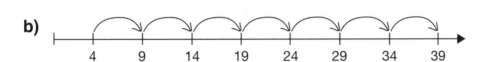

_____

6. Compare the counter pattern with the number pattern.

16, 14, 12, 10, 8, …

How are the patterns the same? _____

_____

How are the patterns different? _____

_____

7. Draw a picture to show the growing pattern.

    2, 4, 6, 8, …

8. Show the first 4 numbers in each pattern.

    a) Start at 11 and add 4 again and again.

_____

    b) Start at 20 and subtract 1, then subtract 2, then 3, and so on.

_____

Solutions and Key to Pathways

Name:_____ Date:_____

Patterns

1. Circle the smallest part of the pattern that repeats. Describe each pattern.

a)

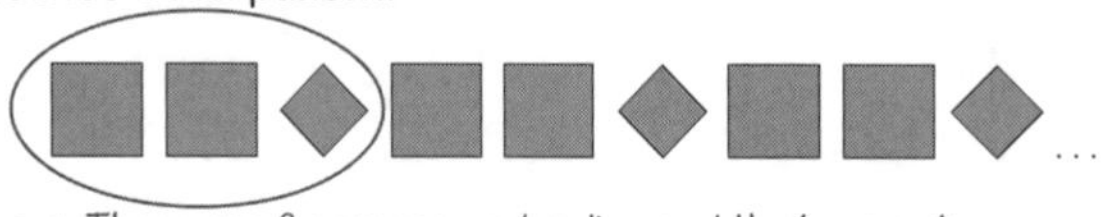

e.g., There are 2 squares and a diamond that repeat.

b) 34, 24, 44, 34, 24, 44, 34, 24, 44, 34, …

e.g., 34, 24, 44 is repeated over and over.

2. How are these patterns the same? How are they different?

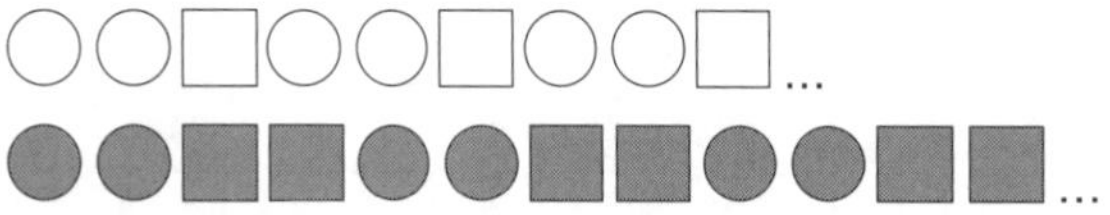

same: e.g., Both have circles and squares; both include 2 circles.

_____

different: e.g., in first pattern only 1 square repeats, but in second 2 squares

repeat; not shaded and shaded; 3 parts repeat or 4 parts repeat

3. Draw a pattern to fit this pattern rule:
Start with a small shape and then make it bigger. Repeat.

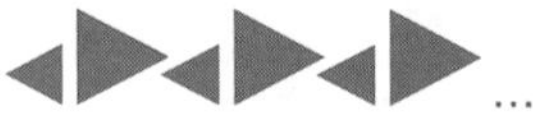

4. Extend each pattern until there are a *total* of 5 repeats.

a)

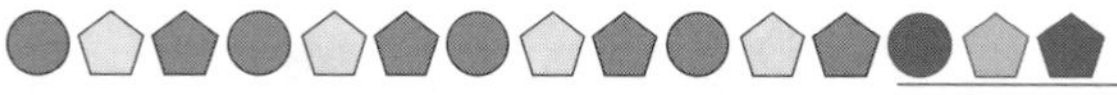

b) 100, 50, 0, 100, 50, 0, 100, 50, 0, 100, 50, 0, 100, 50, 0, …

c) M, N, O, P, M, N, O, P, M, N, O, P, M, N, O, P, M, N, O, P, …

Pathway 2

Name:_____ Date:_____

5. Describe how the pattern grows or shrinks.

a) 100, 90, 80, 70, …

e.g., The pattern starts at 100 and shrinks by 10 each time.

b)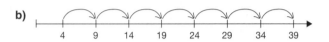

4   9   14   19   24   29   34   39

e.g., The pattern start at 4 and grows by 5 each time.

6. Compare the counter pattern with the number pattern.

 …

16, 14, 12, 10, 8, …

How are the patterns the same? _e.g., Both are shrinking patterns_

patterns that decrease by 2 each time.

How are the patterns different? _e.g., The first pattern uses circles._

The second one uses numbers. They start at different numbers.

7. Draw a picture to show the growing pattern.

2, 4, 6, 8, …

_e.g.,_

|| |||| |||||| ||||||||

8. Show the first 4 numbers in each pattern.

a) Start at 11 and add 4 again and again.

_11, 15, 19, 23, …_

b) Start at 20 and subtract 1, then subtract 2, then 3, and so on.

_20, 19, 17, 14, …_

Copyright © 2011 by Nelson Education Ltd.   _Leaps and Bounds_   Patterns, Diagnostic Tool **101**

Pathway 1

Copyright © 2011 by Nelson Education Ltd.   _Leaps and Bounds 3/4_   Patterns and Algebra: Patterns   **103**

Growing and Shrinking Patterns

- a variety of objects for patterning (e.g., counters, pattern blocks, square tiles, toothpicks, or craft sticks)
- index cards (optional)
- number lines (BLM 4)
- Student Resource pages 100–101

Open-Ended Intervention

Before Using the Open-Ended Intervention

Model a pattern by clapping once, twice, 3 times, then 4 times. Ask:

▶ Describe the pattern. What makes it a pattern?
(e.g., *It's a growing pattern. The number of claps increases by 1 each time.*)

▶ What would the next 2 items in the pattern be? (*5 claps, then 6 claps*)

▶ How could you model this growing pattern using counters instead of claps?
(e.g., *1 counter, then a group of 2 counters, then a group of 3 counters, and so on.*)

Invite students to start at 10 and count backwards by 2s to create a shrinking pattern.

▶ Why does this describe a shrinking pattern? (e.g., *The number pattern is 10, 8, 6, 4, 2 and the numbers decrease by 2 each time.*)

▶ How could you model this pattern using claps, or counters, or a number line?
(e.g., *10 claps, 8 claps, 6 claps, 4 claps, 2 claps. On a number line I'd jump backwards from 10 to 8 to 6 to 4 to 2.*)

Using the Open-Ended Intervention   (Student Resource pages 100–101)

Together, read through the tasks on the student pages. Provide counters so students can create the dot patterns before recording them. Students might like to record the dot pictures on blank cards so they can move the pictures around. Have other patterning materials available, as well as number lines (BLM 4) that students might use for creating other pictures of their patterns.

Allow students time to work, ideally in pairs.

Observe students and use questions as necessary to bring out the following:

- Different growing patterns or shrinking patterns can contain similar groups of items, but it is the order of the groups that is important.
- Growing patterns increase and shrinking patterns decrease in a predictable way.
- A pattern rule can be represented in a variety of ways using actions, sounds, objects, pictures, and numbers.
- When a pattern rule is clearly expressed, many representations are possible, but only one mathematical structure is possible.

Consolidating and Reflecting

Ensure understanding by asking questions about students' work:

▶ What strategy did you use to create your pattern?
(e.g., *I looked at what stayed the same and what changed.*)

▶ How can you use your growing pattern to create a shrinking pattern that is like it? (e.g., *Switch the order of the numbers.*)

▶ Which of your patterns were alike? (e.g., *4, 8, 12, 16, … has some of the same numbers as the doubling pattern 1, 2, 4, 8, 16, …*)

▶ Why can the same pattern be represented in more than one way? (e.g., *You can write the numbers, or you can use objects or pictures or actions or sounds.*)

Leaps and Bounds 3/4
Copyright © 2011 by Nelson Education Ltd.

Guided Intervention

Before Using the Guided Intervention

Model a pattern by clapping once, twice, 3 times, then 4 times. Ask:

▶ What would the next 2 items in the pattern be? (*5 claps, then 6 claps*)
▶ How could you model this pattern using toothpicks instead of claps?
  (e.g., *1 toothpick, then a group of 2 toothpicks, then 3 toothpicks, and so on*)

Invite students to start at 12 and count backwards by 2s. Ask:

▶ Why is this a shrinking pattern? (e.g., *The numbers decrease by 2 each time.*)
▶ How could you model this shrinking pattern using claps or dots or a number
  line? (e.g., *12 claps, 10 claps, 8 claps, 6 claps, …*)

Using the Guided Intervention (Student Resource pages 102–105)

Provide a variety of objects for patterning (e.g., counters, square tiles, pattern blocks,
toothpicks). Also have number lines (BLM 4) available and blank cards for drawing
each item in a pattern. Work through the instructional section of the student page
together. Have students build the patterns using trapezoid pattern blocks. Then
have students work through the **Try These** questions in pairs or individually.

Observe whether students can

• write a pattern rule by identifying the start number and the amount by which
  the pattern changes repeatedly (Question 1)
• relate different representations of given growing and shrinking patterns
  (e.g., using different concrete materials, pictures, numbers) (Question 2)
• extend a pattern when the pattern rule is given (Questions 3, 6)
• compare patterns (Question 4)
• describe growing or shrinking patterns (Question 5)
• create a pattern based on conditions provided (Questions 7, 8)

Consolidating and Reflecting

Ensure understanding by asking students the following questions:

▶ How do you describe a pattern so that someone else can create it exactly?
  (e.g., *You write a pattern rule. It tells you where to start and how much you increase
  or decrease the amount by each time.*)
▶ What strategy did you use to extend a pattern when there was no pattern rule?
  (e.g., *I looked at what stayed the same and what changed each time.*)
▶ Why can the same pattern be represented in more than one way?
  (e.g., *The pattern rule is the same. You can write the numbers, or you can show how
  many, using objects or pictures or actions or sounds.*)
▶ How did you create your shrinking patterns in Question 8?
  (e.g., *I started with 8 and thought of a growing pattern to help me fill in the first
  2 blanks.*)

You will need

• a variety of objects
  for patterning
  (e.g., counters,
  pattern blocks,
  toothpicks or craft
  sticks, square tiles)
• number lines
  (BLM 4)
• Student Resource
  pages 102–105

Repeating Patterns

You will need

- a variety of objects for patterning (e.g., pattern blocks, attribute blocks, counters, square tiles, toothpicks or craft sticks)
- coloured pencils
- Student Resource page 106

Open-Ended Intervention

Before Using the Open-Ended Intervention

Provide square and triangle pattern blocks. Have students create a repeating pattern using the blocks. Ask:

▶ Describe your repeating pattern. (e.g., *square, triangle, repeat*)

▶ How many blocks are in the repeating part (the pattern core)? (e.g., *2*)

Show students how to describe a repeating pattern like that as an AB pattern. This indicates that there are 2 items in the core of the pattern (the part that repeats) and that the 2 items are different. Ask what an AAB pattern might look like.

Make a 2-attribute repeating pattern with attribute blocks, so that students can see a different way that attributes can be manipulated. You might vary shape and size, or shape and number.

Using the Open-Ended Intervention ⬭ Student Resource page 106

Provide a variety of objects that students can use to create patterns. Together, read through the task on the student page. Encourage students to write their pattern rules so that an exact pattern can be recreated and no other pattern is possible. Allow students time to work, ideally in pairs.

Observe whether students

- satisfy the repeating pattern criteria (i.e., a pattern core with 3 or more items in it; repeating the pattern core at least 3 times)
- include other possibilities, such as varying the colour or size or orientation of the shapes, or the number of items in the part that repeats (e.g., one pattern has a core of 4 elements, while a different pattern has a core of 3 elements)
- describe their pattern rule such that the pattern can be recreated with no other possible pattern
- represent their pattern, using letters

Consolidating and Reflecting

Ensure understanding by asking questions about students' work:

▶ What part repeats in your pattern? How many items repeat? (e.g., *The part that repeats is large triangle, large circle, large circle, small square. That's 4 items.*)

▶ How does this pattern compare with that one?
(e.g., *Mike's and mine both have the same pattern rule but use different objects.*)

▶ How did you or could you represent your pattern using letters?
(e.g., *I gave a different letter to each different item. Since I have 3 items, I used the 3 letters J, O, E. My pattern in letters is JOEJOEJOE…*)

Repeating Patterns

GUIDED INTERVENTION

Before Using the Guided Intervention

Have students create a repeating pattern using triangle and trapezoid pattern blocks. Ask:

▸ Describe your repeating pattern. What is the smallest repeating part (the pattern core)? How many blocks are in the repeating part?
(e.g., *triangle, trapezoid, triangle, trapezoid, triangle, trapezoid, over and over; The part that repeats is triangle, trapezoid. That's 2 blocks.*)

▸ How can you make a different repeating pattern using triangles and trapezoids?
(e.g., *Maybe we can change how they are placed—I can turn the triangle or the trapezoid—or maybe change the number of each shape that I use.*)

Using the Guided Intervention ⟮Student Resource pages 107–110⟯

Provide a variety of objects for patterning (e.g., counters, square tiles, pattern blocks, toothpicks). Work through the instructional section of the student pages together. Help students realize that a pattern involving two attributes can sometimes be described focusing on only one of those attributes (e.g., square, square, circle, square, square, circle, or grey, white, grey, white, rather than grey square, white square, grey circle, white square, grey square, white circle).

Have students work through the **Try These** questions in pairs or individually.

Observe whether students can
- identify the part that repeats and fill in missing items in a pattern (Questions 1, 2, 3, 6)
- describe repeating patterns (Questions 3, 6)
- compare repeating patterns (Question 4)
- draw a repeating pattern when the pattern rule is given (Question 5)
- create patterns based on a given pattern rule (Questions 7 and 8)

Consolidating and Reflecting

Ensure understanding by asking students the following questions:

▸ What is changing in the repeating pattern in Question 1?
(e.g., *part a) size, b) shape and number, c) number, d) shape and size and shading*)

▸ Which shapes in Question 2 and 6 show a change in the position (orientation)?
(*in Question 2 part c), triangle; in Question 2 part d), arrow; in Question 6 part b), triangle*)

▸ Why can a repeating pattern be represented in more than one way as in Question 8? (e.g., *The pattern rule stays the same. You can just replace the items using objects or pictures or letters or numbers or actions or sounds.*)

You will need
- a variety of objects for patterning (e.g., pattern blocks, attribute blocks, counters, square tiles, toothpicks or craft sticks)
- coloured pencils
- Student Resource pages 107–110

Planning For This Topic

Materials for assisting students with equality consist of a diagnostic tool and 2 intervention pathways. The pathways for this topic differ in the numbers used: numbers to 20 or numbers to 100.

Each pathway has an open-ended option and a guided option. Choose the type of intervention most suitable for your students' needs and your particular circumstances.

Professional Learning Connections

PRIME: Patterns and Algebra, Background and Strategies (Nelson Education, 2005), page 61

Making Math Meaningful to Canadian Students K–8 (Nelson Education Ltd., 2008), page 583

Big Ideas from Dr. Small Grades K–3 (Nelson Education Ltd., 2010), pages 12–13

Good Questions (dist. by Nelson Education Ltd., 2009), pages 125, 131

Curriculum Connections

Grades 1 to 4 curriculum connections for this topic are provided online. See www.nelson.com/leapsandbounds. The main focus is on one-step addition and subtraction equations with one- and two-digit numbers.

Why might students struggle with equality?

Students might struggle with equality because they might
- incorrectly interpret an equal sign as meaning "here comes the answer" on the right side of the equal sign, such as when you press the equal sign on a calculator (e.g., They would think ■ = 8 in the equation $5 + 3 = ■ + 2$.)
- use equal signs to incorrectly link a string of calculations for an expression to a number (e.g., For $27 + 38 = 65$, students might write $20 + 30 = 50 + 7 = 57 + 8 = 65$.)
- have little familiarity with determining equality using strategies that focus on number relationships rather than on computation (e.g., If you add [or take away] the same amount on both sides of the equation, then the equation is still balanced.)

Diagnostic Tool: Equality

Use the diagnostic tool to determine the most suitable intervention pathway for equality. Provide Diagnostic Tool: Equality, Teacher's Resource pages 110 and 111, and have students complete it in writing or orally. Students may want to use base ten blocks, a pan balance and linking cubes (or centicubes), and number lines (BLM 4).

See solutions on Teacher's Resource pages 112 and 113.

Intervention Pathways

The purpose of the intervention pathways is to help students apply strategies for determining the equivalence of addition and subtraction expressions using a variety of approaches, and for discerning which approaches are more efficient. The focus is to prepare them for determining equivalence with other operations and developing algebraic reasoning.

There are 2 pathways:
- Pathway 1: Equality: Using Numbers to 100
- Pathway 2: Equality: Using Numbers to 20

Use the chart below (or the Key to Pathways on Teacher's Resource pages 112 and 113) to determine which pathway is most suitable for each student or group of students.

Diagnostic Tool Results	Intervention Pathway
If students struggle with Questions 6 to 10	use Pathway 1: Equality: Using Numbers to 100 *Teacher's Resource pages 114–115* *Student Resource pages 111–116*
If students struggle with Questions 1 to 5	use Pathway 2: Equality: Using Numbers to 20 *Teacher's Resource pages 116–117* *Student Resource pages 117–121*

Name: ______________________ Date: ______________

Equality

Diagnostic Tool

1. Show 2 different equations for each number.

   a) 10 = ______ + ______

   10 = ______ + ______ + ______

   b) 8 = ______ − ______

   8 = ______ − ______

2. Write an equation to show how you might make each addition easier. For example, 7 + 5 + 3 = 10 + 5.

   a) 4 + 9 + 6 = ______ + ______

   b) 8 + 3 + 5 + 4 = ________

3. Circle the expressions that are worth the same.

   a) 7 + 7   6 + 8   3 + 10   11 + 4   0 + 9 + 5

   b) 14 − 8   15 − 8   10 − 4   16 − 10   11 − 5

4. Are the 2 expressions worth the same? Tell how you know.

   a) 6 + 0 + 4 + 10 and 10 + 4 + 1 + 6

   b) 16 − 7 and 18 − 9

5. What is the missing number? Tell how you know.

   a) 5 + 3 = ■ + 2

   ____

   ____

   b) 5 = 9 − ■

   ____

   ____

 Copyright © 2011 by Nelson Education Ltd.

6. Show 2 different equations for each number.

a) $35 =$ _____ $+$ _____   **b)** $50 =$ _____ $-$ _____

$35 =$ _____ $+$ _____ $+$ _____ $50 =$ _____ $-$ _____

7. Group the numbers to write an equivalent expression.
For example, $3 + 9 + 1 + 7 = 10 + 10$.

a) $14 + 7 + 6 + 23 =$ _____ $+$ _____

b) $33 + 17 - 3 =$ _____

8. Circle the expressions that are worth the same.

a) $38 + 47$ $40 + 49$ $35 + 50 + 0$ $45 + 40$ $15 + 70$

b) $36 - 12$ $42 - 18$ $34 - 10$ $85 - 62$ $10 + 14$

9. Are the 2 expressions worth the same? Tell how you know.

a) $24 + 55 + 16 + 9$ and $16 + 9 + 24 + 55$

b) $35 - 12$ and $45 - 20 - 2$

10. What is the missing number? Tell how you know.

a) $22 + 35 = \blacksquare + 36$

_____

_____

b) $53 - \blacksquare = 55 - 19$

_____

_____

Solutions and Key to Pathways

Name:_____ **Date:**_____

Equality

1. Show 2 different equations for each number.

a) $10 = \underline{\quad 3 \quad} + \underline{\quad 7 \quad}$ **b)** $8 = \underline{\quad 9 \quad} - \underline{\quad 1 \quad}$

$10 = \underline{\quad 3 \quad} + \underline{\quad 4 \quad} + \underline{\quad 3 \quad}$ $8 = \underline{\quad 15 \quad} - \underline{\quad 7 \quad}$

2. Write an equation to show how you might make each addition easier. For example, $7 + 5 + 3 = 10 + 5$.

a) $4 + 9 + 6 = \underline{\quad 10 \quad} + \underline{\quad 9 \quad}$

b) $8 + 3 + 5 + 4 = \underline{\quad 8 + 8 + 4 \quad}$

3. Circle the expressions that are worth the same.

a) $\boxed{7 + 7}$ $\boxed{6 + 8}$ $3 + 10$ $11 + 4$ $\boxed{0 + 9 + 5}$

b) $\boxed{14 - 8}$ $\boxed{15 - 8}$ $10 - 4$ $\boxed{16 - 10}$ $11 - 5$

4. Are the 2 expressions worth the same? Tell how you know.

a) $6 + 0 + 4 + 10$ and $10 + 4 + 1 + 6$

> e.g., $10 + 10 = 20$ $10 + 10 + 1 = 21$
> No. 20 and 21 are not equal.

b) $16 - 7$ and $18 - 9$

> e.g., $16 - 7 = 9$ $18 - 9 = 9$
> Yes. Both expressions are equal to 9.

5. What is the missing number? Tell how you know.

a) $5 + 3 = \blacksquare + 2$

6, e.g., The left side is 8, so to make the right side 8, $2 + 6 = 8$.

_____

b) $5 = 9 - \blacksquare$

4, e.g., The left side is 5, so the right side must be 5, so the missing

number must be 4.

Pathway 2

Name:_____   Date:_____

6. Show 2 different equations for each number.

a) 35 = ___30___ + ___5___   **b)** 50 = ___75___ − ___25___

35 = ___30___ + ___3___ + ___2___   50 = ___62___ − ___12___

7. Group the numbers to write an equivalent expression.
For example, 3 + 9 + 1 + 7 = 10 + 10.

a) 14 + 7 + 6 + 23 = ___20___ + ___30___

b) 33 + 17 − 3 = ___30 + 17___

8. Circle the expressions that are worth the same.

a) (38 + 47)   40 + 49   (35 + 50 + 0)   (45 + 40)   15 + 70

b) (36 − 12)   (42 − 18)   (34 − 10)   85 − 62   (10 + 14)

9. Are the 2 expressions worth the same? Tell how you know.

a) 24 + 55 + 16 + 9 and 16 + 9 + 24 + 55

> e.g., Yes, both show the same numbers but in a different order.

b) 35 − 12 and 45 − 20 − 2

> e.g., Yes, 35 − 12 = 23 and 45 − 20 − 2 = 23

10. What is the missing number? Tell how you know.

a) 22 + 35 = ■ + 36

21, e.g., 35 and 36 are close numbers. When you add 1 to 35, then

you have to subtract 1 from the other number. 22 − 1 = 21

b) 53 − ■ = 55 − 19

17, e.g., The first numbers are 2 apart, so the second numbers

must be 2 apart

Copyright © 2011 by Nelson Education Ltd.   *Leaps and Bounds*   Patterns and Algebra: Equality, Diagnostic Tool   **111**

Pathway
1

Equality: Using Numbers to 100

You will need

- linking cubes or centicubes
- pan balances (actual or online)
- base ten blocks
- number lines (optional, BLM 4)
- Student Resource pages 111–112

Open-Ended Intervention

Before Using the Open-Ended Intervention

Put 20 red cubes and 11 blue cubes on one side of a pan balance, and 21 white cubes and 10 black cubes on the other side. (Use any 4 colours of cubes.) If you do not have a pan balance, draw a picture of one and use it to demonstrate the function of the equal sign. Ask the following questions:

▸ What equation represents what you see on the balance? (e.g., *20 + 11 = 21 + 10*)

▸ The 2 sides balance. Why? (e.g., *They have the same number of cubes.*)

Write the equation $34 - 14 = 35 - \blacksquare$. Ask:

▸ How can you figure out what the missing number is? (e.g., *Subtract 34 − 14 on the left side and get 20. To get 20 on the other side, I think, what number do I add to 20 to get 35? The missing number is 15.*)

Using the Open-Ended Intervention (Student Resource pages 111–112)

Read through the tasks with students and make sure they realize that numbers can be used more than once. Have available base ten blocks, a pan balance with linking cubes, and number lines (optional, BLM 4). Give students time to work in pairs.

Observe whether students use a variety of strategies for

- choosing numbers (e.g., numbers that are "friendly" and easy to calculate or manipulate, such as multiples of 5s and 10s; *or* numbers that are close in value to facilitate comparison across expressions)
- comparing expressions to see if they are equivalent by calculating the values of the left side and the right side and comparing, *or* by looking for the same numbers on both sides and adjusting as necessary, *or* by looking at complementary relationships between numbers on both sides (e.g., If one addend is 2 less, then the other should be 2 more.)

Consolidating and Reflecting

Ensure understanding by asking students the following questions:

▸ What is the missing number in this equation: $50 + 1 = \blacksquare + 25$? How do you know? (*26. e.g., If I add another 25 on the right side, I get 50, so the missing number must be 25 + 1, which is 26.*)

▸ What is the missing number in this equation: $41 - 17 = 42 - \blacksquare$? How do you know? (e.g., *18. The difference between the numbers has to stay the same. You add 1 to 41 to get 42, so you have to add 1 to 17 to get 18.*)

▸ Did you always have to calculate the value of each side to determine if they were equal? (e.g., *No, sometimes I could see the distance between the numbers would not have changed, since you shifted both the same. Sometimes I could tell that the same total was just split into 2 slightly different-sized parts.*)

Leaps and Bounds 3/4
Copyright © 2011 by Nelson Education Ltd.

Equality: Using Numbers to 100

Guided Intervention

Before Using the Guided Intervention

Put 20 red cubes and 11 blue cubes on one side of a pan balance, and 21 white cubes and 10 black cubes on the other side. (Use any colours.) Ask:

▸ What equation represents what you see on the balance?
(e.g., $20 + 11 = 21 + 10$)

▸ Why do the 2 sides balance? (e.g., *They have the same number of cubes.*)

Write the equation $24 + 18 = 26 +$ ▪. Ask:

▸ How can you figure out the missing number? (e.g., *I could add the numbers on the left side to get 42, and then subtract 26 to get 16.*)

Using the Guided Intervention   (Student Resource pages 113–116)

Work through the instructional section of the student pages together, discussing solutions and strategies for determining equivalence. Have available base ten blocks, a pan balance with linking cubes, and number lines (optional, BLM 4). Have students work through the **Try These** questions in pairs or individually.

Observe whether students

- recognize that an equation describes a balance (Questions 1, 2)
- recognize that an equation is a way to show 2 representations of the same number (Questions 4, 5, 6)
- have a variety of strategies for determining the equivalence of expressions (e.g., calculating the left- and right-side expressions separately and comparing them *or* looking for and using number relationships (Questions 1, 2, 3, 7, 8)
- recognize that an unknown must be replaced by a number that makes the expressions on both sides of the equation equivalent (Questions 1, 2, 3, 8)

Consolidating and Reflecting

Ensure understanding by asking students the following questions:

▸ What is one of the equations you wrote for Question 5? How did you figure it out? (e.g., *I wrote $33 - 1 = 32$, since I know if you take 1 from 33, you're left with 32.*)

▸ What was the missing number in Question 3 part b)? How did you figure it out? (e.g., *It was 10. I thought of 13 from 24 on the number line, so if I started 3 ahead at 27 and wanted to land at the same place, I had to jump 3 less.*)

▸ Why were there different ways to complete Question 8? (e.g., *You could choose one of the missing values to be anything you wanted and then just make the other value work.*)

▸ Did you always have to calculate the value of each side to decide if they were equal? (e.g., *No, sometimes I could see that the distance between the numbers would not have changed, since you shifted both the same. Sometimes I could tell that the same total was just split up into 2 slightly different-sized parts.*)

You will need

- linking cubes
- pan balances (actual or online)
- base ten blocks
- number lines (optional, BLM 4)
- Student Resource pages 113–116

Equality: Using Numbers to 20

You will need

- linking cubes
- a pan balance
- base ten blocks
- number lines (optional, BLM 4)
- Student Resource page 117

Open-Ended Intervention

Before Using the Open-Ended Intervention

Put 7 red cubes and 11 blue cubes on one side of a pan balance, and 6 red cubes and 12 blue cubes on the other side. (Use any colours of cubes.) Ask:

▸ Why would the equation $7 + 11 = 6 + 12$ describe what you see? (e.g., *One side has 7 + 11 and the other side has 6 + 12.*)

▸ Why do the 2 sides balance? (e.g., *They have the same number of cubes.*)

▸ What is another equation for this that has only one number on the right side? (e.g., *7 + 11 = 18*)

Turn the balance around so that the sides are reversed and read the equation.

Write the equation $18 - 9 = 10 + 8 - \blacksquare$. Ask:

▸ How can you figure out the missing number? (e.g., *I would subtract the numbers on the left side to get 9, and add 10 + 8 to get 18, and then subtract 9. The number is 9.*)

Using the Open-Ended Intervention   (Student Resource page 117)

Provide base ten blocks, a pan balance with linking cubes, and number lines (optional, BLM 4). Read the task with students and make sure they realize that numbers can be used more than once. Allow students time to work, ideally in pairs.

Observe whether students use a variety of strategies for

- choosing numbers (e.g., numbers that are "friendly" and easy to calculate or manipulate, such as multiples of 5s and 10s; *or* numbers that are close in value to facilitate comparison across expressions)
- comparing expressions to see if they are equivalent

Consolidating and Reflecting

Ensure understanding by asking students the following questions:

▸ How do you know when 2 expressions describe the same number? (e.g., *The number expressions have the same value.*)

▸ What is one of the equations you wrote? How did you create it? (e.g., *8 + 3 + 7 + 2 = 5 + 8 + 3 + 5 − 1; I made 2 groups of 10 on 1 side, and on the other side I made a group of 10 and a group of 11, so I had to subtract 1.*)

▸ How would you complete this equation: $9 - 8 = 8 + 7 - \blacksquare$? (e.g., *I would calculate the left side, which is 1, and then figure out the right side: 15 – what number gives 1? The missing number is 14.*)

▸ Which of your equations were easy for you to figure out and which were harder? (e.g., *It was easy to write 5 + 1 = 6 − 1 + 1, since I just replaced 5 with 6 − 1. It was harder to write ones involving bigger numbers, since I had to think harder about what to replace the numbers with.*)

Guided Intervention

Before Using the Guided Intervention

Put 7 red cubes and 11 blue cubes on one side of a pan balance, and 6 red cubes and 12 blue cubes on the other side. (Use any colours of cubes.) Ask:

▸ Why would the equation $7 + 11 = 6 + 12$ describe what you see? (e.g., *One side has 7 + 11 and the other side has 6 + 12.*)

▸ What is another equation for this that has only one number on the right side? (e.g., *7 + 11 = 18*)

Turn the balance around so that the sides are reversed.

Write the equation $18 - 9 = 10 + 8 - \blacksquare$. Ask:

▸ How can you figure out the missing number? (e.g., *Subtract on the left side to get 9, and add 10 + 8 to get 18, and then subtract 9. The number is 9.*)

▸ Do you have to subtract to figure it out? (*No. e.g., If you notice that 18 is the same as 10 + 8, then all you have to do is make the last number the same, 9.*)

Using the Guided Intervention (Student Resource pages 118–121)

Provide base ten blocks or linking cubes, a pan balance, and number lines (optional, BLM 4). Work through the instructional section of the student pages together, discussing solutions and strategies for determining equivalence. Have students work through the **Try These** questions in pairs or individually.

Observe whether students
- recognize that an equation describes a balance (Questions 1, 2)
- recognize that an equation is a way to show two representations of the same number (Questions 4, 6, 9)
- have a variety of strategies for determining the equivalence of expressions (Questions 1 to 3, 5, 7, 8)
- recognize that an unknown must be replaced by a number that makes the expressions on both sides of the equation equivalent (Questions 1 to 3, 8)

Consolidating and Reflecting

Ensure understanding by asking the following questions:

▸ How do you know when 2 expressions describe the same number? (e.g., *when the numbers have the same value*)

▸ Which equation in Question 3 did you find easiest to figure out? Why? (e.g., *I thought part b) was easy, since I know that 9 is 7 + 2.*)

▸ How did you decide on two equations in Question 6 part c)? (e.g., *I knew I should start with something bigger than 11 and then take away enough to get 11. First I started 1 above and took away 1, but then I started 10 above, at 21, so I took away 10.*)

▸ How did you solve Question 8 part b)? (e.g., *I chose a value for* ■ *and then figured out other values to make it work.*)

Copyright © 2011 by Nelson Education Ltd.

You will need

- linking cubes or centicubes
- pan balances (actual or online)
- base ten blocks
- number lines (optional, BLM 4)
- Student Resource pages 118–121

Strand: Geometry

Geometry Strand Overview

How were the geometry topics chosen?

This resource provides materials for assisting students with 3 geometry topics. These topics were drawn from the curriculum outcomes from across the country for Grades 1 to 3. Topic selections are also based on research about what aspects of each topic students struggle with. Topics are divided into distinct levels, called pathways, which address gaps in students' prerequisite skills and knowledge.

What geometry topics were omitted?

Geometry topics for this grade do not include symmetry, as it is not addressed under the WNCP curriculum until Grade 4. Although other curricula cover it earlier, symmetry is not typically an area of struggle at this level. Angle measurement has also been excluded from the geometry and measurement topics, as has the term *congruence*. Building 3-D shapes from nets and building models and skeletons is not addressed because additional learning on these topics is warranted before a student is deemed struggling.

How were the pathways determined?

The pathways for 3-D geometry focus on describing and building, allowing students to become familiar with 3-D shapes and develop more precise geometric vocabulary. Pathways for 2-D geometry are based on describing shapes and on creating 2-D shapes by composing and decomposing other shapes. Location pathways focus on either using positional vocabulary, a simpler approach to describing location, or the use of grids and maps, a more sophisticated approach.

Leaps and Bounds 3/4 Copyright © 2011 by Nelson Education Ltd.

Materials

Materials for assisting students who are struggling with geometry topics will likely already be in the classroom or easily accessible. These are listed below. Blackline masters are also listed below and are provided at the back of this resource.

3-D objects (prisms, pyramids, spheres, cylinders, cones)
building blocks or geoblocks
linking cubes
pattern blocks
paper and scissors
coloured pencils
building objects
counters

BLM 6: 1 cm Square Grid Paper
BLM 7: 2 cm Square Grid Paper
BLM 10: 3-D Shapes
BLM 11: Polygons
BLM 12: Tangrams
BLM 13: Pattern Blocks: Triangle/Grid
BLM 14: Pattern Blocks: Square
BLM 15: Pattern Blocks: Rhombus A
BLM 16: Pattern Blocks: Rhombus B
BLM 17: Pattern Blocks: Trapezoid
BLM 18: Pattern Blocks: Hexagon
BLM 27: Venn Diagram

Geometry Topics and Pathways

Topics and pathways in this strand are shown below.
Each pathway has an open-ended intervention and a guided intervention.

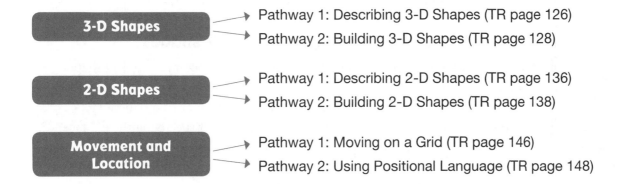

3-D Shapes → Pathway 1: Describing 3-D Shapes (TR page 126)
→ Pathway 2: Building 3-D Shapes (TR page 128)

2-D Shapes → Pathway 1: Describing 2-D Shapes (TR page 136)
→ Pathway 2: Building 2-D Shapes (TR page 138)

Movement and Location → Pathway 1: Moving on a Grid (TR page 146)
→ Pathway 2: Using Positional Language (TR page 148)

3-D Shapes

Planning For This Topic

Materials for assisting students with describing and comparing 3-D shapes consist of a diagnostic tool and 2 intervention pathways. One pathway focuses on describing and comparing 3-D shapes; the other focuses on composing and decomposing shapes.

Each pathway has an open-ended option and a guided option. Choose the type of intervention most suitable for your students' needs and your particular circumstances.

Curriculum Connections

Grades 1 to 4 curriculum correlations for this topic are provided online. See www.nelson.com/leapsandbounds. Note that the WNCP curriculum requires very little constructing of 3-D objects until Grade 4, which focuses on constructing rectangular and triangular prisms (also referred to as rectangle-based prisms and triangle-based prisms). Pathway 1 may not be relevant to students in jurisdictions following the WNCP curriculum.

Note also that different jurisdictions use different terms for 3-D. *3-D shapes* is used here as a neutral term. Other terms for describing these objects (*shapes, objects, skeletons, solids, figures*) are acceptable and should be encouraged.

Why might students struggle with 3-D shapes?

Students might struggle with building, describing, and comparing 3-D shapes because they might
- confuse the vocabulary associated with 2-D shapes and 3-D shapes (e.g., indicates a tissue box to identify a rectangle, without specifying the flat face)
- have difficulty remembering the names associated with 3-D shapes (e.g., hexagonal prism, triangle-based pyramid [or triangular pyramid])
- confuse edges and vertices on a 3-D shape
- lose track of the number of faces, edges, and vertices counted on 3-D shapes
- be able to manipulate individual 3-D shapes, but be unable to combine them to make a new 3-D shape
- have few strategies for visualizing smaller 3-D shapes in a composite 3-D shape

---

Professional Learning Connections

PRIME: Geometry, Background and Strategies (Nelson Education, 2007), pages 42–44, 46–48, 73–74

Making Math Meaningful to Canadian Students K–8 (Nelson Education Ltd., 2008), pages 287–292

Big Ideas from Dr. Small Grades K–3 (Nelson Education Ltd., 2010), pages 65–68, 73

Good Questions (dist. by Nelson Education Ltd., 2009), pages 63, 67, 79

Leaps and Bounds 3/4 Copyright © 2011 by Nelson Education Ltd.

Diagnostic Tool: 3-D Shapes

Use the diagnostic tool to determine the most suitable intervention for 3-D shapes. Provide Diagnostic Tool: 3-D Shapes, Teacher's Resource pages 122 and 123, and have students complete it in writing or orally. Have available 3-D objects, such as solids, skeletons, constructed nets, linking cubes, and pattern blocks for students to use.

See solutions on Teacher's Resource pages 124 and 125.

Intervention Pathways

The purpose of the intervention pathways is to help students describe and compare 3-D shapes in a variety of ways so that ultimately they can do the same with additional geometric properties and more complex polyhedra.

There are 2 pathways:
- Pathway 1: Describing 3-D Shapes
- Pathway 2: Building 3-D Shapes

Use the chart below (or the Key to Pathways on Teacher's Resource pages 124 and 125) to determine which pathway is most suitable for each student or group of students.

Diagnostic Tool Results	Intervention Pathway
If students struggle with Questions 4 to 6	Pathway 1: Describing 3-D Shapes *Teacher's Resource pages 126–127* *Student Resource pages 122–127*
If students struggle with Questions 1 to 3	Pathway 2: Building 3-D Shapes *Teacher's Resource pages 128–129* *Student Resource pages 128–132*

3-D Shapes

1. **a)** Use 4 linking cubes to make an object.
   Draw or describe what the object looks like from the front.

You will need
- linking cubes
- 3-D objects
- pattern blocks

b) Make 1 more object using linking cubes.
   Sketch or describe it.

2. Circle the 3-D shape that could be made by stacking triangle pattern blocks.

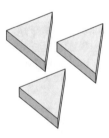

3. **a)** Draw lines on this shape to show how it can be cut into smaller 3-D shapes.

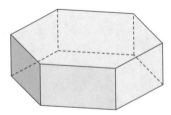

b) Name the shapes of the smaller 3-D shapes you created.

_____

Leaps and Bounds Copyright © 2011 by Nelson Education Ltd.

Name:_____ Date:_____

4. Draw a line to match each description to a 3-D shape.
   One shape will be left over.

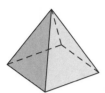 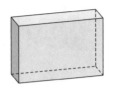 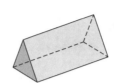 

6 faces   square base   all triangular faces

5. Use a geometry word or words to name each shape.

a)   b)   c)    d)

_____   _____   _____   _____

6. A triangular prism has 5 faces, 6 vertices, and 9 edges.
   Fill in the chart to describe each 3-D shape shown.

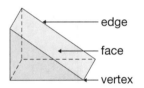

edge
face
vertex

3-D shape	Shapes of faces or surfaces	Number of faces	Number of vertices	Number of edges

Copyright © 2011 by Nelson Education Ltd. *Leaps and Bounds*

Solutions and Key to Pathways

Pathway
2

3-D Shapes

Diagnostic Tool

Name:_____   Date:_____

1. **a)** Use 4 linking cubes to make an object.
Draw or describe what the object looks like from the front.

You will need
- linking cubes
- 3-D objects
- pattern blocks

e.g., My object has 3 cubes on the bottom and one on top of the left cube.

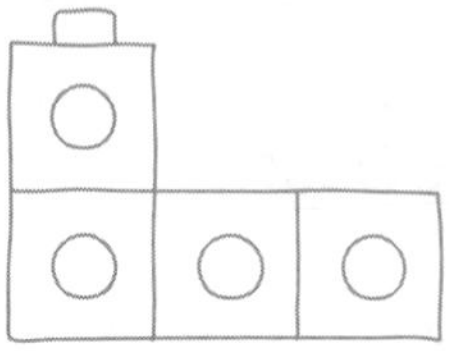

b) Make 1 more object using linking cubes.
Sketch or describe it.

e.g., My object has 3 cubes on the bottom and one on top of the middle cube.

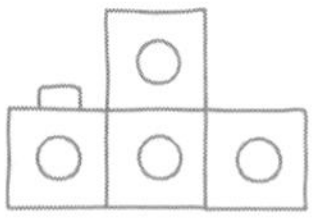

2. Circle the 3-D shape that could be made by stacking triangle pattern blocks.

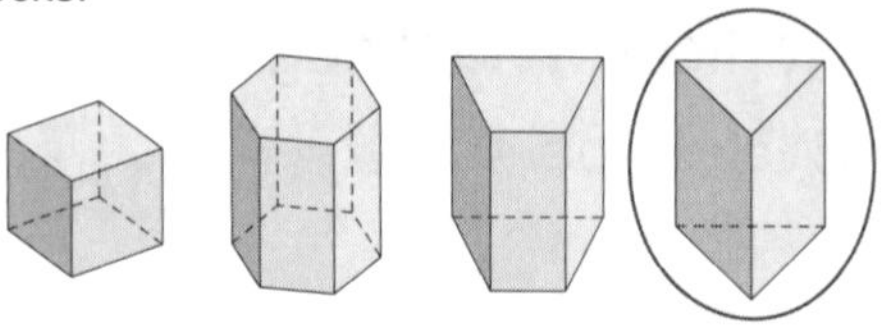

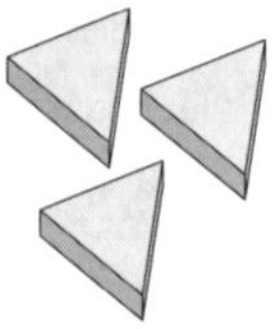

3. **a)** Draw lines on this shape to show how it can be cut into smaller 3-D shapes.

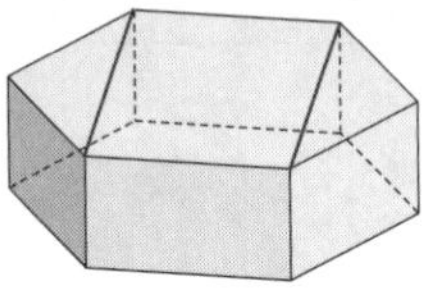

b) Name the shapes of the smaller 3-D shapes you created.

e.g., 2 triangular prisms and 1 rectangular prism

Name:_____ Date:_____

4. Draw a line to match each description to a 3-D shape.
   One shape will be left over.

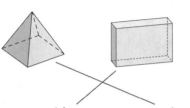

6 faces   square base   all triangular faces

5. Use a geometry word or words to name each shape.

a)   b)   c)   d)

___cone___   ___cube___   ___cylinder___   ___sphere___

Pathway
1

6. A triangular prism has 5 faces, 6 vertices, and 9 edges.
   Fill in the chart to describe each 3-D shape shown.

edge
face
vertex

3-D shape	Shapes of faces or surfaces	Number of faces	Number of vertices	Number of edges
	triangle, square faces	5	5	8
	rectangle faces	6	8	12
	circle faces, rectangle surface	2	0	2

Copyright © 2011 by Nelson Education Ltd.   *Leaps and Bounds*   Geometry: 3-D Shapes, Diagnostic Tool **123**

You will need

- 3-D shapes (prisms, pyramids, sphere, cylinder, cone)
- 3-D Shapes (BLM 10)
- scissors
- Student Resource pages 122–123

Open-Ended Intervention

Before Using the Open-Ended Intervention

Provide 3-D shapes (rectangular prism, square-based pyramid, and cylinder) for students to examine. Ask the following questions:

▸ What are the names of these 3-D shapes?
(e.g., *rectangular prism, square-based pyramid, cylinder*)

▸ How are these 3-D shapes similar? How are they different?
(e.g., *They all have faces but they have different faces [rectangle, triangle, and circle]. A prism and a pyramid have flat faces, and a cylinder has a curved surface.*)

Encourage students to describe the shapes using geometric attributes such as the number of faces, edges, and vertices and the shapes of the faces. Ask:

▸ What strategy can you use to count the vertices? (e.g., *I mark each vertex as I count it.*)

Using the Open-Ended Intervention (Student Resource pages 122–123)

Provide 3-D shapes that match the shapes pictured on the student pages and 3-D Shapes (BLM 10). Students may sort using the objects, then record their sorting using the cutout shapes.

Read through the tasks together. Give students time to work, ideally in pairs.

Observe students as they work and use questions to bring out the following:

- descriptions of objects in terms of geometric attributes (e.g., the shapes of faces, the number of faces, whether faces are or are not identical, the number of vertices, whether the shapes can or cannot be stacked)
- ability to sort the same group of objects in different ways
- use of very simple or more elaborate sorting rules (e.g., sorting by pyramids, prisms, or by number of vertices)

Consolidating and Reflecting

Have students examine a triangle-based pyramid and a triangular prism. Ask:

▸ Describe the attributes of each 3-D shape. (e.g., *A triangle-based pyramid has 4 triangular faces, 6 vertices, and 9 edges; a triangular prism has 5 faces, 2 triangular faces and 3 rectangular faces, 6 vertices, and 9 edges.*)

Provide a square-based pyramid, a rectangular prism, and a triangular prism. Ask:

▸ What attributes can you use to sort these 3-D shapes?
(e.g., *I can sort by number and type of faces, vertices [corners], or edges.*)

▸ What attribute do these three 3-D shapes have in common?
(e.g., *All have at least 1 rectangular face.*)

▸ Choose a fourth 3-D shape that is different from these three 3-D shapes
(e.g., *triangle-based pyramid*), and describe its attributes.

triangular prism or
triangle-based prism

triangular pyramid or
triangle-based pyramid

Describing 3-D Shapes

Guided Intervention

Before Using the Guided Intervention

Provide 3-D shapes (rectangular prism, square-based pyramid, and cylinder). Ask:

▸ What are the names of these 3-D shapes?
(e.g., *rectangular prism, square-based pyramid, cylinder*)

▸ How are these 3-D shapes similar? How are they different?
(e.g., *They all have faces but they have different faces [rectangle, triangle, and circle]. A prism and a pyramid have flat faces, and a cylinder has a curved surface.*)

Encourage students to describe the shapes using geometric attributes such as the number of faces, edges, and vertices and the shapes of the faces.

Using the Guided Intervention (Student Resource pages 124–127)

Provide 3-D shapes and Venn Diagrams (BLM 27). Work through the instructional section on sorting 3-D shapes together. Have students use 3-D shapes and Venn diagrams or charts to sort; then compare their sorting to the groups pictured on the student page.

Have students work through the **Try These** questions in pairs or individually.

Observe whether students

• relate 3-D shapes to real objects (Question 1)
• describe and identify 3-D shapes using geometric attributes (Questions 2 to 4)
• use geometric attributes to sort and classify (Question 5)

Consolidating and Reflecting

Have students examine the triangular pyramid and the triangular prism. Ask:

▸ Describe the attributes of each 3-D shape.
(e.g., *A triangle-based pyramid has 4 triangular faces, 6 vertices, and 9 edges; a triangular prism has 5 faces, 2 triangular faces and 3 rectangular faces, 6 vertices, and 9 edges.*)

Provide a square-based pyramid, a rectangular prism, and a triangular prism. Ask:

▸ What attributes can be used to sort these 3-D shapes? What attribute do they have common?
(e.g., *I can sort by number and type of faces, vertices, or edges. All have at least 1 rectangular face.*)

▸ Compare the square-based pyramid to the rectangular prism and triangular prism. How are pyramids and prisms similar? How are they different?
(e.g., *Prisms and pyramids are named by the shapes of their bases, like the triangular prism and square-based pyramid. Prisms have more rectangular faces, and pyramids have more triangular faces.*)

You will need

• 3-D objects (prisms, pyramids, spheres, cylinders, cones)
• Venn Diagrams (BLM 27)
• 3-D Shapes (BLM 10)
• scissors
• Student Resource pages 124–127

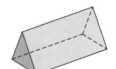

triangular prism or triangle-based prism

triangular pyramid or triangle-based pyramid

Building 3-D Shapes

- building blocks, geoblocks
- linking cubes
- pattern blocks
- Student Resource page 128

Open-Ended Intervention

Before Using the Open-Ended Intervention

Provide building blocks, geoblocks, linking cubes, or pattern blocks. Ask:

▶ What 3-D shapes are in your set(s) of building materials?
(e.g., *The building blocks have a cylinder, a rectangular prism, a squared-based pyramid, and a cone. The geoblocks have rectangular prisms, cubes, triangular prisms, and a square-based pyramid. The linking cubes have rectangular prisms and cubes. The pattern blocks are prisms.*)

▶ Could you build the same things if you used different building materials?
(e.g., *No, I can make hexagon-shaped things with the pattern blocks, but not with linking cubes.*)

Using the Open-Ended Intervention ⟨Student Resource page 128⟩

Provide any of the following: building blocks, geoblocks, linking cubes, and pattern blocks. Read the task on the student page together. Have students stack or join the blocks and cubes to make structures of their own. Tell students that when they make a new 3-D shape from other 3-D shapes, it is called *composing*. Taking apart a 3-D shape to create smaller 3-D shapes is called *decomposing*.

Observe students as they work and use questions to bring out their knowledge of
- strategies for composing and decomposing 3-D shapes
- the names of 3-D shapes (e.g., cube, cylinder, rectangular prism, square-based pyramid)

Consolidating and Reflecting

Ensure students' understanding by using the following prompts and questions:

▶ 3-D shapes can be made up of smaller 3-D shapes. How did you use smaller 3-D shapes to make larger shapes in your structure?
(e.g., *This 3-D shape is made up of 3 cubes and 1 triangular prism.*)

▶ What strategies did you use to make 3-D shapes, using smaller 3-D shapes?
(e.g., *I connected linking cubes to make a rectangular prism. I stacked pattern blocks to make a 3-D shape made up of rectangular and triangular prisms.*)

▶ 3-D shapes can be cut up into smaller 3-D shapes. Look at a triangular prism. What smaller 3-D shapes can you make by taking it apart? (e.g., *I can make 2 smaller triangular prisms even when I cut it in 2 different ways—through the middle and up and down.*)

▶ What strategies did you use to imagine how a 3-D shape could be broken up into smaller 3-D shapes?
(e.g., *I imagined where I could cut the 3-D shape so that it would make smaller 3-D shapes that I could recognize, like a rectangular prism or a triangular prism. I tried to think of where to cut the 3-D shape so that it would make the same type of 3-D shape, just shorter or thinner.*)

Leaps and Bounds 3/4
Copyright © 2011 by Nelson Education Ltd.

Building 3-D Shapes

Guided Intervention

Before Using the Guided Intervention

Provide building blocks, geoblocks, linking cubes, or pattern blocks. Ask:

▸ What 3-D shapes are in your set(s) of building materials? (e.g., *The building blocks have a cylinder, a rectangular prism, a squared-based pyramid, and a cone. The geoblocks have rectangular prisms, cubes, triangular prisms, and a square-based pyramid. The linking cubes have rectangular prisms and cubes. The pattern blocks are prisms.*)

▸ Could you build the same things if you used different building materials? (e.g., *No, I can make hexagon-shaped things with the pattern blocks, but not with linking cubes.*)

Using the Guided Intervention (Student Resource pages 129–132)

Provide building blocks, geoblocks, linking cubes, and pattern blocks. Read through the instructional section of the student pages together. Have students stack or join blocks and cubes to make the structures shown. If some materials are not available, have students examine the pictures. Tell students that when they make a new 3-D shape from other 3-D shapes, it is called *composing*. Taking apart a 3-D shape to create smaller 3-D shapes is called *decomposing*.

Have students work through the **Try These** questions in pairs or individually, using pattern blocks and linking cubes.

Observe whether students
- recognize that prisms can be made by stacking smaller prisms (Question 1)
- are able to name 3-D shapes (Question 1)
- have strategies for composing 3-D shapes (Questions 2, 5)
- are able to explain how a 3-D shape can be decomposed (Questions 3, 4)

Consolidating and Reflecting

Ensure students' understanding by using the following prompts and questions:

▸ What strategies did you use to make 3-D shapes using smaller 3-D shapes? (e.g., *I connected linking cubes to make a 3-D shape made up of rectangular prisms. I stacked pattern blocks to make a 3-D shape made up of rectangular prisms and triangular prisms.*)

▸ 3-D shapes can be cut or decomposed into smaller 3-D shapes. Look at a triangular prism. What smaller 3-D shapes can you make by breaking down the triangular prism? (e.g., *I can make 2 smaller triangular prisms even when I cut it in 2 different ways—through the middle and up and down.*)

▸ What strategies did you use to imagine how a 3-D shape could be broken down into smaller 3-D shapes? (e.g., *I imagined where I could cut the 3-D shape so that it would make smaller 3-D shapes that I could recognize, like a rectangular prism or triangular prism. I tried to think of where to cut the 3-D shape so that it would make the same type of 3-D shape, just shorter or thinner.*)

Copyright © 2011 by Nelson Education Ltd.   *Leaps and Bounds 3/4*

2-D Shapes

Planning For This Topic

Materials for assisting students with 2-D shapes consist of a diagnostic tool and 2 intervention pathways. Pathway 1 focuses on describing and comparing 2-D shapes, and Pathway 2 focuses on composing and decomposing 2-D shapes.

Each pathway has an open-ended option and a guided option. Choose the type of intervention most suitable for your students' needs and your particular circumstances.

Curriculum Connections

Grades 1 to 4 curriculum connections for this topic are provided online. See www.nelson.com/leapsandbounds. If the topic of square corners or benchmark angles has not been addressed, any sorting involving the use of angles may be omitted.

Why might a student struggle with 2-D shapes?

Students might struggle with describing, comparing, composing, and decomposing 2-D shapes because they might

- think that every 2-D shape is a polygon (i.e., A polygon is a closed figure with straight sides; a circle is not a polygon.)
- perceive a change in orientation of a polygon as a change in the type of polygon (e.g., They think that a square that is rotated 45° to look like a diamond is no longer considered a square.)

- not realize that some polygons have more than one name because they can be described by several attributes (e.g., A square is a quadrilateral, a parallelogram, and a rectangle.)
- not recognize that when shapes are put together they must be put together so that parts of edges meet

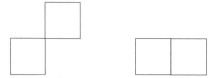

- have trouble keeping track of the number of sides of a shape with many sides
- focus on non-geometric attributes of a shape to sort or describe (e.g., colour), as opposed to properties like side lengths or numbers of sides
- focus on sorting only by number of sides (since we name polygons this way) rather than noticing other properties, such as the shapes that make them up or the kinds of corners or side length relationships

Professional Learning Connections

PRIME: Geometry, Background and Strategies (Nelson Education, 2007), pages 42–44, 50–53, 72, 74–78

Making Math Meaningful to Canadian Students K–8 (Nelson Education Ltd., 2008), pages 287–296, 310–315

Big Ideas from Dr. Small Grades K–3 (Nelson Education Ltd., 2010), pages 65, 73–75

Good Questions (dist. by Nelson Education Ltd., 2009), pages 61, 63–64, 68, 70–72, 81, 83, 85

Leaps and Bounds 3/4 Copyright © 2011 by Nelson Education Ltd.

Diagnostic Tool: 2-D Shapes

Use the diagnostic tool to determine the most suitable intervention for 2-D shapes. Provide Diagnostic Tool: 2-D Shapes, Teacher's Resource pages 132 and 133, and have students complete it in writing or orally.

See solutions on Teacher's Resource pages 134 and 135.

Intervention Pathways

The purpose of the intervention pathways is to help students construct, describe, and compare polygons in a variety of ways so that ultimately they can describe more complex polygons with additional geometric attributes and properties.

There are 2 pathways:
* Pathway 1: Describing 2-D Shapes
* Pathway 2: Building 2-D Shapes

Use the chart below (or the Key to Pathways on Teacher's Resource pages 134 and 135) to determine which pathway is most suitable for each student or group of students.

Diagnostic Tool Results	Intervention Pathway
If students struggle with Questions 4 to 6	use Pathway 1: Describing 2-D Shapes *Teacher's Resource pages 136–137* *Student Resource pages 133–137*
If students struggle with Questions 1 to 3	use Pathway 2: Building 2-D Shapes *Teacher's Resource pages 138–139* *Student Resource pages 138–141*

2-D Shapes

1. Name the smaller shapes that make up each quadrilateral.

a)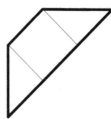

b)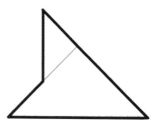

_____

_____

_____

_____

You will need

- pattern blocks
- a straightedge

2. **a)** Show how to divide the square into smaller squares and rectangles.

b) Show how to divide the square into triangles.

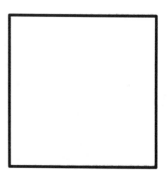

3. Make each 2-D shape using 2 or more different pattern blocks. Sketch the shape. Name pattern blocks you used.

a) triangle

b) 6-sided shape

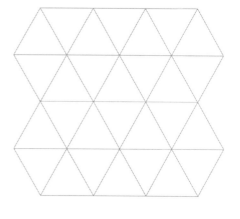

_____

_____

_____

_____

4. **a)** The shapes were sorted into 4 groups.
What might the sorting rule be?

sorting rule: _____

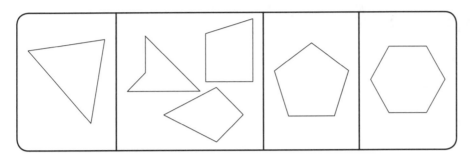

b) Sort the shapes from part a) into 2 groups.
What is your sorting rule?

sorting rule: _____

5. Draw a line to match each name with a shape.

hexagon   square   parallelogram   trapezoid

6. Sketch 2 different examples of each shape.
How are they the same? How are they different?

Shape sketches	Same	Different
quadrilateral		
pentagon		

Copyright © 2011 by Nelson Education Ltd.   *Leaps and Bounds*

Solutions and Key to Pathways

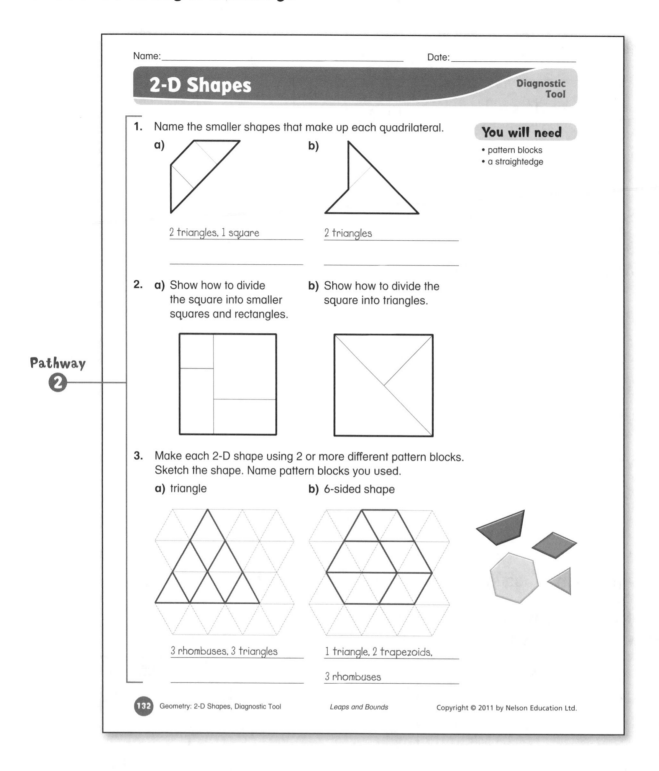

Pathway
2

2-D Shapes

Name: _____   Date: _____

2-D Shapes

Diagnostic Tool

1. Name the smaller shapes that make up each quadrilateral.

   a)

   2 triangles, 1 square _____

   _____

   b)

   2 triangles _____

You will need
- pattern blocks
- a straightedge

2. a) Show how to divide the square into smaller squares and rectangles.

   b) Show how to divide the square into triangles.

3. Make each 2-D shape using 2 or more different pattern blocks. Sketch the shape. Name pattern blocks you used.

   a) triangle

   3 rhombuses, 3 triangles _____

   b) 6-sided shape

   1 triangle, 2 trapezoids, _____

   3 rhombuses _____

Name:_____   Date:_____

4. **a)** The shapes were sorted into 4 groups.
What might the sorting rule be?

sorting rule: _e.g., number of sides_ _____

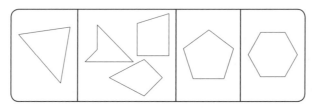

b) Sort the shapes from part a) into 2 groups.
What is your sorting rule?

sorting rule: _quadrilaterals and not quadrilaterals_ _____

5. Draw a line to match each name with a shape.

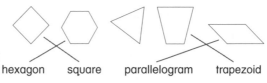

hexagon   square   parallelogram   trapezoid

6. Sketch 2 different examples of each shape.
How are they the same? How are they different?

Shape sketches	Same	Different
quadrilateral	4 sides	one has all same side lengths and the other has no sides the same length
pentagon	5 sides	side lengths are different one has some square corners and the other has no square corners

Pathway
1

Copyright © 2011 by Nelson Education Ltd.   *Leaps and Bounds*   Geometry: 2-D Shapes, Diagnostic Tool   **133**

Copyright © 2011 by Nelson Education Ltd.   *Leaps and Bounds 3/4*   Geometry: 2-D Shapes   **135**

Describing 2-D Shapes

You will need

- paper, scissors
- Polygons (BLM 11)
- Student Resource pages 133–134

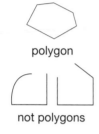

polygon

not polygons

Open-Ended Intervention

Before Using the Open-Ended Intervention

Draw some 2-D shapes, including some that are polygons and some that are not polygons. Ask:

▸ Which one of these shapes is a polygon? What makes it different?
(e.g., *The polygon has straight sides and is closed. The other shapes are not polygons because they are open or they have curved sides.*)

Cut out and display the polygons from BLM 11, Polygons. Explain that different kinds of polygons are named by the number of sides they have. Ask:

▸ What are the names of these polygons? (*triangle, hexagon, quadrilateral, pentagon*)

Using the Open-Ended Intervention   (Student Resource pages 133–134)

Read through the tasks on the student pages together. Use the cutout shapes from Polygons (BLM 11) so that students can sort the shapes. They may want to glue the pieces to show their groups on the second page. Allow students time to work, ideally in pairs.

Observe student responses and use questions to bring out the following:

- Polygons can be described by attributes such as the number of sides or number of vertices (corners).
- Polygons can be sorted into groups according to geometric attributes.
- Shapes can be sorted using 2 or more geometric attributes at the same time.

Consolidating and Reflecting

On the board or on a separate piece of paper, draw a rectangle and a square. Ask:

▸ Name these shapes. How are these shapes the same?
(*rectangle, square; e.g., They have 4 sides, 4 vertices, and 4 square corners.*)

▸ How are these shapes different? (e.g., *All the sides are the same length in a square. Opposite sides are the same length in a rectangle.*)

▸ Is every square a rectangle? Is every rectangle a square?
(e.g., *A square is a rectangle, but not every rectangle is a square.*)

Show a triangle, a hexagon, and a square and ask:

▸ How can you describe these shapes? (e.g., *A triangle has 3 sides and 3 vertices; a rectangle has 4 sides and 4 vertices; a hexagon has 6 sides and 6 vertices.*)

Show a right-angled triangle and a square and ask:

▸ How are these shapes the same? How are they different?
(e.g., *They have straight sides that all meet. Both shapes have a square corner. They have a different number of sides, and the sides are different lengths.*)

▸ How is it possible to sort polygons using more than one geometric attribute at the same time?
(e.g., *You could sort by the kinds of corners and the number of sides.*)

Describing 2-D Shapes

Guided Intervention

Before Using the Guided Intervention

Draw some 2-D shapes, including some that are polygons and some that are not polygons. Ask:

▶ Which of these shapes are polygons? What makes them polygons?
(e.g., *The polygon has straight sides and is closed. The other shapes are not polygons because they are open or they have curved sides.*)

polygon   not polygons

Display a tangram (Tangrams, BLM 12). Ask:

▶ What polygons do you see? (e.g., *triangle, square, quadrilateral*)

Outline a 6-sided shape on a tangram and ask:

▶ What is this shape called? (*a hexagon*)

Using the Guided Intervention   (Student Resource pages 135–137)

Work through the instructional section of the student page together. Challenge students to find more triangles in a tangram by outlining different sections. Students should notice that all of the triangles have 3 sides and 3 vertices. Some might notice that these triangles all have a square corner.

Have students work through the **Try These** questions in pairs or individually. They might like to use Tangrams and Polygons (BLMs 11 and 12) so they can handle the shapes.

Observe whether students

- can identify where shapes are seen in the environment (Question 1)
- can describe shapes, focusing on different aspects of the shapes (e.g., number of sides, number of vertices) (Questions 2, 3)
- can create shapes to meet certain conditions (Questions 4, 5)
- can recognize different polygons share some geometric attributes (Questions 1, 6)

Consolidating and Reflecting

Draw a rectangle and a square. Ask the following questions:

▶ What are these shapes? How are they the same?
(*rectangle, square; e.g., They both have 4 sides, 4 vertices, and 4 square corners.*)

▶ How are the shapes different? (e.g., *All the sides are the same length in a square, and opposite sides are the same length in a rectangle.*)

▶ Is every square a rectangle? Is every rectangle a square?
(e.g., *A square is a rectangle, but not every rectangle is a square.*)

▶ How can you sort polygons using more than one geometric attribute?
(e.g., *You could use kinds of corners or the number of sides.*)

You will need

- tangram (or Tangrams, BLM 12)
- Polygons (BLM 11)
- Student Resource pages 135–137

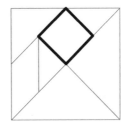

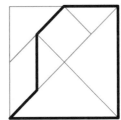

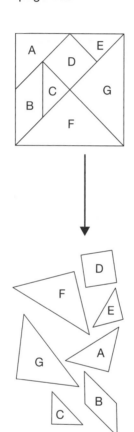

Building 2-D Shapes

You will need

- tangrams (or Tangrams BLM 12)
- paper, scissors
- Student Resource page 138

Open-Ended Intervention

Before Using the Open-Ended Intervention

Provide a tangram set arranged as a square, and ask the following questions:

▶ A tangram square is broken apart into smaller, individual shapes. What shapes do you see?
(e.g., *3 different-sized triangles, 1 square, 1 parallelogram*)

▶ Use at least 2 tangram pieces to make another shape. Describe the shape.
(e.g., *I made squares [from 2 medium triangles and 2 larger triangles], a larger triangle [from 2 large triangles], and a trapezoid [from a parallelogram and a small triangle].*)

When a polygon is broken into smaller shapes, it is called *decomposing*, and when polygons are put together to make a larger shape, it is called *composing*.

Using the Open-Ended Intervention (Student Resource page 138)

Read through the tasks on the student page together. Provide paper and scissors for students to cut out 5 polygons. Allow students time to work, ideally in pairs. Some students may need prompts to get started, but give students sufficient time to start on their own first. Use the following prompts and questions:

- Make 1 straight-line cut. How many polygons did you make? (e.g., *2 polygons*)
- Take one of the 2 polygons that you made and make a second straight-line cut. Now, how many polygons have you made? (e.g., *3 polygons*)

Observe student responses and use questions to bring out the following:

- descriptions and names of polygons in relation to the number of sides
- the identification of square corners within a polygon
- strategies for building (composing) and breaking apart (decomposing) polygons

Consolidating and Reflecting

Ensure students' understanding by asking the following questions:

▶ What strategies did you use to make a larger polygon into a set of smaller polygons?
(e.g., *I made straight-line cuts to divide the polygon into different polygons. I made straight-line cuts to make the same polygon in different sizes. I imagined that 2 squares could make a rectangle.*)

▶ What strategies did you use to make a new, larger polygon from the smaller polygons?
(e.g., *I joined the sides of the polygons that matched up. I put shapes together with no gaps.*)

Leaps and Bounds 3/4
Copyright © 2011 by Nelson Education Ltd.

Building 2-D Shapes

Guided Intervention

Before Using the Guided Intervention

Provide pattern blocks and ask:

▸ What are the names of the pattern blocks?
(e.g., *hexagon, trapezoid, rhombus, triangle, square, and parallelogram*)

▸ What different polygons can you make with 2 trapezoid pattern blocks?
Describe and name the polygons.
(e.g., *a hexagon with 6 sides and a parallelogram with 4 sides*)

▸ What pattern blocks can you put together to cover a yellow hexagon completely
with no gaps or overlaps?
(e.g., *2 red trapezoids, or 6 green triangles, or 1 red trapezoid and 3 green triangles,
or 3 blue rhombuses, or 2 blue rhombuses and 2 green triangles*)

Using the Guided Intervention (Student Resource pages 139–141)

Read through the instructional section of the student pages together. Prompt
students to trace the triangles and parallelograms with their fingers. Have students
verify the number of sides of a parallelogram and triangle (i.e., a parallelogram has
4 sides; a triangle has 3 sides). Ask the following questions:

▸ How are the triangle, trapezoid, and hexagon different?
(e.g., *They have different numbers of sides.*)

▸ How are the triangle, trapezoid, and hexagon the same?
(e.g., *They are made from triangles, or triangles and parallelograms.*)

Have available pattern blocks and tangrams (or Tangrams, BLM 12). Have
students work through the **Try These** questions in pairs or individually.

Observe whether students

• can build new shapes from ones given (Questions 1, 2)

• can decompose simple shapes from ones given (Questions 3, 4).

Consolidating and Reflecting

Ensure understanding by asking the following questions:

▸ What strategies did you use to make a larger polygon into a set of smaller
polygons? (e.g., *I made straight-line cuts to divide the polygon into different
polygons. I made straight-line cuts to make the same polygon in different sizes.
I imagined that 2 squares could make a rectangle.*)

▸ What strategies did you use to make a larger polygon from smaller polygons?
(e.g., *I joined sides of polygons that matched up. I put shapes together with no gaps.*)

You will need

• pattern blocks
• paper
• scissors
• tangrams
(or Tangrams,
BLM 12)
• Student Resource
page 139–141

Copyright © 2011 by Nelson Education Ltd.   *Leaps and Bounds 3/4*

Planning For This Topic

Materials for assisting students with describing movement and location consist of a diagnostic tool and 2 intervention pathways. One pathway is about moving on a grid, and the other is about positional language.

Each pathway has an open-ended option and a guided option. Choose the type of intervention most suitable for your students' needs and your particular circumstances.

Curriculum Connections

Grades 1 to 4 curriculum connections for this topic are provided online. See www.nelson.com/leapsandbounds. Note that there are no specific outcomes related to location in the WNCP curriculum.

Also note that transformations are introduced in Grade 3 in Ontario but not until Grade 5 for WNCP. Because a student would not be considered significantly behind in their understanding of transformations in Grade 3 or Grade 4 even in Ontario, this topic is not covered here.

Why might students struggle with identifying and describing movement and location?

Students might struggle with identifying and describing movement and location for the following reasons:

- They might misinterpret terms (e.g., *Above* is thought to mean directly above, like looking up at the sky).
- They may not realize that *front* and *back* are relative to one's position.
- They might have difficulty differentiating right from left.
- They may not realize that sometimes more than one positional relationship is needed to locate something.
- They may not realize that diagonal movements on a grid are different in size than up and down or right and left movements.
- They might determine movement by counting the starting point rather than only the number of squares or steps *after* the starting point to the next point.

Professional Learning Connections

PRIME: Geometry, Background and Strategies (Nelson Education, 2007), pages 94–96

Making Math Meaningful to Canadian Students K–8 (Nelson Education Ltd., 2008), pages 337–341

Big Ideas from Dr. Small, Grades K–3 (Nelson Education Ltd., 2010), pages 77–80

Good Questions (dist. by Nelson Education Ltd., 2009), pages 64–65

Diagnostic Tool: Movement and Location

Use the diagnostic tool to determine the most suitable intervention for describing movement and location. Provide Diagnostic Tool: Movement and Location, Teacher's Resource pages 142 and 143, and have students complete it in writing or orally.

See solutions on Teacher's Resource pages 144 and 145.

Intervention Pathways

The purpose of the intervention pathways is to provide support for students to describe movement and relative locations using positional language.

There are 2 pathways:
* Pathway 1: Moving on a Grid
* Pathway 2: Using Positional Language

Use the chart below (or the Key to Pathways on Teacher's Resource pages 144 and 145) to determine which pathway is most suitable for each student or group of students.

Diagnostic Tool Results	Intervention Pathway
If students struggle with Questions 4 to 6	use Pathway 1: Moving on a Grid *Teacher's Resource pages 146–147* *Student Resource pages 142–146*
If students struggle with Questions 1 to 3	use Pathway 2: Using Positional Language *Teacher's Resource pages 148–149* *Student Resource pages 147–150*

Movement and Location

1. Angie put her drawings in a scrapbook.

   a) Picture A is to the left of Picture _____.

   b) Picture _____ is above Picture B.

   c) Picture _____ is below and to the right of Picture A.

front

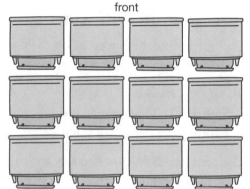

2. Write the names on the desks so that *all* of these statements are true.

   • Dan is sitting to the right of Pam.

   • Tye is sitting behind Pam.

   • Nara is sitting in front of Dan and in front of and to the right of Pam.

3. Make a statement about the location of each shape. Use these positional words: *left, below, right, in front of, behind, inside, back, between, next to*

   a) The triangle is _____.

   b) The square is _____.

   c) The heart is _____.

   d) The circle is _____.

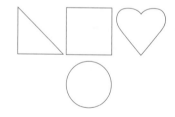

4. Complete these statements to make them true.

   a) A is ____ spaces to the right of B.

   b) D is ____ spaces down from B.

   c) To get from A to C, you go ____ spaces down

   and ____ spaces left.

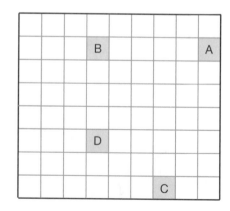

5. Describe the path of the arrows from start to end.
Tell the number of spaces and the direction of each arrow.

a) start at letter: _____

_____

_____

end at letter: _____

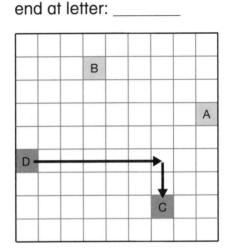

b) start at letter: _____

_____

_____

end at letter: _____

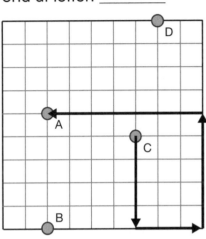

6. Draw the routes on these maps, using arrows between
the letters. Tell where you end up.

a) Start at square A, and move
   8 squares left
   2 squares down

end at letter: ____

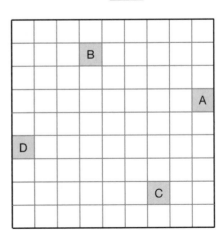

b) Start at point A, and move
   3 units left
   7 units up
   1 unit left

end at letter: ____

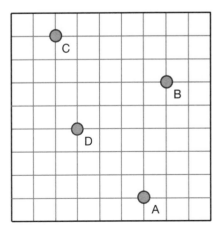

Copyright © 2011 by Nelson Education Ltd.   *Leaps and Bounds*

Solutions and Key to Pathways

Name:_____ Date:_____

Movement and Location

1. Angie put her drawings in a scrapbook.

   a) Picture A is to the left of Picture ___C___.

   b) Picture ___A___ is above Picture B.

   c) Picture ___D___ is below and to the right of Picture A.

2. Write the names on the desks so that *all* of these statements are true.

   • Dan is sitting to the right of Pam.

   • Tye is sitting behind Pam.

   • Nara is sitting in front of Dan and in front of and to the right of Pam.

3. Make a statement about the location of each shape. Use these positional words: *left, below, right, in front of, behind, inside, back, between, next to*

   a) The triangle is <u>to the left of the heart</u>.

   b) The square is <u>above the circle</u>.

   c) The heart is <u>next to the square</u>.

   d) The circle is <u>below the square</u>.

4. Complete these statements to make them true.

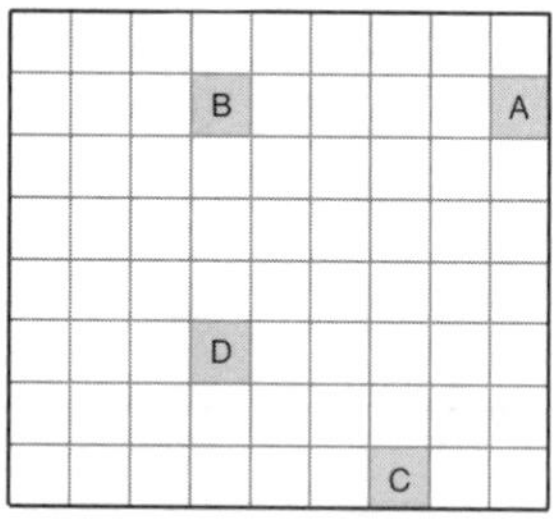

   a) A is ___5___ spaces to the right of B.

   b) D is ___4___ spaces down from B.

   c) To get from A to C, you go ___6___ spaces down and ___2___ spaces left.

Leaps and Bounds   Copyright © 2011 by Nelson Education Ltd.

Leaps and Bounds 3/4   Copyright © 2011 by Nelson Education Ltd.

Name:_____ Date:_____

5. Describe the path of the arrows from start to end.
Tell the number of spaces and the direction of each arrow.

a) start at letter: _____D_____

6 spaces right

2 spaces down

end at letter: _____C_____

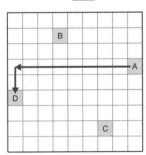

b) start at letter: _____C_____

4 units down, 3 units right,

5 units up, 7 units left

end at letter: _____A_____

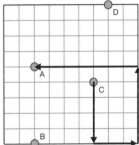

Pathway

6. Draw the routes on these maps, using arrows between
the letters. Tell where you end up.

a) Start at square A, and move

8 squares left
2 squares down

end at letter: _D_

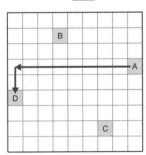

b) Start at point A, and move

3 units left
7 units up
1 unit left

end at letter: _C_

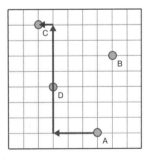

Moving on a Grid

You will need

- grid paper (BLM 7) or grid chart paper
- counters
- Student Resource page 142

Open-Ended Intervention

Before Using the Open-Ended Intervention

Place a counter in a square of a large grid. Move the counter up 2 squares. Ask:

▸ How would you describe how I moved the counter?
(*2 squares up*)

▸ Show how to move it 3 squares to the right.

▸ Show how to move it 1 square down and 2 squares left.

Put another counter on the grid so that there are 3 empty squares between the 2 counters. Move the first counter over to the second one. Ask:

▸ How could you describe the movement of the counter? (e.g., *4 spaces to the right*)

Make sure students notice that they did not count the starting square but only each square they moved to, and through (including the final square).

Using the Open-Ended Intervention (Student Resource page 142)

Read through the tasks on the student page together. Make sure students understand that they can use only letters from the grid. You might want to provide words for students to choose from rather than asking them to make up their own words (e.g., bagel, bag, work, code, burger, bear, start, toast, rock, blue).

Discuss how to record the total number of spaces moved in each direction. (e.g., Moving 2 down and then 1 right is written as "2 down, 1 right," and not "1 down, 1 down, 1 right.")

Provide counters for students who want to use them to show the movements on the grid. Allow students time to work, ideally in pairs.

Observe student responses and use questions to bring out the following:

- Movements on a grid are always horizontal or vertical in this particular task.
- Describing a movement involves direction and a number of spaces.
- A new count starts when the direction changes.

Consolidating and Reflecting

Ensure understanding by asking questions based on students' work:

▸ What are some of the words you found?
(e.g., *bed, blue, back, dare*)

▸ How is telling how to go from W to K different from going from W to R?
(e.g., *Both are one space, but one is right and the other is down.*)

▸ How did you decide how many spaces you needed to get from one letter to the next?
(e.g., *I put a counter on the first letter and counted how many times I had to move it to get to the next letter.*)

Moving on a Grid

Guided Intervention

Before Using the Guided Intervention

Place a counter in a square of a large grid. Move the counter up 2 squares. Ask:

▶ How did I move the counter? (*up 2 squares*)
▶ Show how to move it 3 squares to the right.
▶ Show how to move it 1 square down and 2 squares left.

Put another counter on the grid so that there are 3 empty squares between the 2 counters. Move the first counter over to the second one. Ask:

▶ How can you describe the movement of the counter? (e.g., *4 spaces to the left*)

Make sure students notice that they did not count the starting square but just each square they moved to, and through (including the final square).

Using the Guided Intervention (Student Resource pages 143–146)

Work through the instructional section about Daniel's routes on the student page together. Prompt students to say aloud the directions and trace the routes. Have them work through the **Try These** questions in pairs or individually.

Observe whether students
- follow directions in sequence and draw the appropriate path (Questions 1, 3)
- correctly record a sequence for a path (Questions 2, 3)
- recognize how to predict directions if going from end to start (Question 4)
- realize that directions can be square to square or point to point (Questions 3, 6)
- create, draw, and describe paths to meet given conditions (Questions 3, 5, 6)

Consolidating and Reflecting

Use a blank grid. Have students interpret these directions and draw the path with arrows:

▶ Mark a square in the middle of the grid. Move down 4 squares, right 6 squares, up 3 squares, and left 5 squares. Where do you end up compared with where you started? (e.g., *1 square down and 1 square to the right of the start*)

Have students draw a route on the grid that has 3 directions. Ask:

▶ Describe the directions for your route.
(e.g., *I start here; then I go 2 squares down, 1 square right, and 6 squares left.*)
▶ I start here (mark the grid) and go 3 squares down and 1 square right. But I want to get back to where I started. What directions would work?
(e.g., *1 square left and 3 squares up*)

Use Question 3 parts a) and b) to point out the 2 ways of moving on a grid (i.e., spaces, points).

▶ What is different about the way you moved on these grids?
(e.g., *I moved using spaces in part a) and then I moved using points in part b).*)

You will need

- grid paper (BLM 6 or 7) or grid chart paper
- counters that fit in the grid
- Student Resource pages 143–146

Using Positional Language

You will need

- building blocks (or everyday objects, e.g., cans, boxes, etc., or toys)
- large sheet of paper
- coloured pencils
- Student Resource page 147

Open-Ended Intervention

Before Using the Open-Ended Intervention

Build a simple structure using building blocks. Alternatively, provide students with 5 different blocks and have them build a simple block structure. Ask:

▸ Which block is *above* which other block?
(e.g., *The tall grey one is above the black one.*)

▸ Which is *below*? (e.g., *The black block is below the grey ones.*)

▸ How would you describe the position of the white block compared with the position of the black one? (e.g., *The white block is in front of the black one.*)

▸ Are any blocks *between* other blocks?
(e.g., *A grey block is between the tall grey and the black block.*)

Continue questioning about positions of objects in the classroom, using positional words such as *over, under, behind, inside, outside, to the right, to the left,* and *next to.*

Using the Open-Ended Intervention (Student Resource page 147)

Read through the task on the student page with students. Provide blocks or other 3-D objects (e.g., cans, boxes, etc.) or toys. Explain to students that their scenes could include one structure or several separate parts. Ensure that students understand they are to describe their scenes using positional words to compare the positions of objects in the scene.

Observe student responses and use questions to bring out the following:

- The location of an object is always in relation to the location of another object or objects.
- Positional vocabulary includes words like *over, under, above, below, in front of, behind, inside, outside, next to, between, to the right of,* and *to the left of.*
- There is some flexibility in positional vocabulary (e.g., to the right could mean close to the right or far to the right).
- To say that an object is behind or in front of something, one must know the location of the front and back.

Consolidating and Reflecting

Ensure understanding by asking questions based on students' work:

▸ When are you most likely to use the words *above* or *over*?
(e.g., *when one thing is higher than another*)

▸ If something is *between* 2 other things, does one of them have to be to the right of that thing? (e.g., *No, one might be behind one and in front of another.*)

▸ If one block is *to the right of* another, what else do you know for sure?
(e.g., *that one of the blocks is to the left of the other*)

▸ Suppose 2 objects are both indoors. When would you ever talk about *inside* or *outside*? (e.g., *if one is in one room and one is in another room, or maybe if one is inside a box and the other is outside of it*)

Using Positional Language

Guided Intervention

Before Using the Guided Intervention

Build a simple structure using building blocks. Or provide students with 5 different blocks and have them build a simple block structure. Ask:

▸ Which block is *above* which other block? (e.g., *The white cube is above the grey block.*)

▸ Which is below? (e.g., *The longer grey block is below the longer white one.*)

▸ How would you describe the position of the black block compared with the position of the grey one? (e.g., *The black block is in front of the grey one.*)

▸ Are any blocks between other blocks?
(e.g., *The white one is between the grey blocks.*)

Continue questioning about positions of objects in the classroom, using positional words such as *over, under, behind, inside, outside, to the right, to the left,* and *next to.*

Using the Guided Intervention (Student Resource pages 148–150)

Have students discuss the scene pictured on the student page. Draw attention to the words *front, back, right,* and *left* to orient the picture. Make sure students understand the positional words used. Have them work through the **Try These** questions in pairs or individually.

Observe whether students

• realize that the location of an object is always in relation to the location of another object or objects (Questions 1 to 6)

• correctly use positional vocabulary (*over, under, above, below, in front of, behind, inside, outside, next to, between, to the right of, to the left of*) (Questions 1 to 6)

• understand there is some flexibility in positional vocabulary (e.g., *to the right* could mean close to the right or far to the right) (Questions 1, 5)

• realize they need to know the location of the front and back in order to say that an object is behind or in front of something, or even to the right or left of it (Questions 1, 2, 4)

Consolidating and Reflecting

Ensure students' understanding by asking the following questions:

▸ When are you most likely to use the words *above* or *over?*
(e.g., *when one thing is higher than another*)

▸ If something is *between* 2 other things, does one of them have to be to the right of that thing? (e.g., *No, one might be behind one and in front of another.*)

▸ If one playground area is *to the right of* another, what else do you know for certain? (e.g., *that one of the areas is* to the left of *the other*)

▸ The parking lot was outside the playground in Question 1. When else might you ever talk about inside or outside? (e.g., *if one object is in one room and one is in another room*)

You will need

• building blocks (or everyday objects, e.g., cans, boxes, etc., or toys)
• large sheet of paper
• coloured pencils
• Student Resource pages 148–150

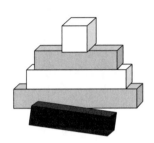

Measurement Strand Overview

How were the measurement topics chosen?

This resource provides materials for assisting students with 5 measurement topics. These topics were drawn from curriculum outcomes across the country for Grades 1 to 3. Topic selections are also based on research about what aspects of each topic students struggle with. Topics are divided into distinct levels, called pathways, which address gaps in students' prerequisite skills and knowledge.

What measurement topics were omitted?

The length topic does not include millimetres or kilometres because although these units are introduced in Grade 3 or Grade 4 in some jurisdictions, students would not be considered to be struggling with these.

The 24-hour clock is not included in the time section because it is not introduced before Grade 4 in any curriculum

These pathways do not include the topic of temperature.

The topic of area is new to Grade 4 under the WNCP curriculum but is included since it is covered in earlier grades in Ontario.

The topic of grams is introduced in Grade 3 under the WNCP curriculum, but not until Grade 4 in Ontario, so it is included in a separate pathway.

How were the pathways determined?

The pathways were determined in different ways for the different measurement topics. For length, mass, capacity, and to a certain extent time, pathways are built on the kind of unit used, whether non-standard or standard. Grams and kilograms are addressed separately, since some regions of the country cover grams earlier than others. An additional pathway in time focused on clock reading. Because standard unit work in area is new to Grade 4, the distinction between the 2 area pathways focuses on whether or not a standard grid is used and how precisely partial units are considered in describing the area, not on whether standard or non-standard units are used.

Materials

Materials for assisting students who are struggling with measurement topics will likely already be in the classroom or easily accessible. These are listed below. Blackline masters are provided at the back of this resource.

coloured pencils
centimetre rulers, metre sticks
string, scissors
classroom objects and household
    objects
objects to measure with (e.g., toothpicks,
    paper clips, Cuisenaire rods)
centimetre cubes, linking cubes
square tiles
pattern blocks
counters
a shoe
a large spoon
pencil case and pencils
pan balances, a bathroom scale
standard masses
coins
1 L containers, other containers

pourable material
chart paper
a business envelope
digital and analog clocks
calendars
small and large sand timers
a metronome (actual or online)
BLM 6: 1 cm Square Grid Paper
BLM 7: 2 cm Square Grid Paper
BLM 19: Coloured Rods
BLM 20: Objects in Grams
BLM 21: Objects in Kilograms
BLM 22: Pizza Shapes
BLM 23: Wrapping Paper
    (Rectangle)
BLM 24: Wrapping Paper (Hexagon)
BLM 25: Calendar
BLM 26: Time Line

Measurement Topics and Pathways

Topics and pathways in this strand are shown below.
Each pathway has an open-ended intervention and a guided intervention.

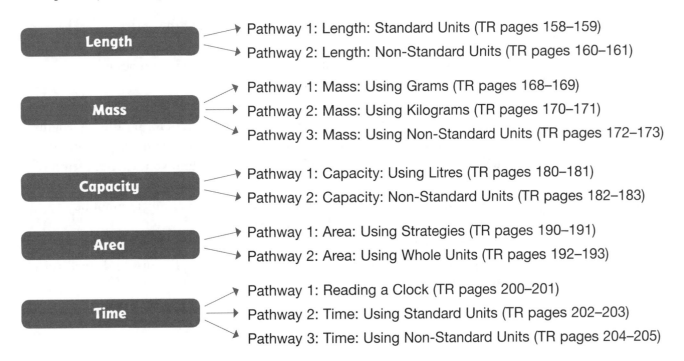

Length
→ Pathway 1: Length: Standard Units (TR pages 158–159)
→ Pathway 2: Length: Non-Standard Units (TR pages 160–161)

Mass
→ Pathway 1: Mass: Using Grams (TR pages 168–169)
→ Pathway 2: Mass: Using Kilograms (TR pages 170–171)
→ Pathway 3: Mass: Using Non-Standard Units (TR pages 172–173)

Capacity
→ Pathway 1: Capacity: Using Litres (TR pages 180–181)
→ Pathway 2: Capacity: Non-Standard Units (TR pages 182–183)

Area
→ Pathway 1: Area: Using Strategies (TR pages 190–191)
→ Pathway 2: Area: Using Whole Units (TR pages 192–193)

Time
→ Pathway 1: Reading a Clock (TR pages 200–201)
→ Pathway 2: Time: Using Standard Units (TR pages 202–203)
→ Pathway 3: Time: Using Non-Standard Units (TR pages 204–205)

Length

Planning For This Topic

Materials for assisting students with length consist of a diagnostic tool and 2 intervention pathways. The pathways for this topic differ in the nature of the units used for measuring: standard units (metres and centimetres) or non-standard units.

Each pathway has an open-ended option and a guided option. Choose the type of intervention most suitable for your students' needs and your particular circumstances.

Curriculum Connections

Grades 1 to 4 curriculum connections for this topic are provided online. See www.nelson.com/leapsandbounds. Note that the standard units in the Ontario Grade 3 curriculum include kilometres. Kilometres are not part of the interventions here because students are still developing a sense of kilometres, so they would not be considered behind in this topic. Perimeter is touched on but is not a focus in the interventions.

Why might a student struggle with length?

Students might struggle with length for any of the following reasons:

- They might have difficulty comparing lengths indirectly (e.g., they might have difficulty comparing the lengths of 2 items if they cannot move one over to the other for a direct comparison).
- They might not realize that when comparing lengths of objects, the objects have to line up at one end.
- They might align the end of the ruler with the end of the object rather than aligning 0 for measuring.
- They might not recognize that the same unit must be used repeatedly or multiples of the same unit must be used.
- They might overlap or leave gaps when using concrete materials for measuring.
- They might have difficulty choosing an appropriate tool for measuring lengths.
- They might not recognize that the number of units required depends on the unit used (e.g., if you are measuring with a longer unit, you will need fewer of them).
- They might not realize that items measured in different units cannot be compared without knowing how the units compare.
- They might not have a personal referent for 1 m or 1 cm.
- They might not realize that the length measurement of a curve is defined as its straightened-out length.

Professional Learning Connections

PRIME: Measurement, Background and Strategies (Nelson Education Ltd., 2010), pages 44–51

Making Math Meaningful to Canadian Students K–8 (Nelson Education Ltd., 2008), pages 370–380

Big Ideas from Dr. Small Grades K–3 (Nelson Education Ltd., 2010), pages 91–96

Good Questions (dist. by Nelson Education Ltd., 2009), pages 95–98 and 107, 109

Leaps and Bounds 3/4   Copyright © 2011 by Nelson Education Ltd.

Diagnostic Tool: Length

Use the diagnostic tool to determine the most suitable intervention pathway for length. Provide Diagnostic Tool: Length, Teacher's Resource pages 154 and 155, and have students complete it in writing or orally. Provide paper clips, Cuisenaire rods (or Coloured Rods, BLM 19), centimetre rulers, and metre sticks (or 1 m lengths of string).

See solutions on Teacher's Resource pages 156 and 157.

Intervention Pathways

The purpose of the intervention pathways is to help students measure length with non-standard units or metres or centimetres. The focus is to prepare them for more complex situations, such as measuring lengths associated with composite shapes, measuring with more than one unit or with more precise units, and for using formulas involving linear measurement.

There are 2 pathways:
- Pathway 1: Length: Standard Units
- Pathway 2: Length: Non-Standard Units

Use the chart below (or the Key to Pathways on Teacher's Resource pages 156 and 157) to determine which pathway is most suitable for each student or group of students.

Diagnostic Tool Results	Intervention Pathway
If students struggle with Questions 5 to 9	use Pathway 1: Length: Standard Units *Teacher's Resource pages 158–159* *Student Resource pages 151–156*
If students struggle with Questions 1 to 4	use Pathway 2: Length: Non-Standard Units *Teacher's Resource pages 160–161* *Student Resource pages 157–161*

Name: _____   Date: _____

Length

1. Which is longer? Circle the correct answer.

   a) your shoe *or* your eraser

   b) a pair of scissors *or* a belt

2. Circle the line that is longer. Tell how you know.

   a)

   _____

   _____

   b)

   _____

   _____

You will need

• paper clips
• coloured rods
• a centimetre ruler
• a metre stick (or 1 m lengths of string)

3. **a)** Estimate how many paper clips long this paper is.

   Estimate: about _____ paper clips

   b) Use paper clips to measure the length of this paper.

   Measure: _____ paper clips

4. The length of a table is 10 dark rods.
About how many light rods long is the table?
Circle the best answer.

   3   10   20   30

Name:_____ Date:_____

5. Estimate and then measure each length in centimetres.

a)

b)

Estimate: about _____ cm   Estimate: about _____ cm

Measure: _____ cm   Measure: _____ cm

6. Name 2 objects you would probably measure using centimetres.

_____

7. Name 2 objects you would probably measure using metres.

_____

8. Circle all the sentences that make sense.

- One metre (1 m) is about the distance from the floor to a doorknob.

- One centimetre (1 cm) is about the width of your fingertip.

- The length of 2 shoes, lined up toe to heel, is more than a metre.

- 1 m is about 1000 cm.

9. What is the total distance around the triangle?

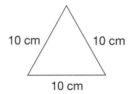

Total distance around: _____ cm

Copyright © 2011 by Nelson Education Ltd.   *Leaps and Bounds*   Measurement: Length, Diagnostic Tool

Solutions and Key to Pathways

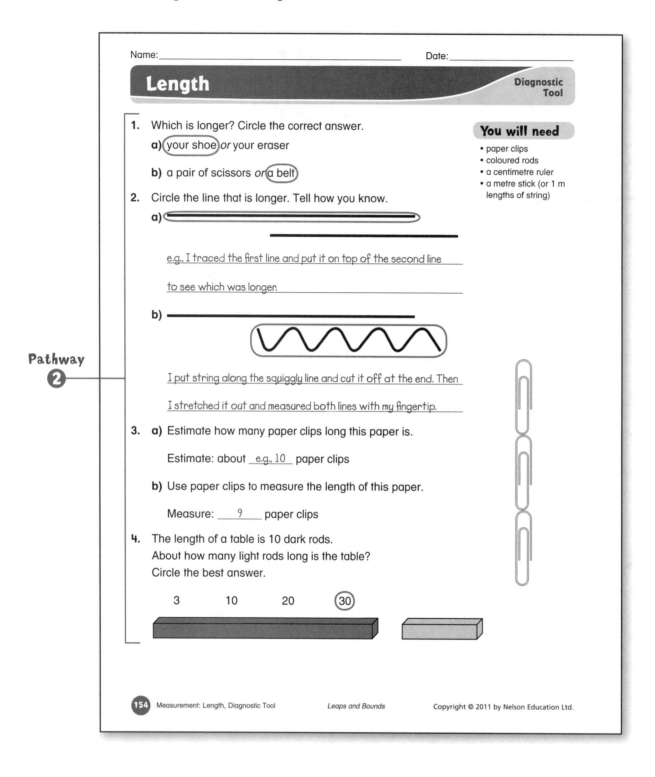

Pathway 2

Name: _____ Date: _____

Length

Diagnostic Tool

You will need
- paper clips
- coloured rods
- a centimetre ruler
- a metre stick (or 1 m lengths of string)

1. Which is longer? Circle the correct answer.
   a) (your shoe) *or* your eraser
   b) a pair of scissors *or* (a belt)

2. Circle the line that is longer. Tell how you know.
   a) ⊂══════════⊃

   e.g., I traced the first line and put it on top of the second line
   to see which was longer.

   b) ──────────

   I put string along the squiggly line and cut it off at the end. Then
   I stretched it out and measured both lines with my fingertip.

3. a) Estimate how many paper clips long this paper is.
   Estimate: about _e.g., 10_ paper clips
   b) Use paper clips to measure the length of this paper.
   Measure: _9_ paper clips

4. The length of a table is 10 dark rods.
   About how many light rods long is the table?
   Circle the best answer.

   3   10   20   (30)

154 Measurement: Length, Diagnostic Tool   *Leaps and Bounds*   Copyright © 2011 by Nelson Education Ltd.

Name:_____   Date:_____

5. Estimate and then measure each length in centimetres.

a)

b)

Estimate: about ___e.g., 4___ cm

Measure: ___5___ cm

Estimate: about ___e.g., 5___ cm

Measure: ___4___ cm

6. Name 2 objects you would probably measure using centimetres.

_e.g., a crayon, a pair of scissors_____

7. Name 2 objects you would probably measure using metres.

_e.g., a bulletin board, a hallway in the school_____

8. Circle all the sentences that make sense.

- (One metre (1 m) is about the distance from the floor to a doorknob.)

- (One centimetre (1 cm) is about the width of your fingertip.)

- The length of 2 shoes, lined up toe to heel, is more than a metre.

- 1 m is about 1000 cm.

9. What is the total distance around the triangle?

10 cm   10 cm

10 cm

Total distance around: ___30___ cm

Copyright © 2011 by Nelson Education Ltd.   *Leaps and Bounds*   Measurement: Length, Diagnostic Tool **155**

Copyright © 2011 by Nelson Education Ltd.   *Leaps and Bounds 3/4*   Measurement: Length **157**

Length: Standard Units

You will need

- centimetre cubes
- centimetre rulers
- string and scissors
- metre sticks
- a shoe
- coloured pencils
- Student Resource pages 151–152

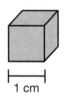

1 cm

Open-Ended Intervention

Before Using the Open-Ended Intervention

Provide centimetre rulers and centimetre cubes. Have students check that the length of a centimetre cube is 1 cm. Ask:

▶ What other object do you know that is about the length of a centimetre? (e.g., *the width of your fingertip, the height of a raisin*)

Have a student hold the end of a string on the floor. Then demonstrate how to mark (or cut) a piece of string that is 1 m long, using the metre stick. Ask:

▶ What other object do you know that is about the length of a metre? (e.g., *the height of a doorknob from the floor, the width of a bed*)

▶ Suppose I want to measure the length of my shoe. Why would I probably measure in centimetres rather than metres? (e.g., *Shoes are smaller than metres.*)

Demonstrate how to measure the shoe, and write the length to the nearest whole number of centimetres.

Using the Open-Ended Intervention (Student Resource pages 151–152)

Provide coloured pencils, centimetre rulers, and metre sticks (or 1 m lengths of string). Also have string and scissors available for measuring or creating curved paths. Together, read through the tasks on the student pages. Ensure that students estimate and then measure. Give students time to work, ideally in pairs.

Observe whether students

- use referents to estimate distances of various lengths using centimetres or metres
- use the correct tool to measure short distances (centimetres) or long distances (metres)
- correctly align the measuring tool to get an accurate measurement
- use the measurement of one length to help them estimate other length measurements
- can judge whether a distance is relatively short, medium, or long
- measure a length by using one unit repeatedly
- measure the length of a path that is not straight by laying a string on it, straightening the string, and then measuring

Consolidating and Reflecting

Ensure understanding by asking students questions about their work:

▶ How do you know it is the shortest path for the ladybug? (e.g., *I think the shortest path is a straight line with no turns from the edge of the rock to the lily pad.*)

▶ What made your path long? (e.g., *I made the path zigzag back and forth lots of times.*)

▶ This string is not straight. How can you measure its length? (e.g., *I will straighten it out and then measure using a ruler.*)

▶ To measure the path to the doorway, how did you know which units to use? (e.g., *I used a metre stick because it would take too long to measure in centimetres.*)

Length: Standard Units

Guided Intervention

You will need

- centimetre cubes
- centimetre rulers
- metre sticks (or 1 m lengths of string)
- string and scissors
- a variety of objects to measure (e.g., Cuisenaire rods [or Coloured Rods, BLM 19], shoelaces)
- Student Resource pages 153–156

Before Using the Guided Intervention

Provide centimetre rulers and centimetre cubes. Have students use their rulers to check that the length of a centimetre cube is 1 cm. Make sure they align the starting place on the ruler with the edge of the cube. Ask:

▸ What else do you know that is about the length of a centimetre?
(e.g., *the width of your fingertip, the distance across a pea or a raisin*)

Have a student hold the end of a string on the floor. Then demonstrate how to mark (or cut) a piece of string that is 1 m long, using a metre stick. Ask:

▸ What else do you know that is about the length of a metre?
(e.g., *the height of a doorknob from the floor, the length of a giant step*)

Using the Guided Intervention   (Student Resource pages 153–156)

Provide centimetre cubes, centimetre rulers, and metre sticks (or 1 m lengths of string). Guide students as they measure the length of the feather using centimetre cubes and a ruler, and record each measurement using a whole number of units.

Have students work through the **Try These** questions in pairs or individually.

Observe whether students can
- estimate the lengths of objects in centimetres (Questions 2 to 4)
- measure the lengths of objects in centimetres (Questions 1, 3, 7, 8, possibly 10)
- estimate the lengths of objects in metres (Questions 5, 6, 9)
- measure the lengths of objects in metres (Question 9, possibly 10)
- use appropriate units of measure (Questions 2, 3, 7, 8, 10)

1 cm

Consolidating and Reflecting

Ensure understanding by asking students the following questions:
▸ How do you know that your objects are close to the required length?
(e.g., *I can compare the objects to something I know, such as the length of a tape holder, which is about 10 cm.*)
▸ Can you tell by looking at shapes which has the shortest distance around? How did you measure the distances? (e.g., *No, it's hard to tell for sure. The sides in a shape look about the same length, so I just measured 1 side at a time and added the lengths.*)
▸ When you measured the length of the hallway, how did you know which units to use? (e.g., *I used a metre stick because it's longer, and metres are good for measuring longer distances. It would take too long to measure in centimetres.*)
▸ Why is it easy to imagine something 40 cm long if you know an object that is 20 cm long? (e.g., *If you double 20, you get 40, so the object should be twice as long.*)
▸ This shoelace is not straight. How would you measure its length?
(e.g., *I will straighten it out and then measure using a ruler.*)

Length: Non-Standard Units

You will need

- paper clips (regular and large)
- a pencil case
- a variety of identical objects to measure with (e.g., paper clips, toothpicks, Cuisenaire rods [or Coloured Rods, BLM 19], linking cubes)
- a large piece of paper and coloured pencils
- string and scissors
- Student Resource page 157

Open-Ended Intervention

Before Using the Open-Ended Intervention

Provide regular-sized paper clips and ask students to estimate the number of paper clips it would take to measure the width of a pencil case. Have them measure by placing the paper clips end to end in a straight line.

Next, show some large-sized paper clips. Ask:

▶ If you measure the same distance using these paper clips, would you need more or fewer of them? Why? (e.g., *Fewer; these paper clips are longer.*)

▶ Why can't you report a measurement as 10 paper clips if you used some big ones and some little ones? (e.g., *All of the objects have to be identical so we all get the same number.*)

Using the Open-Ended Intervention   (Student Resource page 157)

Provide linking cubes, paper clips, toothpicks, or other identical objects that can be used as non-standard units for measuring length. Each student will need a large piece of paper and coloured pencils. Also have string and scissors available so students can create and/or measure curvy paths. Together, read through the task on the student page. Give students time to work in pairs.

Observe whether students can

- estimate the lengths using non-standard units
- measure the lengths using a series of the same non-standard units
- measure the lengths by iterating a single non-standard unit
- judge whether a distance is relatively short, medium, or long
- compare the lengths of objects by comparing the numbers when the same units are used
- measure the length of a path that is not straight by placing a string on it, straightening the string, and then measuring

Consolidating and Reflecting

Ensure understanding by asking students questions based on their work:

▶ Would you describe the distance as short or long?
  (e.g., *I think it is a short path because I can measure it with just paper clips.*)

▶ When you used one unit, what did you do?
  (e.g., *I marked where the unit starts and ends, and kept moving it along the measuring line. Then I counted how many times I moved the unit along.*)

▶ How can you predict whether it would take more or fewer toothpicks than the other units you chose?
  (e.g., *A toothpick is longer than a paper clip, so you don't need as many.*)

▶ This string is not straight. How would you measure its length?
  (e.g., *I will straighten it out and then measure using a ruler.*)

Length: Non-Standard Units

Guided Intervention

Before Using the Guided Intervention

Provide regular-sized paper clips and ask students to predict how many paper clips it would take to measure the length of their pencil case. Have them measure by placing the paper clips end to end in a straight line.

Next, show some large-sized paper clips. Ask:

▸ If you measure the same distance using these paper clips, would you need more or fewer of them? Why? (e.g., *Fewer; these paper clips are longer.*)

▸ Why can't you report a measurement as 10 paper clips if you used some big ones and some little ones?
  (e.g., *All of the objects have to be identical so we all get the same number.*)

▸ How can you measure using only 1 paper clip? (e.g., *Place the paper clip at the end of the line and mark where the paper clip ends. Then place the paper clip at the end of the first mark, and mark where the paper clip ends. Repeat this over and over until you're at the end of the line. Then count the number of spaces between the marks.*)

Using the Guided Intervention   (Student Resource pages 158–161)

Provide a variety of identical objects that can be used as non-standard units for measuring length. Also provide string and scissors. Read through the instructional section of the student pages together. Guide students as they measure the lengths of the worms using non-standard units. Encourage them to measure other lengths of objects using non-standard units.

Have students work through the **Try These** questions individually or in pairs.

Observe whether students can
* compare lengths (Questions 1, 4, 6, 7, 9, 10)
* estimate lengths using non-standard units (Questions 3, 5)
* measure lengths using non-standard units (Questions 2, 3, 4, 6, 8, 9)
* recognize how the choice of unit affects the measure (Question 8)

Consolidating and Reflecting

Ensure understanding by asking students the following questions:

▸ How did you find the books that would fit or were too tall for the shelf, in Question 4? (e.g., *I placed 8 green rods in a line to see how much space I had. Then I chose a book close to that size and a book that was much taller.*)

▸ Which is longer, the 10 linking cubes or the 5 new pencils? How do you know? (e.g., *5 new pencils are longer than the 10 linking cubes. I know because I lined up 2 new pencils and it was longer than the 10 linking cubes.*)

▸ Would someone else get the same measurement as you did for the distance around the paper? the squiggly line? Explain.
  (e.g., *Yes, we should get the same number if we both use the same unit.*)

You will need

* paper clips (regular and large)
* a pencil case
* a variety of identical objects to measure with (e.g., paper clips, toothpicks, Cuisenaire rods [or Coloured Rods, BLM 19], linking cubes)
* string and scissors
* Student Resource pages 158–161

Planning For This Topic

Materials for assisting students with understanding mass consist of a diagnostic tool and 3 intervention pathways. The pathways differ in the types of units used: standard (grams and kilograms) and non-standard.

Each pathway has an open-ended option and a guided option. Choose the type of intervention most suitable for your students' needs and your particular circumstances.

Curriculum Connections

Grades 1 to 4 curriculum connections for this topic are provided online. See www.nelson.com/leapsandbounds. Note that in the Ontario curriculum, grams are not covered until Grade 4. For these students, items referring to grams in the diagnostic tool could be omitted and Pathway 1 need not be considered.

Why might students struggle with mass?

Students might struggle with mass for any of the following reasons:
- They might not recognize that the same unit must be used repeatedly or multiples of the same unit must be used (e.g., a paper clip placed over and over or a number of paper clips placed end to end).
- They might not recognize that the number of units required depends on the unit used (e.g., if you are measuring with a larger unit, you will need fewer of them).
- They might not realize that the mass of an object is independent of its other measures, such as its dimensions or volume (e.g., they think a larger object has a greater mass).
- They might think that breaking an object into smaller parts would change its total mass.
- They might not realize that items measured in different units cannot be compared without knowing how the units compare.
- They might not have a personal referent, or benchmark, for 1 kg or 1 g (e.g., 1 kg is about the mass of my dictionary).

**Professional
Learning
Connections**

*PRIME: Measurement,
Background and
Strategies* (Nelson
Education Ltd., 2010),
pages 92–101
*Making Math Meaningful
to Canadian Students
K–8* (Nelson Education
Ltd., 2008),
pages 430–441
*Big Ideas from Dr. Small
Grades K–3* (Nelson
Education Ltd., 2010),
pages 112–114
Good Questions (dist. by
Nelson Education Ltd.,
2009), page 100

Leaps and Bounds 3/4
Copyright © 2011 by Nelson Education Ltd.

Diagnostic Tool: Mass

Use the diagnostic tool to determine the most suitable intervention for mass. The tool focuses on estimating and measuring mass. Provide Diagnostic Tool: Mass, Teacher's Resource pages 164 and 165, and have students complete it in writing or orally. Have available pan balances, linking cubes, and centimetre cubes for students to use.

See solutions on Teacher's Resource pages 166 and 167.

Intervention Pathways

The purpose of the intervention pathways is to prepare students to measure mass with either non-standard units or grams or kilograms so that ultimately they can use a broader range of mass units in a variety of situations.

There are 3 pathways:
- Pathway 1: Mass: Using Grams
- Pathway 2: Mass: Using Kilograms
- Pathway 3: Mass: Using Non-Standard Units

Use the chart below (or the Key to Pathways on Teacher's Resource pages 166 and 167) to determine which pathway is most suitable for each student or group of students.

Diagnostic Tool Results	Intervention Pathway
If students struggle with Questions 7 to 9	use Pathway 1: Mass: Using Grams *Teacher's Resource pages 168–169* *Student Resource pages 162–165*
If students struggle with Questions 4 to 6	use Pathway 2: Mass: Using Kilograms *Teacher's Resource pages 170–171* *Student Resource pages 166–169*
If students struggle with Questions 1 to 3	use Pathway 3: Mass: Using Non-Standard Units *Teacher's Resource pages 172–173* *Student Resource pages 170–172*

Mass

1. Jill says that the ping-pong ball has a greater mass than the marble because it is bigger. Do you agree? Explain.

You will need
• a pan balance
• linking cubes
• centimetre cubes

_____

_____

2. A pan balance shows that object A balances 10 pennies and object B balances 10 marbles. Can you be sure which object is heavier? Explain your thinking.

_____

_____

3. Circle the sentence or sentences that are true.

• A taller object might be heavier or lighter than a shorter object.

• A large pail is always heavier than a small pail.

• Two of an object have to be heavier than one of that object.

• A package that is long and wide is never lighter than one that is shaped like a cube.

4. Circle all the sentences that are true.

• One kilogram (1 kg) might be the mass of a bag of sugar.

• A potato might have a mass of one kilogram (1 kg).

• One kilogram (1 kg) is heavier than a small pencil case with 10 pencils in it.

• One kilogram (1 kg) is the mass of 10 pairs of skates.

Name:_____ Date:_____

5. Match the measures that make sense.
One mass will have no match.

4 kg

a) a textbook

1 kg

b) a 10-year-old student

35 kg

c) a baby

15 kg

d) a laptop computer

2 kg

6. Name an object for each mass.

a) 10 kg _____

b) one half kilogram _____

7. Circle the objects that have a mass of about 5 g.

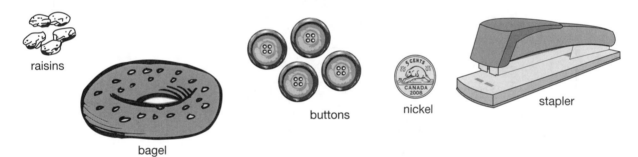

raisins

bagel

buttons

nickel

stapler

8. Circle the best estimate for the mass of the newspaper.
Explain your choice.

50 g   350 g   2000 g

_____

_____

9. Circle all the sentences that make sense.

• 1 kg is 1000 g.   • An eraser is about 80 g.

• A slice of bread is about 30 g.   • A CD is about 40 g.

Solutions and Key to Pathways

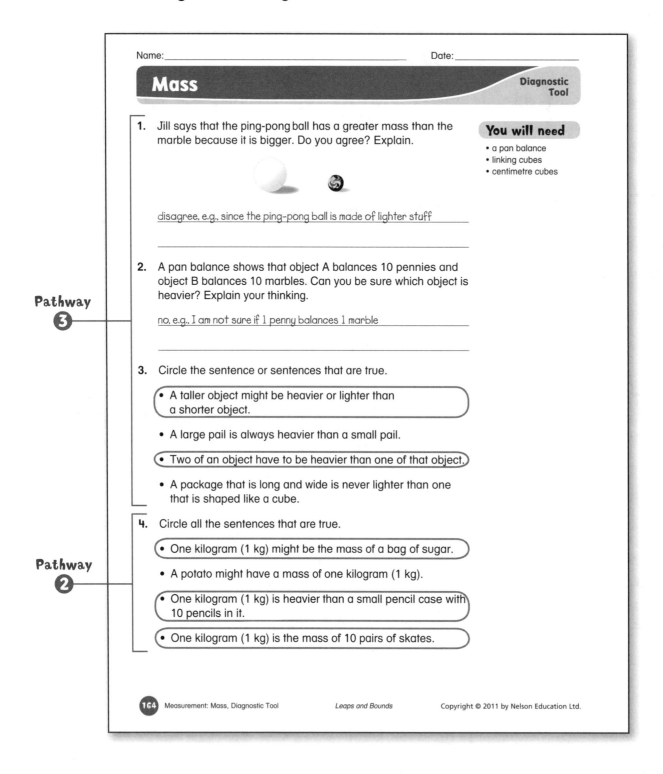

Name: _____ Date: _____

Mass

Diagnostic Tool

1. Jill says that the ping-pong ball has a greater mass than the marble because it is bigger. Do you agree? Explain.

You will need
- a pan balance
- linking cubes
- centimetre cubes

disagree, e.g., since the ping-pong ball is made of lighter stuff
_____

Pathway 3

2. A pan balance shows that object A balances 10 pennies and object B balances 10 marbles. Can you be sure which object is heavier? Explain your thinking.

no, e.g., I am not sure if 1 penny balances 1 marble
_____

3. Circle the sentence or sentences that are true.

- (A taller object might be heavier or lighter than a shorter object.)

- A large pail is always heavier than a small pail.

- (Two of an object have to be heavier than one of that object.)

- A package that is long and wide is never lighter than one that is shaped like a cube.

Pathway 2

4. Circle all the sentences that are true.

- (One kilogram (1 kg) might be the mass of a bag of sugar.)

- A potato might have a mass of one kilogram (1 kg).

- (One kilogram (1 kg) is heavier than a small pencil case with 10 pencils in it.)

- (One kilogram (1 kg) is the mass of 10 pairs of skates.)

164 Measurement: Mass, Diagnostic Tool   *Leaps and Bounds*   Copyright © 2011 by Nelson Education Ltd.

Name:______________________ Date:______________

Pathway 2

5. Match the measures that make sense.
One mass will have no match.

a) a textbook

b) a 10-year-old student

c) a baby

d) a laptop computer

4 kg
1 kg
35 kg
15 kg
2 kg

6. Name an object for each mass.

a) 10 kg e.g., a 2-year-old child

b) one half kilogram e.g., a bag of rice

Pathway 1

7. Circle the objects that have a mass of about 5 g.

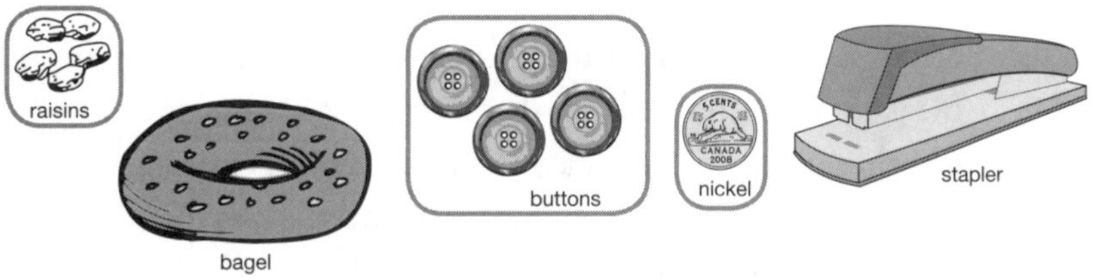

raisins
bagel
buttons
5 CENTS
CANADA
2008
nickel
stapler

8. Circle the best estimate for the mass of the newspaper.
Explain your choice.

THE NEWS

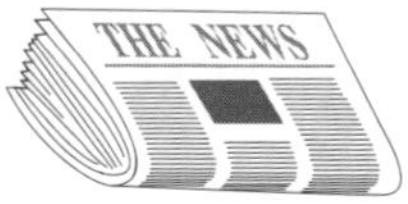

50 g   (350 g)   2000 g

e.g., 50 g is really light–like 2 small snack bags, and 2000 g is as heavy as 2 textbooks, so that is too much.

9. Circle all the sentences that make sense.

- (1 kg is 1000 g.)
- An eraser is about 80 g.
- (A slice of bread is about 30 g.)
- (A CD is about 40 g.)

Mass: Using Grams

You will need

- pan balances
- gram masses (e.g., 10 g, 20 g, 50 g, 100 g, 250 g)
- a variety of items to measure, including light ones such as pencils, large paper clips, linking cubes, coins, and heavier ones such as water bottles, juice boxes, eyeglasses, staplers, pencil cases
- Objects in Grams (BLM 20, optional)
- Internet access (optional)
- Student Resource page 162

Open-Ended Intervention

Before Using the Open-Ended Intervention

Make sure students understand how a pan balance works. Place a 20 g mass on the balance. Introduce *mass* as a term used to describe how heavy something is. Ask:

▸ Suppose you want to balance this mass. Will you use a heavy object or a light one? (e.g., *a light one, since I can see that the mass didn't bring the balance down all that much*)

▸ How many pencils do you think might balance the 20 g? (e.g., *5 or 6*)

▸ Do you think it would take more or fewer large paper clips to balance the mass? Why? (*More. e.g., A large paper clip is lighter than a pencil.*)

Using the Open-Ended Intervention   (Student Resource page 162)

Provide pan balances, gram masses, and some classroom items. Read through the tasks on the student page together. Give students time to work, ideally in pairs.

Make sure students estimate and then test their estimates. Encourage them to measure when possible by using the masses, but they might also use the Internet or other resources (such as BLM 20: Objects in Grams) to confirm their estimates. For example, students might do an Internet search for "mass small apple" to get a sense of a typical mass for a small apple.

Observe student responses, and bring out the following:

- It takes many lighter items to make up 500 g, but fewer heavier items.
- Although heavier objects can be measured in grams, it usually makes sense to measure lighter ones in grams.
- Mass can be determined by balancing an object against known masses.
- What you know about one mass can help you estimate other masses.

Consolidating and Reflecting

Ensure understanding by asking questions based on students' work:

▸ Imagine that an item balances 100 g. When you pick up the item, will it seem heavy? (e.g., *No, it's not really light, but it's not really heavy.*)

▸ If you know the mass of an object, can you be sure how big it is? (e.g., *No, it could be really big and light or really heavy and small.*)

▸ What objects did you use to balance about 500 g? (e.g., *a stapler and a calculator*)

▸ Why does that make sense? (e.g., *Neither is really heavy but not really light either.*)

▸ What kinds of everyday items might come in packages that are labelled in grams? (e.g., *snack bags, granola bars*)

▸ Why might it be useful to use grams to measure mass instead of, for example, using linking cubes to measure? (e.g., *so we all have the same idea when we talk about the measurement*)

Mass: Using Grams

Guided Intervention

Before Using the Guided Intervention

Make sure students understand how a pan balance works. Place a 20 g mass on the balance. Introduce *mass* as a term used to describe how heavy something is. Ask:

▸ Suppose you want to balance this mass. Will you use a heavy object or a light one? (e.g., *a light one, since I can see that the mass didn't bring the balance down all that much*)

▸ How many square tiles do you think might balance the 20 g? (e.g., *7 or 8*)

▸ Do you think it would take more or fewer linking cubes to balance the mass? Why? (*fewer, e.g., since a square tile seems heavier than a linking cube*)

Using the Guided Intervention   (Student Resource pages 163–165)

Provide pan balances, Objects in Grams (BLM 20), gram masses, and classroom objects for students to measure. Read through the instructional section of the student pages together. Guide students as they measure and compare the masses of the items on the page.

Have students work through the **Try These** questions in pairs or individually. To help them relate masses in the questions to known masses, they may use the household objects or Objects in Grams (BLM 20) or the Internet.

Observe whether students

• use personal referents, or benchmarks, to compare the masses of objects (Questions 1, 2, 4, 5, 6, 7)

• understand how to interpret what a pan balance shows about how the masses of 2 items compare (Question 3)

• recognize which objects are appropriate to measure in grams (Questions 6, 8)

• realize that mass is independent of size (Question 7)

• recognize the value of using grams as a standard unit (Questions 8, 9)

Consolidating and Reflecting

Ensure understanding by asking students the following questions:

▸ What kinds of everyday items might come in packages that are labelled in grams? (e.g., *small bag of pretzels, granola bar*)

▸ If you know the mass of an object, do you know how big it is? (e.g., *No; it could be really light and big like a balloon or really heavy and small like a metal ball.*)

▸ Suppose you want to know the mass of an object and it is heavier than a 200 g mass, but not a lot heavier. How would you figure out the mass? (e.g., *I would add a light mass to the 200 g side of the balance to try to get both sides balanced.*)

▸ Why might it be useful to use grams to measure mass instead of, for example, using linking cubes to measure?
(e.g., *so we all have the same idea when we talk about the measurement*)

You will need

• pan balances
• gram masses (e.g., 10 g, 20 g, 50 g, 100 g, 250 g)
• a variety of items to measure (e.g., light ones such as pencils, square tiles, linking cubes, coins, and heavier ones such as water bottles, juice boxes, eyeglasses, staplers, pencil cases)
• a variety of household objects labelled in grams or Objects in Grams (BLM 20)
• Internet access (optional)
• Student Resource pages 163–165

Mass: Using Kilograms

You will need

- pan balances
- 1 kg masses
- a bathroom scale (optional)
- a variety of items to measure (e.g., textbooks, a bunch of bananas, a bag of apples, a litre bottle of water or other liquid, a pack of paper)
- Objects in Kilograms (BLM 21, optional)
- Internet access (optional)
- Student Resource page 166

Open-Ended Intervention

Before Using the Open-Ended Intervention

Make sure students understand how a pan balance works. Place a 1 kg mass on one side and a litre bottle of water on the other side. Introduce *mass* as a term used to describe how heavy something is. Ask:

▶ How do you know that the water bottle has a mass of 1 kg? (*They balance.*)
▶ Do you think the package of paper will have a mass greater than 1 kg or less? How will you test your prediction? (e.g., *I think more; it seems heavier than the water. I will test by putting it on the balance.*)
▶ How many kilograms do you think the bag of apples might be? (e.g., *maybe 2 kg*)
▶ We have only one 1 kg mass. How can you test your prediction? (e.g., *I could put a litre bottle of water on the same side of the pan balance as the 1 kg mass.*)

Using the Open-Ended Intervention   (Student Resource page 166)

Provide some 1 kg masses, pan balances or a bathroom scale, and some classroom objects. Read through the tasks on the student page together.

Give students time to work, ideally in pairs. Make sure students estimate the masses of items that are not too heavy, and then check their estimates. Encourage them to measure when possible by using the masses, but they might also use the Internet or Objects in Kilograms (BLM 21) to confirm their predictions.

Observe student responses, and bring out the following:

- A personal referent, or benchmark, for 1 kg might be a textbook; a benchmark for 5 kg might be a small roast turkey (for a family of 4 or so).
- What you know about one mass measurement can help you estimate other mass measurements.

Consolidating and Reflecting

Ensure understanding by asking questions based on students' work:

▶ Imagine that an object balances 3 kg. Will you be able to pick it up? How do you know? (e.g., *Yes, I can carry 3 textbooks easily.*)
▶ If you know the mass of an object, can you be certain how big it is? (*No.* e.g., *It could be really big and light like a huge balloon or really heavy and small like a metal ball.*)
▶ Suppose you had found something that had a mass of 2 kg. How could that have helped you solve the problem? (e.g., *I would just use 5 of those objects for 10 kg, 25 of them for 50 kg, and 50 of them for 100 kg.*)
▶ What kinds of everyday objects might come in packages labelled in kilograms? (e.g., *packs of paper, big boxes of cereal or rice or pasta, big bags of flour*)
▶ Why might it be useful to use kilograms to measure mass instead of, for example, using books to measure? (e.g., *so we all have the same idea when we talk about the measurement*)

Mass: Using Kilograms

Guided Intervention

Before Using the Guided Intervention

Make sure students understand how a pan balance works. Place a 1 kg mass on one side of the balance and a litre bottle of water on the other side. Introduce *mass* as a term used to describe how heavy something is. Ask:

▸ How do you know that the bottle of water has a mass of 1 kg?
(*They balance on the pan balance.*)

▸ Do you think the pack of paper will have a mass greater than 1 kg or less? How will you test your prediction? (e.g., *I think more; it seems heavier than the water. I will test by putting it on the balance.*)

▸ How many kilograms do you think the bag of apples might be? (e.g., *maybe 2 kg*)

▸ We have only one 1 kg mass. How can you test your prediction? (e.g., *I could put a litre bottle of water on the same side of the pan balance as the 1 kg mass.*)

Using the Guided Intervention (Student Resource pages 167–169)

Provide pan balances or a bathroom scale, some objects students can use as benchmarks, such as textbooks or packs of paper, and Objects in Kilograms (BLM 21, optional), for Questions 1 and 2.

Read through the instructional section of the student page together. Encourage students to hold a variety of objects that have a mass of about 1 kg. Have students work through the **Try These** questions in pairs or individually.

Observe whether students
- use personal referents, or benchmarks, to compare masses (Questions 1, 2, 4, 6)
- use what they know about one mass to estimate other masses (Question 5)
- understand that the mass of the container holding items also contributes to the overall mass (Question 5)
- understand what a pan balance actually shows (Questions 3, 5)
- recognize which objects are appropriate to measure in kilograms (Question 7)
- recognize the value of using kilograms as a standard unit (Question 8)

Consolidating and Reflecting

Ensure understanding by asking students the following questions:

▸ Why does it make sense that a big dog might be measured in kilograms?
(e.g., *Kilograms are used to measure heavy things, and big dogs are heavy.*)

▸ What kinds of everyday objects might come in packages labelled in kilograms?
(e.g., *packs of paper, big boxes of cereal or rice or pasta, big bags of flour*)

▸ If you know the mass of an object, do you know how big it is? (*No. e.g., It could be really light and big like a balloon or really heavy and small like a metal ball.*)

▸ What object might have a mass of about 2 kg? (e.g., *an extra-thick textbook*)

▸ What classroom objects make sense to measure in kilograms? Why these items?
(e.g., *furniture or heavy books since they are heavy*)

You will need

- pan balances
- 1 kg masses
- a bathroom scale (optional)
- a variety of items to measure (e.g., textbooks, a bunch of bananas, a bag of apples, a litre bottle of water or other liquid, a pack of paper)
- a variety of household objects measured in kilograms (or Objects in Kilograms, BLM 21)
- Internet access (optional)
- Student Resource pages 167–169

Mass: Using Non-Standard Units

Open-Ended Intervention

You will need

- pan balances
- linking cubes
- 5 objects of different masses, labelled A to E (e.g., small rocks or classroom items), where D is larger but lighter than E
- a variety of identical objects (e.g., plastic Cuisenaire rods or pattern blocks)
- Student Resource page 170

Before Using the Open-Ended Intervention

Make sure students understand how a pan balance works. Place 10 linking cubes on one side of the balance and 1 hexagon pattern block on the other side. (The following assumes that a plastic yellow pattern block is about 2 g and a linking cube is about 1.5 g.) Introduce *mass* as a term used to tell how heavy something is.

▶ How do you know that the group of cubes has a greater mass than the pattern block? (e.g., *The balance is down on the cube side.*)

Put about 8 hexagon pattern blocks on the other side so the pans balance. Ask:

▶ Why can I say that 8 pattern blocks have the same mass as the cubes? (e.g., *The sides balance.*)

▶ What object might need more than 8 pattern blocks to balance it? (e.g., *a big pair of scissors*)

Using the Open-Ended Intervention ⟮Student Resource page 170⟯

Provide pan balances and the labelled objects mentioned in the materials list. Read through the tasks together. Give students time to work, ideally in pairs.

Observe student responses, and bring out the following:

- Personal referents, or benchmarks, can be used to compare the masses of objects.
- Mass is independent of size.
- A pan balance can show which of 2 sets of objects is heavier.
- A mass measurement depends on the size of the unit used.
- Masses can be compared only if the same units are used (or the relationship between the units is known).
- Measuring mass might be useful in a practical situation to describe how heavy something is.

Consolidating and Reflecting

Ensure understanding by asking questions based on students' work:

▶ Suppose one object balances 8 orange rods. How many identical pattern blocks do you think it will take to balance that one object? (e.g., *I think more than 8, since the rods are heavier; maybe it would be 20.*)

▶ How could you use the pan balance to figure out which object will need more linking cubes to balance it? (e.g., *I could put 2 objects on opposite sides of the balance to see which is heavier. The heavier one needs more linking cubes.*)

▶ How did you estimate the number of cubes you could use to balance object E? (e.g., *I knew it took 27 cubes to balance D, and object E looked like it might be twice as heavy, so I estimated 54.*)

▶ Does the largest size mean the greatest mass? (*No. e.g., A is larger than E, but it is lighter.*)

Mass: Using Non-Standard Units

Guided Intervention

Before Using the Guided Intervention

Make sure students understand how a pan balance works. Place 16 linking cubes on one side of the balance and 1 orange rod on the other side. (The following assumes that a plastic orange rod is about 4 g and a linking cube is about 1.5 g.) Introduce *mass* as a term used to tell how heavy something is. Ask:

▸ How do you know that the group of cubes has a greater mass than the orange rod? (e.g., *The balance is down on the cube side.*)

Put 6 orange rods on the other side until the pans balance.

▸ Why can I say that 6 orange rods have the same mass as the cubes? (e.g., *The sides balance.*)

Using the Guided Intervention (Student Resource pages 171–172)

Provide a pan balance, 5 objects of different masses labelled A to E as described in the materials list, linking cubes, and orange Cuisenaire rods (or new pencils). Read through the instructional section of the student page together. Encourage students to make and test predictions about how many linking cubes (or other non-standard units) it takes to balance various objects.

Have students work through the **Try These** questions in pairs or individually.

Observe whether students

• can use personal referents, or benchmarks, to compare masses (Questions 1, 3)
• realize that mass is independent of size (Question 5)
• understand what the pan balance actually shows (Question 2)
• recognize that the mass measurement depends on the size of the unit used (Question 4)
• realize that masses can be compared only if the same units are used (or the relationship between the units is known) (Question 6)
• recognize when measuring mass might be useful (Question 7)

Consolidating and Reflecting

Ensure understanding by asking questions based on students' work:

▸ Show an object such as a large spoon. How many linking cubes do you think might balance the spoon? (e.g., *I think about 25.*)

▸ What if I measured with orange rods instead. Would it take more or fewer? Why? (e.g., *fewer, because an orange rod is heavier than a linking cube*)

▸ If you know the mass of an object, do you know how big it is? (*No. e.g., It could be really light and big like a balloon or really heavy and small like a metal ball.*)

▸ Suppose you measured the mass of an object. If it balanced 8 dice and it also balanced 15 linking cubes, what do you know about the masses of the dice and cubes? (e.g., *I know that a die is about twice as heavy as a linking cube.*)

You will need

• pan balances
• linking cubes
• orange Cuisenaire rods (or items with a similar mass, such as new pencils)
• a large spoon
• scissors
• pattern blocks
• 5 objects labelled A to E (e.g., small rocks or classroom items), where B balances 20 linking cubes (mass is approximately 30 g) and C balances 2 orange Cuisenaire rods (mass is approximately 8 g)
• Student Resource pages 171–172

Planning For This Topic

Materials for assisting students with understanding capacity consist of a diagnostic tool and 2 intervention pathways. Pathway 1 focuses on standard units (litres), and Pathway 2 focuses on non-standard units.

Each pathway has an open-ended option and a guided option. Choose the type of intervention most suitable for your students' needs and your particular circumstances.

Curriculum Connections

Grades 1 to 4 curriculum connections for this topic are provided online. See www.nelson.com/leapsandbounds. Note that in jurisdictions following the WNCP curriculum, the only relevant part of this section might be Pathway 2 at this grade level.

Why might students struggle with capacity?

Students might struggle with capacity because they might not
- recognize that the same size unit must be used repeatedly or multiples of the same unit must be used
- recognize that the number of units required depends on the size of the unit used; for example, if you are measuring with a larger unit, you will need fewer of them
- realize that each whole unit must be completely filled
- realize that the capacity of an object is independent of its other measures, such as its mass
- realize that items measured in different units cannot be compared without knowing how the units compare
- have a personal referent, or benchmark, for 1 L
- be able to estimate measurements using a variety of benchmarks

Professional Learning Connections

PRIME: Measurement Background and Strategies (Nelson Education Ltd., 2010), pages 79–84

Making Math Meaningful to Canadian Students K–8 (Nelson Education Ltd., 2008), pages 416–421

Big Ideas from Dr. Small Grades K–3 (Nelson Education Ltd., 2010), pages 108–111

Diagnostic Tool: Capacity

Use the diagnostic tool to determine the most suitable intervention for capacity. The tool focuses on the estimation and measurement of capacity. Provide Diagnostic Tool: Capacity, Teacher's Resource pages 176 and 177, and have students complete it in writing or orally. Have available a variety of containers for students to use.

Note: The word *cup* is used throughout the materials to mean a drinking cup of some sort. The reference is not to the imperial 1 cup measure. *Cup* is a familiar word for students, and they understand that drinking cups come in many sizes.

See solutions on Teacher's Resource pages 178 and 179.

Intervention Pathways

The purpose of the intervention pathways is to prepare students to measure capacity with either non-standard units or litres, so that ultimately they can use a broader range of capacity units.

There are 2 pathways:
- Pathway 1: Capacity: Using Litres
- Pathway 2: Capacity: Non-Standard Units

Use the chart below (or the Key to Pathways on Teacher's Resource pages 178 and 179) to determine which pathway is most suitable for each student or group of students.

Diagnostic Tool Results	Intervention Pathway
If students struggle with Questions 7 and 8	use Pathway 1: Capacity: Using Litres *Teacher's Resource pages 180–181* *Student Resource pages 173–176*
If students struggle with Questions 1 to 6	use Pathway 2: Capacity: Non-Standard Units *Teacher's Resource pages 182–183* *Student Resource pages 177–179*

Capacity

1. Marc emptied the water from the full pitcher into 1 large and 3 small drinking cups.

Circle the best description of how much the pitcher holds.

You will need

- a variety of containers (e.g., small and large drinking cups, pitchers, bottles)

- 2 large drinking cups
- 4 small drinking cups
- 5 small drinking cups

Explain your thinking.

_____

_____

2. The pitcher is filled using drinking cup A 5 times. Circle the number of times you think you would need to fill drinking cup B to fill the same pitcher.

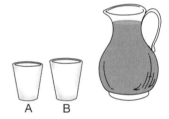

6 of cup B   5 of cup B   4 of cup B   2 of cup B

3. Lee says that the 4 glasses of water would fill the pitcher.
Do you agree?
Explain your thinking.

_____

_____

4. Suppose you filled containers C and D.
Circle the container that you think holds more.
Explain your thinking.

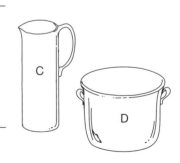

_____

_____

Leaps and Bounds Copyright © 2011 by Nelson Education Ltd.

5. Circle the sentences that are true.

- If you know the capacity of a container, you know how tall it is.

- If you know the capacity of a container, you know how much it holds.

- If you know the capacity of a container, you know how heavy it is.

6. A glass pitcher holds 10 full glasses of water poured from the small glass. A plastic pitcher holds 8 full glasses of water poured from the big glass. Do you know which pitcher has the greater capacity? Explain your thinking.

_____

_____

_____

7. Circle all the statements that are true.

- One litre (1 L) is a huge amount of soup for a family.

- One litre (1 L) of water would be too much for an adult to drink in one day.

- One litre (1 L) is less than the amount of juice in a small juice box.

- A one-litre (1 L) container of milk is not too big to carry.

- One litre (1 L) is more than the amount of water in a drinking cup.

8. Circle all the statements that you agree with.

- Half a litre is an amount a person might drink at one meal.

- A very large cooking pot might hold 10 L of water.

- A teaspoon holds about half a litre of soup.

- A large baking dish might hold 4 L.

Solutions and Key to Pathways

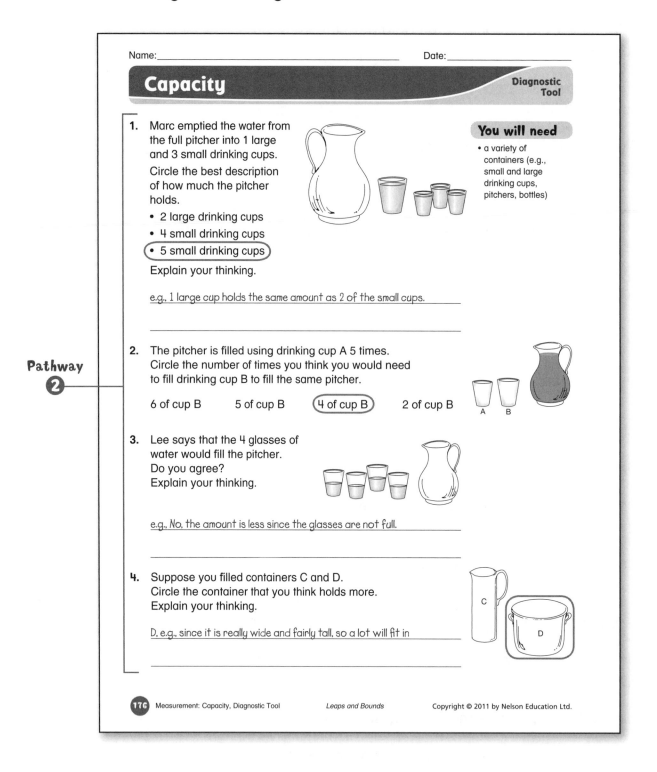

Capacity — Diagnostic Tool

Pathway 2

1. Marc emptied the water from the full pitcher into 1 large and 3 small drinking cups.
Circle the best description of how much the pitcher holds.
   • 2 large drinking cups
   • 4 small drinking cups
   • ⟨5 small drinking cups⟩
   Explain your thinking.

   e.g., 1 large cup holds the same amount as 2 of the small cups.

   You will need
   • a variety of containers (e.g., small and large drinking cups, pitchers, bottles)

2. The pitcher is filled using drinking cup A 5 times.
Circle the number of times you think you would need to fill drinking cup B to fill the same pitcher.

   6 of cup B   5 of cup B   ⟨4 of cup B⟩   2 of cup B

3. Lee says that the 4 glasses of water would fill the pitcher.
Do you agree?
Explain your thinking.

   e.g., No, the amount is less since the glasses are not full.

4. Suppose you filled containers C and D.
Circle the container that you think holds more.
Explain your thinking.

   D, e.g., since it is really wide and fairly tall, so a lot will fit in

Name:_____ Date:_____

5. Circle the sentences that are true.

- If you know the capacity of a container, you know how tall it is.

- If you know the capacity of a container, you know how much it holds.

- If you know the capacity of a container, you know how heavy it is.

Pathway 2

6. A glass pitcher holds 10 full glasses of water poured from the small glass. A plastic pitcher holds 8 full glasses of water poured from the big glass. Do you know which pitcher has the greater capacity? Explain your thinking.

no, e.g., since the glasses are different sizes, and even though the

large glass is bigger, it's hard to tell exactly how much bigger

_____

7. Circle all the statements that are true.

- One litre (1 L) is a huge amount of soup for a family.

- One litre (1 L) of water would be too much for an adult to drink in one day.

- One litre (1 L) is less than the amount of juice in a small juice box.

- A one-litre (1 L) container of milk is not too big to carry.

- One litre (1 L) is more than the amount of water in a drinking cup.

Pathway 1

8. Circle all the statements that you agree with.

- Half a litre is an amount a person might drink at one meal.

- A very large cooking pot might hold 10 L of water.

- A teaspoon holds about half a litre of soup.

- A large baking dish might hold 4 L.

Copyright © 2011 by Nelson Education Ltd. *Leaps and Bounds* Measurement: Capacity, Diagnostic Tool **177**

Capacity: Using Litres

You will need

- a 1 L container (e.g., a water bottle or milk carton)
- large and small containers including various sizes of drinking glasses, some tablespoons, small bowls or pots, a standard-sized drink can, a small garbage can (or other container holding about 6 L), a pail or a paint can, and, if possible, a large, family-sized garbage can
- pourable material, to be reused (e.g., water, aquarium gravel, sand, salt)
- Internet access or other reference materials that deal with sizes of common containers (optional)
- Student Resource page 173

Open-Ended Intervention

Before Using the Open-Ended Intervention

Show a 1 L container to students. Also have available a drinking glass, a drink can, and a pot that holds more than 1 L. Ask:

▶ This container holds one litre of water. How would you describe how much one litre is? (e.g., *It's not a lot, but it is more than just a little bit.*)

▶ How many glasses do you think we could fill with one litre? (e.g., *3 or 4*)

▶ How could we check? (e.g., *Pour water from the full 1 L container into the glass.*)

▶ Do you think it would take more or fewer drink cans to fill the container? Why? (e.g., *fewer, since the cans hold more than the glasses*)

Using the Open-Ended Intervention   (Student Resource page 173)

Provide a variety of containers, including large and small ones, as well as pourable material. If possible, display a large household garbage can and a small waste basket. Together, read through the task on the student page. Give students time to work, ideally in pairs.

Encourage students to estimate and to measure when possible by using the litre containers. They might also use the Internet or other resources to check their estimates.

Observe student responses, and bring out the following:

- It takes many small containers to make up 1 L, but fewer larger containers.
- It is useful to have a personal referent, or benchmark, for 1 L to estimate capacities in litres.
- The capacity of many objects can be measured in full litres or full and part litres.
- Different-looking objects can have the same capacity.
- You can use what you know about one capacity measurement to help you estimate other capacity measurements.

Consolidating and Reflecting

Ensure understanding by asking questions based on students' work:

▶ Imagine a container that can hold 10 L. About how big is it? (e.g., *I think a very large cooking pot might hold 10 L.*)

▶ If you know the capacity of a container, do you know how tall it is? (e.g., *no, since it could be really wide and short or really tall and not as wide and still hold the same amount*)

▶ What did you find out? (e.g., *It takes about 70 tablespoons to make one litre, but only 2 thermoses of water to make one litre. I also found out that the sink holds about 25 L. I looked at the fridge in the teacher's room and I'm pretty sure it would hold about 200 containers of milk if it were full, so that's 200 L.*)

▶ Why might it be useful to measure a capacity in litres instead of, for example, measuring a capacity in glassfuls? (e.g., *Glasses can be different sizes, and another person might not be sure what is meant.*)

Capacity: Using Litres

Guided Intervention

Before Using the Guided Intervention

Display a 1 L container, a baby cup, and a pot that holds more than 1 L. Ask:

▸ This container holds one litre of water. How would you describe how much one litre is? (e.g., *It's not a lot, but it is more than just a little bit.*)

▸ How many baby cups do you think it would take to fill the container? (e.g., *6*)

▸ How could we check? (e.g., *Pour water from the full 1 L container into the glass.*)

▸ Do you think it would take more or fewer drink cans to fill the container? Why? (e.g., *fewer, since the cans hold more than the glasses*)

Using the Guided Intervention (Student Resource pages 174–176)

Provide 1 L containers, one large (e.g., 4 to 6 L) container, a drinking glass, and pourable material. Guide students as they test that it does take 3 or 4 glasses of water to make 1 L. Show another container that holds about 5 or 6 L, and ask students whether seeing that container helps them see why a bathtub or pail might hold the amounts suggested.

Have students work through the **Try These** questions in pairs or individually. For some of the questions, students might also use the Internet to help them estimate the capacity of containers.

As they are working, observe whether students

• relate a personal referent, or benchmark, of one litre to everyday situations (Questions 1, 2, 5, 6, 7)

• realize that capacity measures inside dimensions rather than outside dimensions (Question 3)

• realize that different-looking shapes can have the same capacity (Question 4)

• can compare capacities using litre referents (Questions 5, 7)

• recognize the value of using litres as a standard unit of capacity (Question 8)

Consolidating and Reflecting

Ensure understanding by asking students the following questions:

▸ What kinds of everyday items might come in 1 L or 2 L containers? (e.g., *laundry soap, ice cream, soft drinks*)

▸ If you know the capacity of a container, do you know how tall it is? (e.g., *No, it could be really wide and short or really tall and not as wide and still hold the same amount.*)

▸ Suppose 2 containers look the same on the outside. Do they have to have the same capacity? (e.g., *No, maybe one has much thicker sides than the other, so there's less room on the inside.*)

▸ Why might it be useful to use litres to measure capacity instead of, for example, using glassfuls? (e.g., *so we all have the same idea when we talk about the measurement*)

You will need

• a 1 L container (e.g., a water bottle or milk carton)

• large and small containers including a drinking glass, a baby cup, a standard-sized drink can, some tablespoons

• 2 unmarked containers that are not identical but hold the same amount

• pourable material, to be reused (e.g., water, aquarium gravel, salt, sand)

• Internet access or other reference materials that deal with sizes of common objects (optional)

• Student Resource pages 174–176

You will need

- a small container and a larger container with a capacity 4 times that of the smaller one
- 5 different-sized medium to large containers labelled A to E (e.g., pitchers, pots, pails, jars, bowls)
- 2 different-sized small containers labelled ① and ② (e.g., a teacup and a small yogurt cup)
- pourable material, to be reused (e.g., water, aquarium gravel, sand, salt)
- Student Resource page 177

Open-Ended Intervention

Before Using the Open-Ended Intervention

Provide the small container and larger container (see materials list). Ask:

▸ About how many of the small containers do you think it will take to fill the larger one? (e.g., *4 of them*)

Have the students pour to check. Ask:

▸ You observed that it took about 3 of the small containers to fill the larger one. Suppose I use another container that is a bit bigger than yours. Would I need more or fewer than 3 of them? (*fewer*)

▸ Why do you think it's important to fill the small container all the way to the top? (e.g., *If I don't, then I won't get an accurate number.*)

Using the Open-Ended Intervention   (Student Resource page 177)

Provide the labelled containers mentioned in the materials list. Read through the tasks on the student page together. Give students time to work, ideally in pairs.

Observe student responses to see
- whether their initial predictions seem reasonable
- whether they use the result of one experiment to make a better prediction the next time
- whether they consider the size of the unit when making their estimates
- whether they correctly fill the units and pour carefully

Consolidating and Reflecting

Ensure understanding by asking questions like these based on students' work:

▸ Suppose a container is filled using 6 of container ①. How many of container ② do you think it will take?
(e.g., *I think 8, since container ② is smaller, but not a lot smaller.*)

▸ Why did it take more containers to fill container B than container A?
(e.g., *Container A is taller and wider, so it has to take more to fill it.*)

▸ Suppose 2 students fill container A using container ①. Do they have to get the same number? (e.g., *yes, as long as they both fill each container to the top*)

▸ How did you predict the number of times you could fill container D using container ①? (e.g., *I knew that it took 12 times to fill container C, and container D looked like just a little more than half as big, so I predicted 7 or 8.*)

▸ How did you order the containers from least to greatest capacity?
(e.g., *I looked at the number of same units and ordered the numbers from least to greatest.*)

▸ Why might it be useful to measure capacity?
(e.g., *You might have to know if the pot you picked is big enough to fill 3 big containers with soup for the entire family and 3 guests.*)

Leaps and Bounds 3/4
Copyright © 2011 by Nelson Education Ltd.

Capacity: Non-Standard Units

Guided Intervention

Before Using the Guided Intervention

Provide the small container and larger container (see materials list). Ask:

▶ About how many of the small containers do you think it will take to fill the larger one? (e.g., *3 of them*)

Have the students pour to check. Ask:

▶ Why do you think it's important to fill the small container all the way to the top? (e.g., *If I don't, then I won't get an accurate number.*)

▶ You observed that it took about 3 of the small containers to fill the larger one. Suppose I use another container that is a bit smaller than yours. Would I need more or fewer than 3 of them to fill the large one? (*more*)

Using the Guided Intervention (Student Resource pages 178–179)

Provide the labelled containers described in the materials list. Read through the instructional section together. Guide students as they fill container A using container ①. Ensure that they fill both containers completely. Ask them how their estimate compares with the actual measurement.

Have students work through the **Try These** questions in pairs or individually.

Observe whether students

• use visual cues to predict which container will hold more (Question 1)
• recognize that the number describing the capacity depends on the size of the unit used (Questions 2, 3)
• realize that capacities can be compared only if the same units are used (or the relationship between the units is known) (Questions 3, 5)
• recognize that all of the linear measurements of an object relate to its capacity (Question 4)
• recognize when measuring capacity might be useful (Question 6)

Consolidating and Reflecting

Ensure understanding by asking students the following questions:

▶ Look at container A. What would a container that would be filled using A twice look like? (e.g., *It would be just as wide but twice as high.*)

▶ Suppose you filled container B with 2 different small containers. If it took 8 fills with one container and 15 fills with the other container, what do you know about the small containers?
(e.g., *I know that the second small container was about half as big as the first one.*)

▶ Why might it be useful to measure capacity?
(e.g., *You might have to know if the pot you picked is big enough to fill 3 big containers with soup for the entire family and 3 guests.*)

• a small container and a larger container with a capacity 4 times that of the smaller one
• 5 different-sized medium to large containers, labelled A to E (e.g., pitchers, pots, pails, jars, bowls), where A holds about 3 times as much as container ① and C holds about 6 times as much as container ②
• 2 different-sized small containers, labelled ① and ② (e.g., a drinking cup and a medicine bottle)
• pourable material, to be reused (e.g., water, aquarium gravel, sand, salt)
• Student Resource pages 178–179

Planning For This Topic

Materials for assisting students with area consist of a diagnostic tool and 2 intervention pathways. Both pathways involve non-standard units but differ in how students determine areas using identical shapes—using both whole and parts of units and/or grids or by covering with a whole number of units.

Each pathway has an open-ended option and a guided option. Choose the type of intervention most suitable for your students' needs and your particular circumstances.

Curriculum Connections

Grades 1 to 4 curriculum connections for this topic are provided online. See www.nelson.com/leapsandbounds. Standard units such as square centimetres are not covered at this level. Note that the WNCP curriculum does not introduce area until Grade 4 so students in those jurisdictions would not yet require intervention in this topic.

Why might students struggle with area?

Students might struggle with area for any of the following reasons:
- They might confuse length with area measurements (e.g., a square may have a greater area than a longer and narrower rectangle, but the student focuses on the longer sides).
- They might confuse perimeter and area because they think that the distance around an object is the same as its area.
- They might not consider the effect of the size of the unit on the measurement and use only the number of units when comparing 2 area measurements.
- They might have difficulty estimating the area of the uncovered parts when the non-standard units do not fit exactly, since they might not be comfortable accumulating partial pieces.
- They might not realize that when comparing 2 areas, each area must be covered by the same size of non-standard units.
- They might arrange the measuring units in a haphazard way, making it difficult to see the true area.

Professional Learning Connections

PRIME: Measurement, Background and Strategies (Nelson Education Ltd., 2010), pages 59–64

Making Math Meaningful to Canadian Students K–8 (Nelson Education Ltd., 2008), pages 390–395

Big Ideas from Dr. Small Grades K–3 (Nelson Education Ltd., 2010), pages 104–107

Good Questions (dist. by Nelson Education Ltd., 2009), pages 96, 97, 99, 102, 107–115

Copyright © 2011 by Nelson Education Ltd.

Diagnostic Tool: Area

Use the diagnostic tool to determine the most suitable intervention for area. Provide Diagnostic Tool: Area, Teacher's Resource pages 186 and 187, and have students complete it in writing or orally. Provide pattern blocks, pennies (or round counters), and square tiles for students to use.

See solutions on Teacher's Resource pages 188 and 189.

Intervention Pathways

The purpose of the intervention pathways is to help students with measuring area using non-standard units. The focus is to prepare students for measuring area using standard units in more complex situations.

There are 2 pathways:
- Pathway 1: Area: Using Strategies
- Pathway 2: Area: Using Whole Units

Use the chart below (or the Key to Pathways on Teacher's Resource pages 188 and 189) to determine which pathway is most suitable for each student or group of students.

Diagnostic Tool Results	Intervention Pathway
If students struggle with Questions 4 to 6	use Pathway 1: Area: Using Strategies *Teacher's Resource pages 190–191* *Student Resource pages 180–185*
If students struggle with Questions 1 to 3	use Pathway 2: Area: Using Whole Units *Teacher's Resource pages 192–193* *Student Resource pages 186–190*

Area

1. **a)** Cover this shape using hexagon pattern blocks.

   How many did you use? _____ hexagon blocks

   b) Cover the shape with a different type of pattern block.

   Which pattern block did you use? _____

   How many did you use? _____

   c) Why does it make sense that you need a different number of blocks?

   _____

2. Kyla drew a rectangle that was just big enough to fit about 6 toonies touching each other. Would she need more than 6 pennies or fewer than 6 pennies to fit into the rectangle?

   _____

   Explain your thinking.

   _____

   _____

3. **a)** Predict which shape has the greater area.

_____

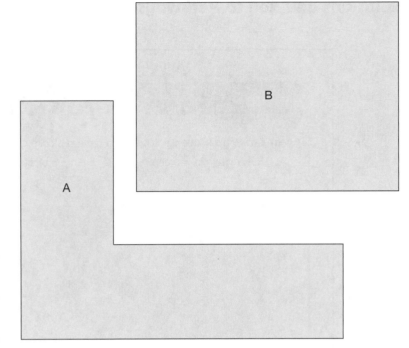

B

A

b) Test your prediction by covering the shapes with square tiles.

c) Was your prediction correct? Why or why not?

_____

_____

_____

_____

4. Why can't you just count the squares in each shape to predict which shape has a greater area?

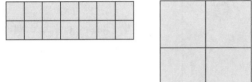

_____

_____

5. What is the area of the shape on this grid in square units?

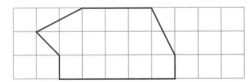

_____

6. Estimate the area of the penguin picture on this square grid.

about _____

Solutions and Key to Pathways

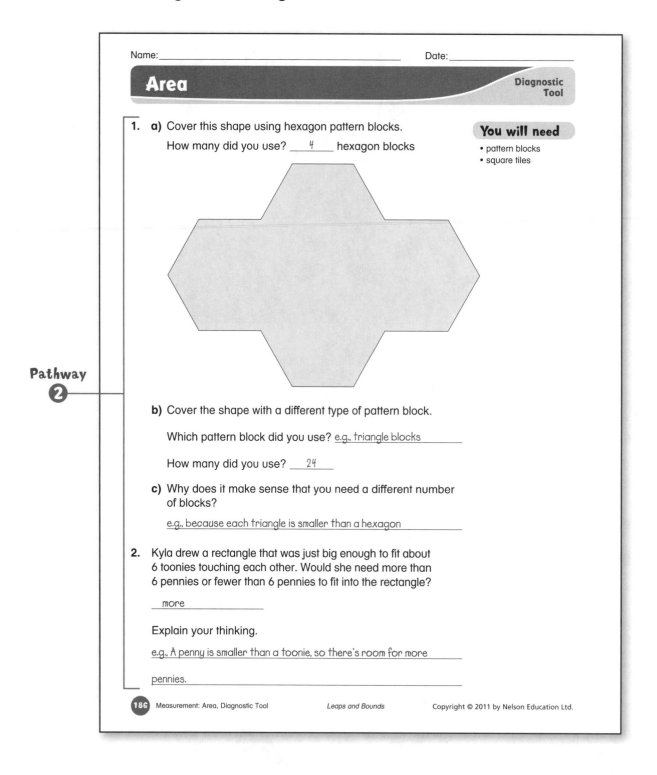

Pathway 2

Name:_____ Date:_____

Area

Diagnostic Tool

1. a) Cover this shape using hexagon pattern blocks.

How many did you use? ___4___ hexagon blocks

You will need
• pattern blocks
• square tiles

b) Cover the shape with a different type of pattern block.

Which pattern block did you use? _e.g., triangle blocks_____

How many did you use? ___24___

c) Why does it make sense that you need a different number of blocks?

_e.g., because each triangle is smaller than a hexagon_____

2. Kyla drew a rectangle that was just big enough to fit about 6 toonies touching each other. Would she need more than 6 pennies or fewer than 6 pennies to fit into the rectangle?

___more_____

Explain your thinking.

_e.g., A penny is smaller than a toonie, so there's room for more_____

_pennies._____

Name: _____   Date: _____

Pathway 2

3. a) Predict which shape has the greater area.

_e.g., B_

b) Test your prediction by covering the shapes with square tiles.

c) Was your prediction correct? Why or why not?

e.g., Yes. For shape A, I used

4 tiles and 1 more makes 5

squares. I used 6 tiles to

almost cover shape B.

A

B

Pathway 1

4. Why can't you just count the squares in each shape to predict which shape has a greater area?

e.g., The squares are not the same size, so you can't

compare the numbers.

5. What is the area of the shape on this grid in square units?

e.g., 12 full squares and 2 or 3 more, or 14 and a half square units

6. Estimate the area of the penguin picture on this square grid.

about _e.g., 15 square units_

Copyright © 2011 by Nelson Education Ltd.   *Leaps and Bounds*   Measurement: Area, Diagnostic Tool **187**

Copyright © 2011 by Nelson Education Ltd.   *Leaps and Bounds 3/4*   Measurement: Area **189**

Area: Using Strategies

You will need

- paper and scissors
- a variety of flat, identical objects (e.g., pattern blocks, square tiles, pennies or round counters, sticky notes)
- Pizza Shapes (BLM 22, optional)
- transparent square grids (from BLM 6)
- Student Resource pages 180–181

Open-Ended Intervention

Before Using the Open-Ended Intervention

Provide an irregular paper shape and some flat objects to measure with, such as pattern blocks, square tiles, and pennies or round counters. Ask:

▶ How might you figure out the area of this shape?
  (e.g., *Cover the shape with something like pattern blocks or square tiles.*)

▶ Which of these units might be good to use? Why? (e.g., *Pennies fit close together, but there are gaps between them. Square tiles or triangles fit together better.*)

Show how to put parts of the uncovered shape together to make a whole unit. Next, show students a transparent square grid (larger than 1 cm is good but not necessary; could be made from 1 cm Square Grid Paper (BLM 6)). Ask:

▶ How can you use this square grid to measure the area of the shape? (e.g., *Put the grid on top of the shape, and count the whole squares and the part squares.*)

Using the Open-Ended Intervention (Student Resource page 180–181)

Provide a variety of identical flat objects (e.g., pattern blocks, square tiles, pennies) and transparent square grids. Together, read the task on the student pages. If students prefer to use 2 given shapes, give them copies of Pizza Shapes (BLM 22). Give students time to work, ideally in pairs.

Encourage students to use the results they get with the first unit to predict whether there will be more or fewer with the second unit.

Observe whether students are able to
- reasonably predict which shape has the greater area
- measure or estimate areas using non-standard units, with as few gaps as possible
- measure or estimate areas in square units, using a square grid
- recognize parts of shapes and, if possible, combine them to make a whole shape
- compare areas by counting the number of same-sized units used and comparing

Consolidating and Reflecting

Ensure understanding by asking questions about students' work:

▶ Were the pizzas the same size or different? How do you know? (e.g., *The area of the rectangular pizza was greater because I used more triangle blocks to cover it.*)

▶ When you used the square grid did you find the same results? (e.g., *The rectangular pizza was still larger than the round one.*)

▶ What would you notice if you used pennies to compare the 2 areas? (e.g., *Both pizzas will have small gaps between the pennies, but you can still estimate the area if they are placed as close together as possible.*)

▶ Suppose 2 shapes are each 5 square units. Would they have to look exactly the same? (*No. e.g., You don't know what shapes they are; you just know the area.*)

Area: Using Strategies

Guided Intervention

Before Using the Guided Intervention

Provide a shape with straight edges cut from paper. Have available some flat objects to measure with, such as triangle pattern blocks, square tiles, and pennies or round counters. Ask:

▶ How might you find the area of this shape?
(e.g., *Cover the shape with something like triangle blocks or square tiles.*)

▶ Which of these units might be good to use? Why? (e.g., *Pennies are all the same, and they fit closely together, but there are spaces between them. Square tiles and triangles fit together better.*)

Have students cover the shape as completely as possible. Ask:

▶ Which unit was the best for covering this shape? Why?
(e.g., *the triangles, because they fit together without any gaps between them, and they fit inside the shape better than the squares did*)

Using the Guided Intervention   (Student Resource pages 182–185)

Provide Pizza Shapes (BLM 22), a variety of flat, identical objects (e.g., pattern blocks, square tiles, pennies), and transparent square grids (any size, but could be made from 1 cm Square Grid (BLM 6)). Guide students as they measure and compare the areas of the 2 pizzas, using non-standard units and a square grid. Have them compare their results to the measurements on the student page. Ask them if the pizzas should be sold for the same amount.

Have students work through the **Try These** questions in pairs or individually.

Observe whether students

- can measure areas using non-standard units (Questions 1 to 7)
- can compare 2 areas (Questions 2, 3, 6, 7)
- can estimate areas (Questions 4, 7)
- can create shapes with a given area (Questions 6 to 8)

Consolidating and Reflecting

Ensure understanding by asking students questions such as the following:

▶ Can you compare the areas of 2 shapes by just looking?
(e.g., *I can guess which is larger or if they are the same size, but I might need to measure both areas to compare them. I could also put one on top of the other.*)

▶ Why is it important to include the units when you measure?
(e.g., *because the number will change if you use different units*)

▶ How do you measure the area when the shape does not fit exactly in the grid lines? (e.g., *I count the whole squares, and then I put parts of squares together to make more whole squares. Sometimes there's still a bit left over.*)

Copyright © 2011 by Nelson Education Ltd.   *Leaps and Bounds 3/4*

You will need

- paper and scissors
- a variety of flat, identical objects (e.g., pattern blocks, square tiles, pennies, or round counters)
- Pizza Shapes (BLM 22)
- transparent square grids (made from BLM 6)
- Student Resource pages 182–185

Area: Using Whole Units

You will need

- a cutout shape
- a variety of flat, identical objects (e.g., pattern blocks, square tiles, a cardboard cutout or sticky notes of any shape, loonies, or large round counters)
- chart paper, coloured pencils, and straightedges
- Student Resource page 186

Open-Ended Intervention

Before Using the Open-Ended Intervention

Provide a cutout rectangle, 2.5 cm by 8 cm. Put 2 square tiles on top of the cutout. Ask:

▸ Why might I say that the rectangle is bigger than 2 tiles? (e.g., *There is still some space left over.*)

Explain that *area* describes how much surface the rectangle covers. Ask:

▸ How many squares would it take to cover the rectangle? (*3*)
▸ Is the answer exact? (e.g., *No, but there isn't much left over.*)
▸ What if you covered the rectangle with loonies? How would you describe the area? (e.g., *I can use 3 loonies, but they don't cover all of the rectangle. There's a little bit not covered, so I'd say the area is a bit more than 3 loonies.*)

Using the Open-Ended Intervention (Student Resource page 186)

Provide a variety of objects for measuring area, including cardboard cutouts that you might make ahead of time (or identical sticky notes). Also provide chart paper, coloured pencils, and straightedges that students can use for drawing.

Read through the task with students. Give students time to work, ideally in pairs.

Observe whether students can

- measure areas using non-standard units with as few gaps as possible
- use many identical units or the same unit repeatedly (iteration)
- recognize that parts of units can be combined to make a whole unit

Consolidating and Reflecting

Ensure understanding by asking questions about students' work:

▸ Why were the game boards different sizes even though they all had 10 sections? (e.g., *The unit used to create each of the equal sections can be anything. It can big like a card or smaller like a square tile.*)
▸ Which shapes were exactly 10 units in area? Which were not? (e.g., *When I used trapezoid blocks or triangle blocks or rhombus blocks, these gave areas that were exact. When I used my sticky-note flower shapes, the area was a bit more than 10 flower units.*)
▸ Which shapes were easiest to use to make your game board? Why? (e.g., *shapes like pattern blocks, because they fit together without any gaps*)
▸ If you made 10 sections by using loonies, would the area be exactly 10 units? (e.g., *No, loonies are round, so they don't fit together exactly. The area would be more than 10 loonie units.*)

Guided Intervention

Before Using the Guided Intervention

Provide a cutout shape, such as a rhombus with dimensions as shown in the margin. Put triangle pattern blocks on top of the cutout. Ask:

▸ Why might I say that the rectangle is bigger than 3 triangles? (e.g., *There is still some space left over.*)

Tell students that *area* describes how much surface the shape covers.

▸ How many triangle blocks would it take to cover the rectangle? (*4*)
▸ Is the answer exact? (e.g., *No, but there isn't much left over.*)
▸ Suppose you covered the shape with pennies. How would you describe the area? (e.g., *I can use 3 pennies but they don't cover all of the shape. There's a lot left over, so maybe the parts could make another penny. The area is about 4 pennies.*)

Using the Guided Intervention — Student Resource pages 187–190

Provide a variety of flat objects (e.g., pattern blocks, square tiles, small cards or sticky notes, pennies), and Wrapping Paper (BLMs 23 and 24). Read through the instructional section with students. Guide them as they measure the areas of the shapes and compare them.

Have students work through the **Try These** questions individually or in pairs. Encourage them to predict the number of units they will use before they measure. Provide a business envelope for Question 4.

Observe whether students
• can measure areas using non-standard units (Questions 1, 2, 5 to 7)
• can estimate areas (Questions 4, 6)
• can compare 2 areas (Questions 2, 3)
• can create shapes with a given area (Questions 5 to 7).

Consolidating and Reflecting

Ensure understanding by asking students the following questions:

▸ If you create 2 shapes that each have an area of 5 units, do you know which is bigger? (e.g., *No, because you don't know how big each unit is.*)
▸ Which units did you use to measure a shape that covered the shape completely? (e.g., *The trapezoid blocks, triangle blocks, or rhombus blocks fit together, and there's nothing left over.*)
▸ Which units did you use to measure a shape that did *not* cover the shape completely? (e.g., *Loonies are round and don't fit together exactly.*)
▸ Can the area of a shape that is long and skinny be the same as a shape that is shorter and wider? (e.g., *Yes. I made a long, skinny rectangle into a square shape, and the areas are almost the same.*)

You will need

• cutout shape
• pattern blocks
• Wrapping Paper (Rectangle) (BLM 23)
• Wrapping Paper (Hexagon) (BLM 24)
• a variety of flat, identical objects (e.g., pattern blocks, square tiles, small cards or sticky notes, pennies or round counters)
• a business envelope (24 cm by 10.5 cm)
• Student Resource pages 187–190

Time

Planning For This Topic

Materials for assisting students with understanding the concepts of telling time and measuring time consist of a diagnostic tool and 3 intervention pathways. Pathway 1 focuses on telling time using both digital and analog clocks. Pathways 2 and 3 focus on measuring time using standard and non-standard units.

Each pathway has an open-ended option and a guided option. Choose the type of intervention most suitable for your students' needs and your particular circumstances.

Curriculum Connections

Grades 1 to 4 curriculum connections for this topic are provided online. See www.nelson.com/leapsandbounds. Although the term *elapsed time* may not formally appear in the curriculum for Grades 1 to 3, nevertheless, there is an indication that students should solve problems involving units of time. The best way to do that is to use simple elapsed time problems, so these sorts of problems are included.

Why might students struggle with time?

Students might struggle with telling time or measuring time for any of the following reasons:

- They might not recognize that any non-standard measuring unit must involve a steady count (e.g., a number of claps, a number of steps).
- They might not recognize that the number of non-standard units required to measure an event's duration depends on the size of the unit used (e.g., if you are measuring with a longer unit, you will need fewer of them).
- They might not realize that times measured in different units cannot be compared without knowing how the unit sizes compare.
- They might not have a personal referent for 1 minute or 1 hour.
- They might not be familiar with the relationship between minutes and hours, hours and days, days and weeks, or months and years.
- They might have difficulty reading a clock when the time is not on the hour.
- They might have difficulty distinguishing between the minute and hour hands on an analog clock.

Professional Learning Connections

PRIME: Measurement, Background and Strategies (Nelson Education Ltd., 2010), pages 103–109

Making Math Meaningful to Canadian Students K–8 (Nelson Education Ltd., 2008), pages 441–448

Big Ideas from Dr. Small, Grades K–3 (Nelson Education Ltd., 2010), pages 98–103

Diagnostic Tool: Time

Use the diagnostic tool to determine the most suitable intervention for time. The tool involves measuring time with non-standard units as well as the relationship between standard units and the reading of clocks. Provide Diagnostic Tool: Time, Teacher's Resource pages 196 and 197, and have students complete it in writing or orally. Have available an analog clock with movable hands for students to use.

See solutions on Teacher's Resource pages 198 and 199.

Intervention Pathways

The purpose of the intervention pathways is to prepare students to measure time with either non-standard units or standard units, or read a clock.

There are 3 pathways:
- Pathway 1: Reading a Clock
- Pathway 2: Time: Using Standard Units
- Pathway 3: Time: Using Non-Standard Units

Use the chart below (or the Key to Pathways on Teacher's Resource pages 198 and 199) to determine which pathway is most suitable for each student or group of students.

Diagnostic Tool Results	Intervention Pathway
If students struggle with Questions 7 to 9	use Pathway 1: Reading a Clock *Teacher's Resource pages 200–201* *Student Resource pages 191–196*
If students struggle with Questions 4 to 6	use Pathway 2: Time: Using Standard Units *Teacher's Resource pages 202–203* *Student Resource pages 197–201*
If students struggle with Questions 1 to 3	use Pathway 3: Time: Using Non-Standard Units *Teacher's Resource pages 204–205* *Student Resource pages 202–205*

Name:_____   Date:_____

Time

1. Circle the statements that make sense.

- You can count up to 8 in the time it takes to write your name.

- You can clap your hands quickly about 2 times in the time it takes to draw a stick figure.

Explain *one* of your answers.

_____

_____

You will need

- a clock with moveable hands

2. Which are units you could use to measure short amounts of time? Circle them.

- number of arm swings

- number of times you could flip a card

- number of textbooks you could read

Explain your thinking for one that is *not* circled.

_____

_____

3. Do you know who took longer to cross the room, Jason or Amil? Explain your thinking.

- Jason walked across the room twice while Mia counted to 100.

- Amil walked across the same room twice while Sandy clapped her hands in a steady beat.

_____

_____

4. Circle all the sentences that are true.

- There are 10 days in a week.

- There are 10 hours in a day.

- There are 100 minutes in an hour.

- There are 12 months in a year.

Leaps and Bounds Copyright © 2011 by Nelson Education Ltd.

5. Name something that might take about each amount of time.

1 hour: _____

2 years: _____

6. How long did each event take?

a) A music lesson started at 5:15 in the afternoon and ended at 6:00 the same day.

_____

b) A project started on November 14 and ended on January 21.

_____

7. Write the time the way it would look on a digital clock.

a)

b)

____ ____:____ ____   ____ ____:____ ____

8. a) The minute hand on a clock is pointing to 7. What do you know about the time?

_____

b) The hour hand on a clock is between 4 and 5. What do you know about the time?

_____

9. Kevin read the time as *quarter after* .... What do you know about where the hands are?

_____

Solutions and Key to Pathways

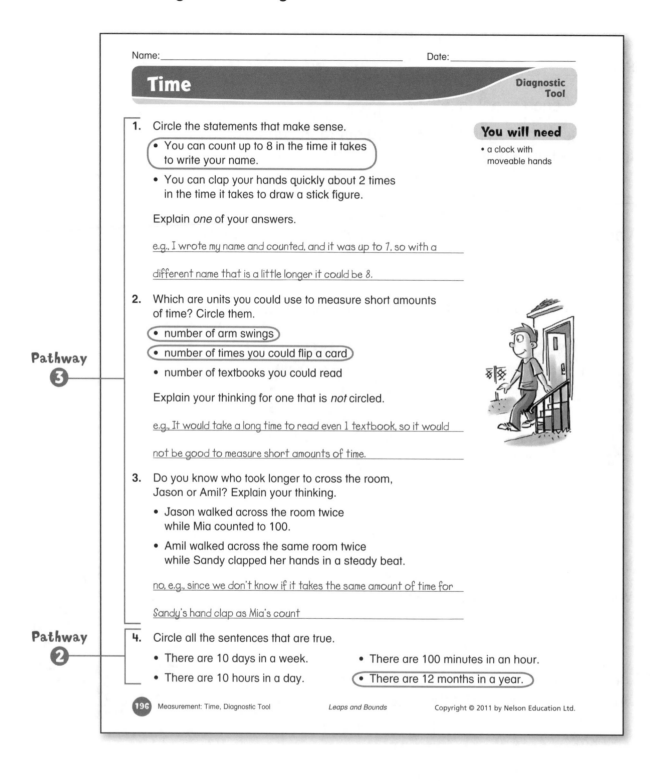

Name: _____ Date: _____

Time

1. Circle the statements that make sense.

(• You can count up to 8 in the time it takes to write your name.)

• You can clap your hands quickly about 2 times in the time it takes to draw a stick figure.

Explain *one* of your answers.

e.g., I wrote my name and counted, and it was up to 7, so with a

different name that is a little longer it could be 8.

You will need

• a clock with moveable hands

2. Which are units you could use to measure short amounts of time? Circle them.

(• number of arm swings)

(• number of times you could flip a card)

• number of textbooks you could read

Explain your thinking for one that is *not* circled.

e.g., It would take a long time to read even 1 textbook, so it would

not be good to measure short amounts of time.

Pathway 3

3. Do you know who took longer to cross the room, Jason or Amil? Explain your thinking.

• Jason walked across the room twice while Mia counted to 100.

• Amil walked across the same room twice while Sandy clapped her hands in a steady beat.

no, e.g., since we don't know if it takes the same amount of time for

Sandy's hand clap as Mia's count

Pathway 2

4. Circle all the sentences that are true.

• There are 10 days in a week.

• There are 10 hours in a day.

• There are 100 minutes in an hour.

(• There are 12 months in a year.)

Name: _____ Date: _____

5. Name something that might take about each amount of time.

    1 hour: *e.g., a TV show* _____

    2 years: *e.g., the time between when I turned 4 and when I turned 6*

6. How long did each event take?

    a) A music lesson started at 5:15 in the afternoon and ended at 6:00 the same day.

    45 minutes _____

    b) A project started on November 14 and ended on January 21.

    2 months and 1 week (or 7 days) _____

7. Write the time the way it would look on a digital clock.

    a)

    b)

    _1_ _0_ : _0_ _5_   ___ _4_ : _4_ _0_

8. **a)** The minute hand on a clock is pointing to 7. What do you know about the time?

    e.g., It is 35 minutes past the hour. _____

    b) The hour hand on a clock is between 4 and 5. What do you know about the time?

    e.g., It is after 4 o'clock but before 5 o'clock. _____

9. Kevin read the time as *quarter after* ....
    What do you know about where the hands are?

    e.g., The minute hand is at 3. It doesn't say where the hour hand is.

Copyright © 2011 by Nelson Education Ltd. *Leaps and Bounds* Measurement: Time, Diagnostic Tool **197**

Copyright © 2011 by Nelson Education Ltd. *Leaps and Bounds 3/4* Measurement: Time **199**

Reading a Clock

You will need

- clocks with moveable hands
- a digital clock
- blank cards (optional)
- Student Resource pages 191–192

Open-Ended Intervention

Before Using the Open-Ended Intervention

Set an analog clock to 4:15 and say the time. Write 4:15 and ask:

▸ What does 4:15 mean? (e.g., *15 minutes after 4*)

Make sure students know the minute hand and the hour hand on the clock. Ask:

▸ How do you know it was 4:15? (e.g., *The hour hand is near 4 and the minute hand is at 3. You count by 5s when you go around the clock, so, you'd say 5, 10, 15.*)

Change the analog clock to show 4:45. Ask:

▸ What time is it now? (*four forty-five, or quarter to five*)
▸ Why did you say 4 o'clock even though the hour hand is not pointing to 4? (*because it's past 4 but not at 5 yet*)

Move the minute hand to each number on the clock to make sure students know how to skip count by 5s to read the minutes. Set the analog clock to several other times, and ask students to read the time.

Using the Open-Ended Intervention   (Student Resource pages 191–192)

Provide a clock with moveable hands. Read through the task on the student pages together. Explain to students that they should use only the times when the minute hand points right at a number on the clock. For the first part of the task, students might draw simple sketches and record the times below.

For the second part of the task, tell students that they can create any descriptions. Give students time to work, ideally in pairs.

Observe student responses, and bring out the following:

- There are always many times that fit any description (other than when a specific time is given).
- You skip count by 5s to read the minutes when the hand is on a number.
- The hour hand is not on one of the 12 numbers unless the minute hand is on 12.
- The hour is always a whole number from 1 to 12, but the minutes can go up to 59. The minutes are also always a whole number.

Consolidating and Reflecting

Ensure understanding by asking students the following questions:

▸ Would the time ever be 12:64? (*no, since the minutes can't be more than 59*)
▸ What do you know about a time if the minute hand points to 8? (*It is 40 minutes after the hour or 20 minutes before the next hour.*)
▸ What description did you make up? (e.g., *that the hands are a bit less than half the circle apart*)
▸ How did you select times to match your description? (e.g., *I set the hour hand and then moved the minute hand so it was almost, but not quite, halfway around the clock.*)

Leaps and Bounds 3/4
Copyright © 2011 by Nelson Education Ltd.

Reading a Clock

Guided Intervention

You will need
- clocks with moveable hands
- a digital clock
- Student Resource pages 193–196

Before Using the Guided Intervention

Set an analog clock to 2:15. Write the digital time 2:15, and read it to students.

▶ What does 2:15 mean? (e.g., *15 minutes after 2*)

Make sure students know the minute hand and the hour hand on the clock. Ask:

▶ How do you know it was 2:15? (e.g., *The hour hand is near 2, and the minute hand is at 3. You count by 5s when you go around the clock, so if the hand points to 3, you'd say 5, 10, 15.*)

You may want to introduce the language *quarter after* 2.

Change the analog clock to show 2:45. Ask:

▶ What time is it now? (*two forty-five, or quarter to three*)

Set the clock for 12 o'clock. Move the hand to each number to make sure students realize how to skip count by 5s to read the minutes. Let students know that we use 2 digits to write the minutes, so we would write 12:05 and not 12:5.

Using the Guided Intervention   (Student Resource pages 193–196)

Provide clocks with moveable hands. Work through the instructional section of the student pages together, modelling the times and moving the hands on the clocks. Have students move the hands on their clocks to 7:05 and then to 8:10.

Have students work through the **Try These** questions in pairs or individually.

Observe whether they
- can read a digital clock (Questions 1, 2, 4, 6)
- can read an analog clock if the minute hand is at 5-minute intervals (Questions 3, 4, 6)
- can write the time from an analog clock in digital form (Question 3)
- recognize the minutes past the hour for different positions of the minute hand (Question 5)
- realize that the hands can be close together or not (Questions 7, 8)
- recognize the rationale for phrases like *quarter after* and *quarter to* (Question 9)

Consolidating and Reflecting

Ensure understanding by asking students the following questions:
Set the analog clock for 3:05.
▶ How could you write this as a digital time? (*3:05*)
▶ What does the 3 mean? (e.g., *It's after 3 o'clock but not yet 4 o'clock.*)
▶ Why did you write 05? (e.g., *because it is 5 minutes after 3 o'clock*)
▶ Would the time ever be 12:64? (*no, since the minutes can't be more than 59*)
▶ What do you know about a time if the minute hand points to 8? (*It is 40 minutes after the hour.*)

Time: Using Standard Units

You will need

- calendars (or BLM 25)
- a clock with moveable hands
- Time Line (BLM 26)
- Student Resource pages 197–198

Open-Ended Intervention

Before Using the Open-Ended Intervention

Provide a calendar for each student. Point out that each row shows a week. Ask:

▸ How does the calendar show the number of days in a week? (*There are 7 columns, one for each day of the week.*)

▸ How many weeks are in a month? (*about 4*)

▸ How can you find out how many days are in each month? (e.g., *You have to look at each month because the number of days is not always the same.*)

Distribute copies of Time Line (BLM 26). Help students see that we start measuring the time for a day at 12 a.m. (midnight) and that we go through 1 o'clock, 2 o'clock, …, to 12 p.m. (noon) and then back through 1 o'clock, 2 o'clock, etc.

Indicate that within each hour the minutes go from 00 minutes after the hour to 59 minutes. Point out the minute markings on a clock.

Draw a segment on the time line from 2 o'clock to 5:30. Ask:

▸ Why is this amount of time 3 hours and 30 minutes? (*It's 3 hours from 2 to 5 and then another half hour, and that's 30 min.*)

▸ How long is it from 2:30 p.m. to 3:15? (e.g., *It's 30 minutes to 3 o'clock and then another 15 minutes, so it is 45 minutes.*)

Using the Open-Ended Intervention (Student Resource pages 197–198)

Provide calendars (or BLM 25) and Time Line (BLM 26). Read through the tasks on the student pages together. Give students time to work, ideally in pairs.

Observe student responses, and bring out the following:

- The minute part of a time is always between 00 and 59; the hour part is always a whole number from 1 to 12.
- To calculate the duration of an event, it is helpful to use hour or half-hour benchmarks. Sometimes it helps to go forwards and other times to go backwards.
- If events are months apart, they are many weeks apart and many more days apart.

Consolidating and Reflecting

Ensure understanding by asking questions based on students' work:

▸ Suppose an activity lasted less than an hour. Do the hour parts of the time have to be the same? (*No.* e.g., *It could be from 8:30 to 9:00, and that's less than an hour, but the hours are different.*)

▸ What 2 important dates did you use? (e.g., *I used my birthday and Christmas.*)

▸ How many months apart are they? (e.g., *more than 3 months*)

▸ How did you figure out the number of weeks? (e.g., *I used a calendar and just counted the number of weeks from the first date to the second one.*)

Leaps and Bounds 3/4

Copyright © 2011 by Nelson Education Ltd.

Time: Using Standard Units

Guided Intervention

Before Using the Guided Intervention

Point out the minute markings on a clock. Indicate that within each hour the minutes go from 00 minutes after the hour to 59 minutes.

Help students get a feel for a minute by asking them when they think a minute ends after you say *Start*. Indicate when the minute is actually over.

Using the Guided Intervention   (Student Resource pages 199–201)

Provide calendars (or BLM 24) and Time Line (BLM 25). Work through the instructional section of the student pages together.

Encourage students to think of other events that might take about one minute, one hour, one day, or one month (e.g., one minute: clap your hands about 100 times; one hour: you can walk about 4 km or 5 km; one day: the amount of time between when you leave school one day and leave school the next day; one month: from the time when you turn an old calendar page to show a new month until the next time you do it).

Point out that each row on a calendar shows a week. Discuss how the calendar shows each month and the number of days in each, and 12 months in a year.

Have students work through the **Try These** questions in pairs or individually.

Observe whether students
- can use facts about the number of minutes in an hour, hours in a day, and so on to relate other time measurements (Questions 1, 2, 3, 4, 7)
- realize that the same amount of time can be described using different units (Questions 2, 3, 6)
- have personal referents, or benchmarks, for various units of time (Question 5)
- realize that to calculate the duration of an event, it is sometimes helpful to use hour or half-hour benchmarks (Question 6)
- recognize the value of measuring the duration of an event (Question 8)

Consolidating and Reflecting

Ensure understanding by asking students the following questions:
- ▶ How many minutes are in 2 and a half hours? (*150*)
- ▶ The time between spring break and the end of school lasts a little more than 3 months. About how many weeks is that? (*12*) about how many days? (*100*)
- ▶ What unit of time would you use to measure the length of a movie? (*minutes or hours*) the length of a school year? (*months*)
- ▶ Jenna has lived in her house for 1 year and 8 months. How many months has she lived there? (*20*)
- ▶ An event started at 11:35 and lasted 2 hours and 30 minutes. When did it end? (*2:05*)

You will need
- calendars (or BLM 25)
- a clock with moveable hands
- Time Line (BLM 26)
- Student Resource pages 199–201

Time: Using Non-Standard Units

You will need

- small sand timers
- larger sand timers (e.g., with 2 or 3 times the amount of sand)
- a metronome—actual or online (optional)
- a pencil case holding about 25 pencils
- Student Resource pages 202–203

Open-Ended Intervention

Before Using the Open-Ended Intervention

Make sure students understand how the timers work.

Ask students to write their names 3 times. As they do, tap steadily. Ask:

▶ Why might I say it took 15 taps on the table for you to write your name 3 times? (*You tapped 15 times and we started and ended together.*)

▶ Do you think it will take more or fewer than 15 turns of the timer for you to write your name 3 times? (e.g., *I think it will be less, since it will take longer for the timer to empty than for you to tap once.*)

If a metronome is available (could be actual or online), demonstrate how it works.

Using the Open-Ended Intervention   (**Student Resource pages 202–203**)

Provide a small sand timer, a larger timer, and a pencil case with 25 pencils in it. Read through the tasks on the student pages together. Make sure students understand that they should estimate the number of times before they actually do the timing. Give students time to work, ideally in pairs.

Observe student responses, and bring out the following:

- A time unit can be used to decide which of 2 events takes longer.
- A time measurement depends on the size of the unit used.
- Times can be compared only if the same units are used (or the relationship between the units is known).

Consolidating and Reflecting

Ensure understanding by asking questions based on students' work:

▶ Suppose it took 6 turns of the small timer to measure a time. How many turns of the large timer do you think it will take? Why? (e.g., *2 turns, since it looked like it was less than half as many for the things I measured*)

▶ Why does it make sense that it took fewer turns? (e.g., *A big timer takes longer to empty, so you wouldn't turn it over as often.*)

▶ Which of your events took the most time? (e.g., *eating an apple*)

▶ Were the time measurements for this event more, no matter what unit you used? Explain your thinking. (*Yes.* e.g., *If something takes longer, it should take more timer turns, or more times filling and emptying a pencil case, or a higher count than for a shorter event.*)

▶ Suppose one event took 3 turns of the large timer, and another event took a count of 300. Can you be sure which lasted longer? (*No.* e.g., *I'm not sure how many numbers I can say in 1 turn of the large timer.*)

Guided Intervention

Before Using the Guided Intervention

You will need

- small sand timers
- Student Resource pages 204–205

Make sure students understand how the timer works. Ask students to write their names 3 times. As they do, tap steadily. Ask:

▶ Why might I say it took 15 taps on the table for you to write your name 3 times? (*You tapped 15 times, and we started and ended together.*)

Repeat the activity but instead of tapping the table, take steps and report the number of steps you took in that amount of time. Ask:

▶ Why might I say it took 8 steps instead? (e.g., *I saw you take 8 steps while I wrote my name 3 times.*)

▶ Do you think it will take more or fewer than 15 turns of the timer for you to write your name 3 times? (e.g., *I think it will be less, since it will take longer for the timer to empty than for you to tap on the table once.*)

Using the Guided Intervention (Student Resource pages 204–205)

Provide students with timers. Read through the instructional section on the student page together. Encourage students to consider how high they could count or how many times they would turn over a timer if they wrote their name 3 times.

Have students work through the **Try These** questions in pairs. Encourage them to perform the experiments and not just guess.

Observe whether students

- can measure times using non-standard units, with steady beats (Question 1)
- can make reasonable decisions about what time unit to use (Question 2)
- realize that different units result in different time-measurement numbers (Question 3)
- have benchmarks, or personal referents, for time units (Questions 4, 6)
- realize that 2 events measured in different units cannot be compared if the relationship between the units is not known (Questions 5, 6)
- have some notions of why one might want to measure durations (Question 7).

Consolidating and Reflecting

Ensure understanding by asking students the following questions:

▶ What would be a good thing to measure with numbers of sleeps? (e.g., *something that wouldn't happen for a lot of days*)

▶ What would be a good event to measure with a number of steps? (e.g., *something that takes a bit of time, such as how long it takes to eat a small snack*)

▶ If we measured how long it takes to fill a page with your name, would it take more turns of the timer or more claps? (*claps, since they are quicker*)

▶ Suppose it took 10 claps for one event and 8 steps for another. Do you know which took longer? (*No. e.g., I don't know if steps or claps are quicker—it depends.*)

Strand: Data Management

Overview

How were the data management topics chosen?

This resource provides materials for assisting students with 2 data management topics. These topics were drawn from the curriculum outcomes from across the country for Grades 1 to 3. Topic selections are also based on research about particular aspects of each topic that students struggle with. These topics are divided into distinct levels, called pathways, which address gaps in students' prerequisite skills and knowledge.

What data management topics were omitted?

Data management topics on creating and using surveys are not addressed directly in these materials. At this level, it is not practical to expect students to work on surveys independently, or even in very small groups. A focus on sorting and presenting data is more useful for students who are struggling.

Probability is also not addressed. In some curricula, the topic is not explored before Grade 4. In others, early expectations are very simple and students would likely not yet be struggling.

How were the pathways determined?

Pathways for sorting differ in whether one or more attributes are being considered at a time.

Pathways for displaying data differ in whether or not a scale (i.e., many-to-one correspondence) is used in the data display. They also differ in the use of bar graphs and pictographs versus concrete and picture graphs to display data, the latter being less abstract.

Materials

Materials for assisting students who are struggling with data management topics will likely already be in the classroom or easily accessible. These are listed below. Blackline masters are also listed below and are provided at the back of this resource.

string, yarn, or small hoops
attribute blocks
pattern blocks
scissors
coloured pencils
buttons
square tiles
linking cubes
paper clips
sticky notes
graphing mats
identical stickers or rubber
   stamps
rulers or straightedges
small cards

BLM 27: Venn Diagram
BLM 28: Sorting Mat
BLM 29: Pet Cards
BLM 30: Fish Cards
BLM 31: Animal Cards
BLM 32: Flip Flop Cards
BLM 33: Waste Cards
BLM 34: Food Cards
BLM 35: Graphing Mat
BLM 36: Graphing Grid
BLM 37: Soccer
BLM 38: T-Shirts

Data Management Topics and Pathways

Topics and pathways in this strand are shown below.
Each pathway has an open-ended intervention and a guided intervention.

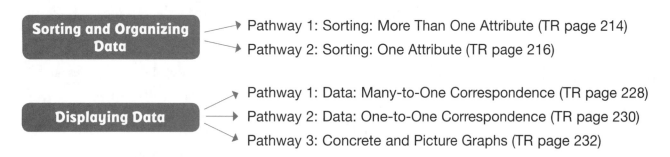

Sorting and Organizing Data
→ Pathway 1: Sorting: More Than One Attribute (TR page 214)
→ Pathway 2: Sorting: One Attribute (TR page 216)

Displaying Data
→ Pathway 1: Data: Many-to-One Correspondence (TR page 228)
→ Pathway 2: Data: One-to-One Correspondence (TR page 230)
→ Pathway 3: Concrete and Picture Graphs (TR page 232)

Sorting and Organizing Data

Planning For This Topic

Materials for assisting students with sorting and organizing data consist of a diagnostic tool and 2 intervention pathways. Pathway 1 focuses on sorting using more than one attribute, and Pathway 2 focuses on sorting using one attribute.

Each pathway has an open-ended option and a guided option. Choose the type of intervention most suitable for your students' needs and your particular teaching circumstances.

Curriculum Connections

Grades 1 to 4 curriculum connections for this topic are provided online. See www.nelson.com/leapsandbounds.

Even though Venn diagrams may not be mentioned specifically, they are commonly used tools for sorting, as are sorting circles, which are used extensively.

Many of the sorting outcomes in both curricula are related to geometry, so sorting is also covered in that strand.

Professional Learning Connections

PRIME: Data Management and Probability, Background and Strategies (Nelson Education Ltd., 2006), pages 42–50

Making Math Meaningful to Canadian Students K–8 (Nelson Education Ltd., 2008), pages 516–524

Big Ideas from Dr. Small Grades K–3 (Nelson Education Ltd., 2010), pages 115–120

Why might students struggle with sorting and organizing data?

Students might struggle with sorting and organizing data for any of the following reasons:

- They might find the terminology confusing (e.g., you sort a set of items by the *attribute* of colour, but use descriptive words like red or blue as the *characteristics* or *sorting rules*).
- They might not realize that many sorting rules are possible for a given attribute (e.g., if asked to sort by an attribute such as colour, possible sorting rules are "red v. not red," "red v. blue v. neither," "red or yellow v. blue," etc.).
- They might have difficulty dealing with items that do not possess the characteristic that is the focus of the sorting rule(s).
- They might have difficulty sorting the same set of items in more than one way.
- They might have difficulty sorting items that require abstract knowledge (e.g., the sorting rules "letters that are vowels," "even numbers," or "animals that eat meat").

Diagnostic Tool: Sorting and Organizing Data

Use the diagnostic tool to determine the most suitable intervention pathway for sorting and organizing data. Provide Diagnostic Tool: Sorting and Organizing Data, Teacher's Resource pages 210 and 211, and have students complete it in writing or orally. Have available sorting materials (including string, yarn, or small hoops for making sorting circles, and paper) as well as Pet Cards (BLM 29).

See solutions on Teacher's Resource pages 212 and 213.

Intervention Pathways

The purpose of the intervention pathways is to help students sort and organize objects and numbers using one attribute or more than one attribute. They use Venn diagrams and charts as forms of data display. This will help prepare them for organizing data into appropriate categories to create a graph, such that each piece of data appears in only one category.

There are 2 pathways:
- Pathway 1: Sorting: More Than One Attribute
- Pathway 2: Sorting: One Attribute

Use the chart below (or the Key to Pathways on Teacher's Resource pages 212 and 213) to determine which pathway is most suitable for each student or group of students.

Diagnostic Tool Results	Intervention Pathway
If students struggle with Questions 4 to 6	use Pathway 1: Sorting: More Than One Attribute *Teacher Resource pages 214–215* *Student Resource pages 206–211*
If students struggle with Questions 1 to 3	use Pathway 2: Sorting: One Attribute *Teacher Resource pages 216–217* *Student Resource pages 212–217*

Sorting and Organizing Data

1. How can you sort these shapes into 2 groups?
   Describe 3 ways.

You will need
• Pet Cards (BLM 29)

_____

_____

2. **a)** Describe how the 6 shapes were sorted.

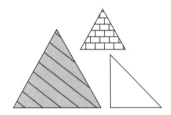   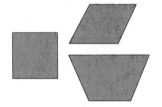

_____

   b) Describe another way to sort the 6 shapes.

_____

3. Sort the 8 pets into 2 groups: birds or dogs.
   Use the Pet Cards to sort, then write the
   letter of each pet below in the group
   where it belongs.
   Some do not belong to either group.

Pets

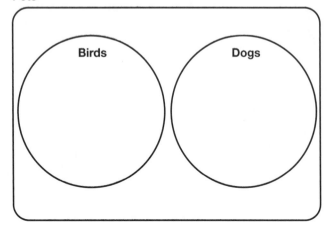

4. Sort these 5 items using the chart below.
Write the letter of each shape where it belongs.

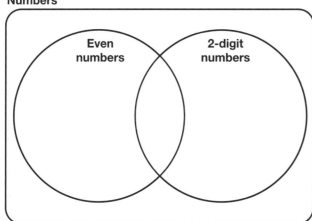

	3-D shape	2-D shape
Grey		
Not grey		

5. Sort these 8 numbers using the Venn diagram.
22, 3, 40, 88, 114, 9, 17, 333

Numbers

Even numbers

2-digit numbers

6. Sort these 10 animals using the chart below.

G: goldfish P: poodle T: terrier   S: Siamese cat B: bulldog

C: canary   L: lizard   K: kangaroo H: hound   W: whale

	Dogs	Not dogs
Animals with fur		
Animals without fur		

Solutions and Key to Pathways

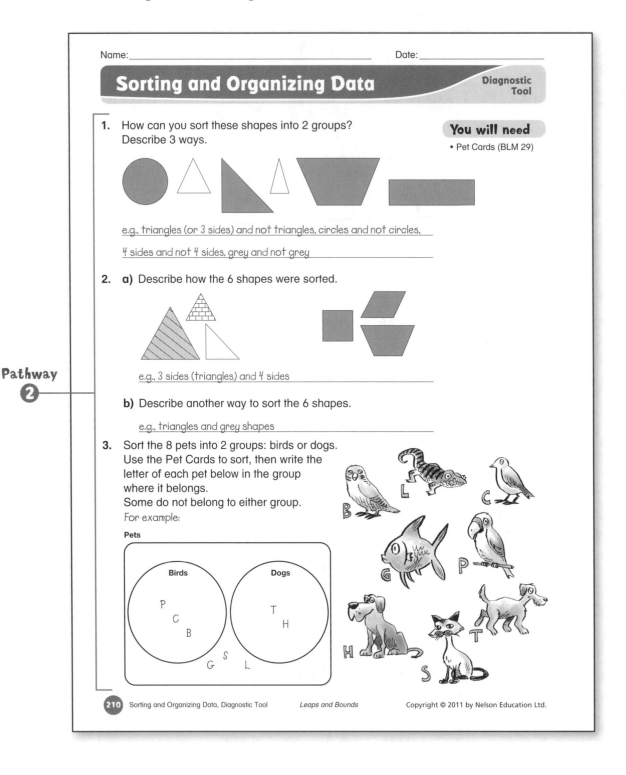

Pathway 2

Name:_____ Date:_____

Sorting and Organizing Data

Diagnostic Tool

1. How can you sort these shapes into 2 groups? Describe 3 ways.

You will need
• Pet Cards (BLM 29)

e.g., triangles (or 3 sides) and not triangles, circles and not circles,

4 sides and not 4 sides, grey and not grey

2. a) Describe how the 6 shapes were sorted.

e.g., 3 sides (triangles) and 4 sides

b) Describe another way to sort the 6 shapes.

e.g., triangles and grey shapes

3. Sort the 8 pets into 2 groups: birds or dogs. Use the Pet Cards to sort, then write the letter of each pet below in the group where it belongs.
Some do not belong to either group.

For example:

Pets

Birds: P, C, B

Dogs: T, H

G S L

210 Sorting and Organizing Data, Diagnostic Tool *Leaps and Bounds* Copyright © 2011 by Nelson Education Ltd.

Name:_____ Date:_____

4. Sort these 5 items using the chart below.
   Write the letter of each shape where it belongs.

	3-D shape	2-D shape
Grey	A	C, E
Not grey	D	B

5. Sort these 8 numbers using the Venn diagram.
   22, 3, 40, 88, 114, 9, 17, 333

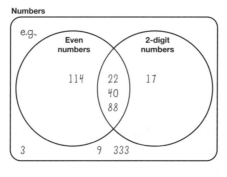

Numbers

e.g.,

Even numbers: 114

2-digit numbers: 17

(overlap): 22 40 88

3   9   333

6. Sort these 10 animals using the chart below.

   G: goldfish   P: poodle   T: terrier   S: Siamese cat   B: bulldog
   C: canary   L: lizard   K: kangaroo   H: hound   W: whale

	Dogs	Not dogs
Animals with fur	P T H B	K S
Animals without fur		G C L W

Copyright © 2011 by Nelson Education Ltd.   *Leaps and Bounds*   Sorting and Organizing Data, Diagnostic Tool   **211**

Sorting: More Than One Attribute

You will need

- attribute blocks or pattern blocks
- Sorting Mat (BLM 28)
- string, yarn, or small hoops
- Fish Cards (BLM 30)
- Venn Diagram (BLM 27)
- Student Resource pages 206–207

2-D Shapes

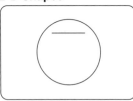

Open-Ended Intervention

Before Using the Open-Ended Intervention

Make a large circle or use the Sorting Mat (BLM 28). Label some pattern blocks or attribute blocks with letters on pieces of tape. Ask:

- ▶ What attributes do these blocks have? Think about how they are the same and different. (e.g., *shape, colour, size, number of sides*)
- ▶ Sort these shapes so that there is only 1 shape in the circle. Write the letter of the shape inside the circle and the other letters outside the circle. What label (or sorting rule) would you use? (e.g., *D is inside, and A, B, and C are outside; the sorting rule is 3 sides/not 3 sides.*)
- ▶ Sort the shapes a different way. What sorting rule would you use? (e.g., *yellow/not yellow: A is inside, and B, C, and D are outside; or 4 sides/not 4 sides: B and C inside the circle, A and D outside the circle*)

Using the Open-Ended Intervention (Student Resource pages 206–207)

Provide the Fish Cards (BLM 30) and string, yarn, small hoops, or a Venn diagram (BLM 27). Read through the tasks on the student pages together. Students may sort using the materials, and then record their sorting by writing the letter for each fish in the Venn diagram on the student page. Students might draw new fish on blank cards and place them on their large model. Allow students time to work, ideally in pairs.

Observe whether students

- are able to sort using more than one attribute
- recognize that many sorting rules are possible when size, type, and pattern vary
- can describe their sorting rules and relate them to the parts of the Venn diagram

Consolidating and Reflecting

Ensure understanding by asking questions based on students' work:

- ▶ What sorting rule did you use to sort the fish? (e.g., *small and spotted*)
- ▶ Why were there 3 fish in the overlapping part of your sorting diagram? (e.g., *They belong in both circles.*)
- ▶ When does a fish go outside the circles but inside the rectangle? (e.g., *If the fish didn't match the sorting rules, it went outside the circles.*)
- ▶ What sorting rule would give no fish in the overlapping part? (e.g., *striped and not striped*)
- ▶ How might the diagram look different if you changed one of the sorting rules? (e.g., *You might have more or fewer fish in each circle, or outside the circles.*)

Sorting: More Than One Attribute

Guided Intervention

Before Using the Guided Intervention

Make a large circle or use the Sorting Mat (BLM 28), and provide attribute blocks or pattern blocks. Label each with a letter on a piece of tape. Ask:

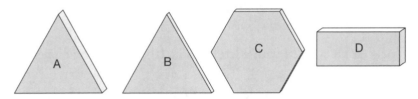

▸ What attributes do these blocks have? (e.g., *shape, colour, size, number of sides*)

▸ Sort these shapes so that there is only 1 shape in the circle. Write the letter of the shape inside the circle and the other letters outside the circle. What label (or sorting rule) would you use? (e.g., *rectangles/not rectangles*)

▸ Sort the shapes a different way. What sorting rule would you use? (e.g., *blue/not blue or 3 sides/not 3-sides.*)

Using the Guided Intervention   (Student Resource pages 208–211)

Provide the sets of cards and string, yarn, or small hoops. Read through the instructional part of the student pages together. Have students sort the cards on a large Venn diagram (e.g., yarn circles or BLM 27), and then record their work by writing the letters of the cards on the smaller Venn diagram on the student page.

Have students work through the **Try These** questions in pairs or individually.

Observe whether students can
• identify attributes and sort when given the sorting rules (Question 1)
• identify attributes and describe the sorting rules (Questions 1, 2, 7)
• use a Venn diagram to organize their sorting (Questions 1, 2, 3, 7)
• use a chart to organize their sorting (Questions 4, 5)

Consolidating and Reflecting

Ensure understanding by asking students the following questions:
▸ What sorting rules could you use to sort the attribute blocks?
   (e.g., *size: large and small, thickness: thick and thin*)

▸ How did you know which objects to put in the overlapping part of the Venn diagram? (e.g., *If the item can go in both circles, it goes in the overlapping part.*)

▸ How did you know which items or numbers to put outside the circles but inside the rectangle? (e.g., *If the item doesn't match the sorting rule on either circle, it goes outside the circles.*)

▸ Do you find it easier to sort using a chart or a Venn diagram? Why? (e.g., *The Venn diagram. I can see where the circles overlap and I can see the items that are in each circle and in both circles.*)

Copyright © 2011 by Nelson Education Ltd.   *Leaps and Bounds 3/4*   Data Management: Sorting and Organizing Data   **215**

You will need

• attribute blocks or pattern blocks
• Sorting Mat (BLM 28)
• string, yarn, or small hoops
• Fish Cards (A to J, BLM 30)
• Animal Cards (BLM 31)
• Flip Flop Cards (BLM 32)
• Waste Cards (BLM 33)
• Venn Diagram (BLM 27)
• Student Resource pages 208–211

2-D Shapes

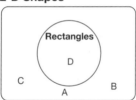

Sorting: One Attribute

You will need

- attribute blocks or pattern blocks
- string, yarn, or small hoops
- Sorting Mat (BLM 28)
- Food Cards A to J (BLM 34)
- Student Resource pages 212–213

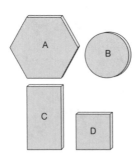

2-D Shapes

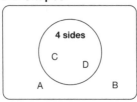

Open-Ended Intervention

Before Using the Open-Ended Intervention

Provide 2 different attribute blocks or pattern blocks, each labelled with a letter.

▶ How are these blocks the same? How are they different? (e.g., *They are flat, the same colour, and the same thickness; they are plastic; A has 6 straight sides and B has no straight sides; A is bigger than B; they are different shapes.*)

Provide 2 more blocks, each labelled with a letter, and a labelled sorting circle (e.g., 4 sides). Ask:

▶ What blocks belong in this sorting circle? (*C and D*)

Write the letter of each to record the sorting.

Using the Open-Ended Intervention (Student Resource pages 212–213)

Provide the Food Cards (BLM 34) and string, yarn, small hoops, or Sorting Mat (BLM 28). Read through the tasks on the student pages together. For the first time they sort, encourage students to use any method they like (e.g., simple groups with no labels). For the second time they sort, students can use a small hoop or yarn circle or sorting mat, and then record their work by writing the letter of each food in the sorting mat on the page. They might draw new foods on blank cards and place them on their large model.

Allow students time to work, ideally in pairs.

Observe whether students
- are able to sort using one attribute
- recognize that different sorting rules are possible
- can describe their sorting rules and relate them to the parts of the sorting mat
- realize that every item must be included on the sorting mat

Consolidating and Reflecting

Ensure understanding by asking questions based on students' work:
▶ Look at the 10 foods again. What sorting rule could you use to sort them? (e.g., *fruits and vegetables/not fruits and vegetables; food names that start with B/not B*)
▶ What do you know about foods inside the sorting circle? (e.g., *They match the sorting rule.*)
▶ When are foods placed outside the circle but inside the rectangle? (*If the food didn't match the sorting rule on the circle, it went outside the circle.*)
▶ What items do you or your family sort? Why is sorting helpful? (e.g., *We sort the laundry into light and dark colours in case colours run onto the light clothes.*)
▶ Does the sorting always change if you change the sorting rule? (e.g., *No, there might be lots of ways of saying the sorting rule.*)

Sorting: One Attribute

Guided Intervention

Before Using the Guided Intervention

Provide 2 different attribute blocks or pattern blocks, each labelled with a letter.

▸ How are these blocks alike?
   (e.g., *They are flat, the same colour, and the same thickness; they are plastic.*)

▸ How are they different? (e.g., *A has 6 straight sides and B has no straight sides; A is bigger than B; they are different shapes.*)

Provide 2 more blocks, each labelled with a letter, and a labelled sorting circle (e.g., No straight sides). Ask:

▸ What blocks belong in this sorting circle? (*B*)

Write the letter of each to record the sorting.

Using the Guided Intervention   (Student Resource pages 214–217)

Provide the sets of cards (cut from the blackline masters) and string, yarn, a small hoop, or Sorting Mat (BLM 28). Read through the instructional part of the student pages together. The first time they sort, encourage students to use any method they like (e.g., simple groups with no labels). The second time they sort, students can use a small hoop or yarn circle or sorting mat and then record their work by writing the letter of each food on the sorting mat on the page.

Have students work through the **Try These** questions in pairs or individually.

Observe whether students can
- sort by one attribute when given the sorting rule (Questions 1a, 6, 7)
- clearly describe the sorting rule used for a given sort (Questions 2, 6)
- use a Venn diagram to help them sort (Questions 1, 2, 4, 6, 7)
- use a chart to help them sort (Question 5)

Consolidating and Reflecting

Ensure understanding by asking students the following questions:

▸ Look at these attribute blocks. How can you sort them?
   (e.g., *by size: large/small; by thickness: thick/thin; by colour: red/yellow*)

▸ How did you know which objects or numbers to put inside the circle on the sorting mat? (e.g., *If it follows the sorting rule, it goes in the circle.*)

▸ How did you know which items or numbers to put outside the circle but inside the rectangle? (e.g., *If it doesn't match the sorting rule, it goes outside the circle.*)

▸ Will there always be items in all parts of the sorting mat—inside the circle, outside the circle? (e.g., *No. For Question 7, if the rule was to sort by one-digit numbers, then all the numbers would be inside the circle and none outside.*)

▸ Does the sorting always change if you change the sorting rule?
   (e.g., *No. There might be lots of ways of saying the sorting rule, as in Question 3.*)

Copyright © 2011 by Nelson Education Ltd.   *Leaps and Bounds 3/4*   Data Management: Sorting and Organizing Data   **217**

You will need

- attribute blocks or pattern blocks
- string, yarn, or small hoops
- Sorting Mat (BLM 28)
- Food Cards (BLM 34)
- Flip Flop Cards (BLM 32)C
- Waste Cards (BLM 33)
- Student Resource pages 214–217

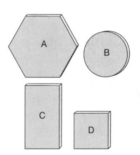

2-D Shapes

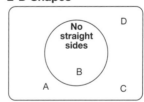

Displaying Data

Planning For This Topic

Materials for assisting students with displaying data consist of a diagnostic tool and 3 intervention pathways. The pathways for this topic differ in the types of graphs being examined (e.g., pictographs, bar graphs, concrete graphs, picture graphs) and whether the scale shows many-to-one or one-to-one correspondence.

Each pathway has an open-ended option and a guided option. Choose the type of intervention most suitable for your students' needs and your particular circumstances.

Curriculum Connections

Grades 1 to 4 curriculum connections for this topic are provided online. See www.nelson.com/leapsandbounds. The interventions emphasize displaying and interpreting data, where students work with given graphs as well as create graphs from given data. Students are not expected to collect their own data or create surveys.

Why might students struggle with displaying data?

Students might struggle with *displaying* data for any of the following reasons:
- They might not align pictures and categories on graphs, or choose consistent symbols when creating pictographs.
- They might have difficulty making the transition from individual squares with pictures or symbols to lengths of bars, when representing data collections.
- They might not know which types of data displays make sense for a particular set of data.
- They might not have a clear understanding of scale (e.g., have difficulty moving from one-to-one correspondence to many-to-one correspondence for pictographs and bar graphs).

Students might struggle with *reading and interpreting* data for any of these reasons:
- They might not make comparisons of data in different categories and interpret graphs correctly, especially when the scale is not 1 or 10.
- They might not consider the scale when comparing data.
- They might have difficulty drawing conclusions about data (e.g., they simply read the data in individual categories).

Professional Learning Connections

PRIME: Data Management and Probability, Background and Strategies (Nelson Education Ltd., 2006), pages 57–68, 77–78, 86–87

Making Math Meaningful to Canadian Students K–8 (Nelson Education Ltd., 2008), pages 472–484

Big Ideas from Dr. Small, Grades K–3 (Nelson Education Ltd., 2010), pages 122–127

Good Questions (dist. by Nelson Education Ltd., 2009), pages 151–156, 165–170

Diagnostic Tool: Displaying Data

Use the diagnostic tool to determine the most suitable intervention pathway for displaying data. Provide Diagnostic Tool: Displaying Data, Teacher's Resource pages 220 to 223, and have students complete it in writing or orally. Have available a graphing mat (BLM 35) and square tiles for students to use.

See solutions on Teacher's Resource pages 224 to 227.

Intervention Pathways

The purpose of the intervention pathways is to help students create, read, and interpret appropriate graphs, including concrete graphs, picture graphs, pictographs, and bar graphs. The focus is to prepare them for creating and interpreting more complex data displays.

There are 3 pathways:
- Pathway 1: Data: Many-to-One Correspondence
- Pathway 2: Data: One-to-One Correspondence
- Pathway 3: Concrete and Picture Graphs

Use the chart below (or the Key to Pathways on Teacher's Resource pages 224 to 227) to determine which pathway is most suitable for each student or group of students.

Diagnostic Tool Results	Intervention Pathway
If students struggle with Questions 6, 7	use Pathway 1: Data: Many-to-One Correspondence *Teacher's Resource pages 228–229* *Student Resource pages 218–223*
If students struggle with Questions 3 to 5	use Pathway 2: Data: One-to-One Correspondence *Teacher's Resource pages 230–231* *Student Resource pages 224–229*
If students struggle with Questions 1, 2	use Pathway 3: Concrete and Picture Graphs *Teacher's Resource pages 232–233* *Student Resource pages 230–235*

Displaying Data

1. Four classes of students made a picture graph to show the dogs they have.

You will need
- Graphing Mat (BLM 35)
- square tiles

Our Dogs

Class A	🐕	🐕	🐕	🐕					
Class B	🐕	🐕	🐕	🐕	🐕	🐕	🐕		
Class C	🐕	🐕	🐕	🐕	🐕	🐕			
Class D	🐕	🐕	🐕	🐕	🐕	🐕	🐕	🐕	🐕

a) How many students in Class B have dogs? _____

b) How many more students in Class D than in Class A have

dogs? _____

c) Nobody in Class E has a dog. How would you show that information?

_____

_____

2. Suppose you reach into a bag of coloured square tiles and pull out some blue tiles, red tiles, and yellow tiles.

Tell how you can use a graphing mat to help you see which colour you have most of, which colour you have least of, and which colour is in the middle.

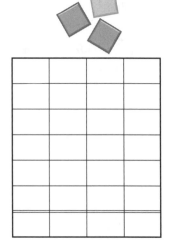

_____

_____

_____

3. Sasha asked some classmates what time they go to bed on a school night: 8:30, 9:00, 9:30, or 10:00 p.m. These are the results.

Bedtimes of Students

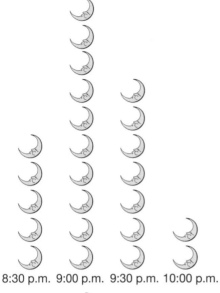

8:30 p.m. 9:00 p.m. 9:30 p.m. 10:00 p.m.

Each 🌙 means 1 student.

a) Which bedtime was chosen least often?

_____

b) How many more students go to bed at

8:30 p.m. than at 10:00 p.m.? _____

c) How many students in all were asked?

_____

4. The students in glee club were asked to choose their favourite colour of T-shirt. Here are the results.

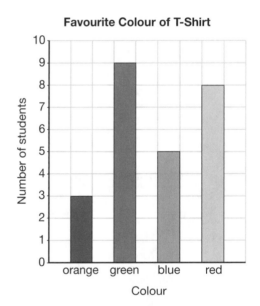

a) Do you agree with the following statement? Explain your thinking.

"More students preferred red to green."

_____

b) How many students were asked? _____

Name:_____ Date: _____

5. A survey of 37 families gave this information about favourite places to go on vacations.

a) Make a bar graph to show the data.

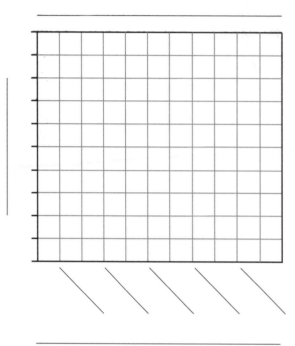

Favourite Family Vacations

Vacation	Number of families
beach	9
cottage	8
big city	9
skiing	4
camping	7

b) Write 2 statements about the bar graph.

_____

_____

6. A soccer team raised money by selling 100 hamburgers at a tournament. This chart shows the number sold for the 4 meals.

Make a pictograph to show the data.
Choose a scale so that all the data fits in the grid.

Hamburger Sales

Meal	Number of hamburgers sold
Saturday lunch	24
Saturday dinner	40
Sunday lunch	20
Sunday dinner	16

Hamburger Sales

Sat. lunch									
Sat. dinner									
Sun. lunch									
Sun. dinner									

Each _____ means _____ hamburgers.

Leaps and Bounds Copyright © 2011 by Nelson Education Ltd.

7. Compare the 2 bar graphs.

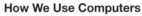

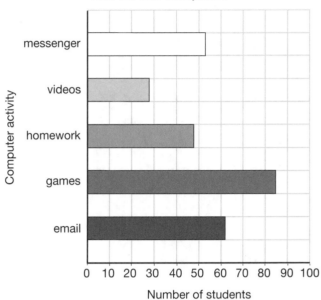

How We Use Computers

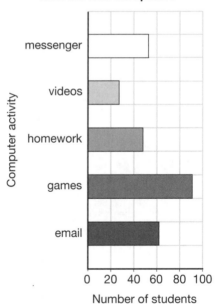

How We Use Computers

How are the graphs the same? _____

_____

_____

How are the graphs different? _____

_____

_____

Solutions and Key to Pathways

Pathway 3

Name: _____ Date: _____

Displaying Data

1. Four classes of students made a picture graph to show the dogs they have.

You will need
- Graphing Mat (BLM 35)
- square tiles

Our Dogs

Class A							
Class B							
Class C							
Class D							

a) How many students in Class B have dogs? _____7_____

b) How many more students in Class D than in Class A have dogs? _____5_____

c) Nobody in Class E has a dog. How would you show that information?

e.g., Add another row, label it Class E, and don't show any

pictures in the row.

2. Suppose you reach into a bag of coloured square tiles and pull out some blue tiles, red tiles, and yellow tiles.

Tell how you can use a graphing mat to help you see which colour you have most of, which colour you have least of, and which colour is in the middle.

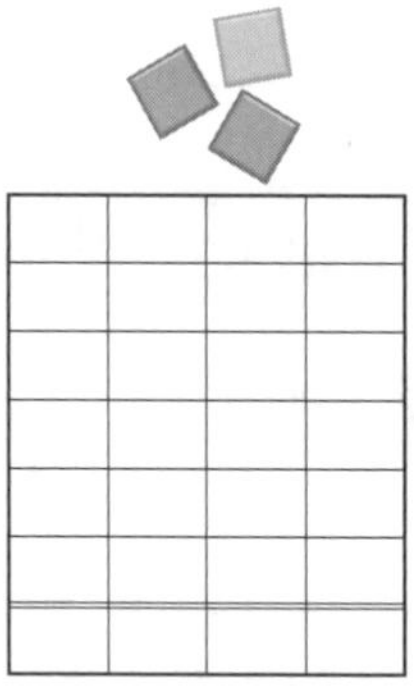

e.g., I would put 1 tile in each box so that all the same colours line

up. Then I can compare the numbers by looking at how long each line

of tiles is.

Leaps and Bounds Copyright © 2011 by Nelson Education Ltd.

Leaps and Bounds 3/4 Copyright © 2011 by Nelson Education Ltd.

Name:_____   Date:_____

3. Sasha asked some classmates what time they go to bed on a school night: 8:30, 9:00, 9:30, or 10:00 p.m. These are the results.

a) Which bedtime was chosen least often?

_10:00 p.m._

b) How many more students go to bed at

8:30 p.m. than at 10:00 p.m.? ___3___

c) How many students in all were asked?

___24___

Bedtimes of Students

8:30 p.m. 9:00 p.m. 9:30 p.m. 10:00 p.m.

Each ☽ means 1 student.

Pathway ❷

4. The students in glee club were asked to choose their favourite colour of T-shirt. Here are the results.

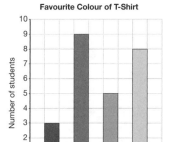

Favourite Colour of T-Shirt

Number of students / Colour

orange green blue red

a) Do you agree with the following statement? Explain your thinking.

"More students preferred red to green."

e.g., No, 9 chose green and only 8 chose red.

b) How many students were asked? ___25___

Copyright © 2011 by Nelson Education Ltd.   *Leaps and Bounds*   Displaying Data, Diagnostic Tool **221**

5. A survey of 37 families gave this information about favourite places to go on vacations.

a) Make a bar graph to show the data.

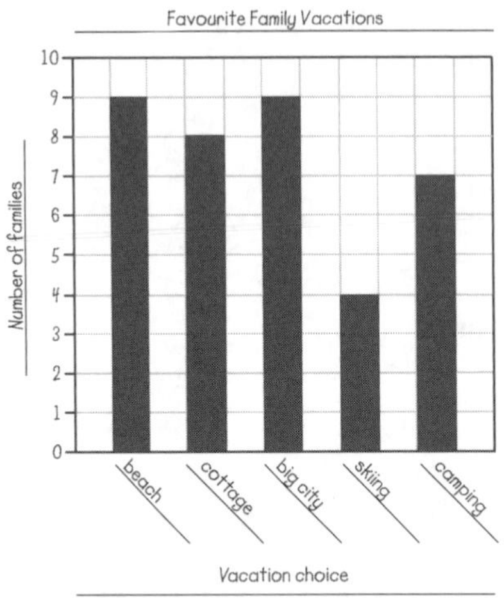

Favourite Family Vacations

Vacation	Number of families
beach	9
cottage	8
big city	9
skiing	4
camping	7

Favourite Family Vacations

Number of families (vertical axis, 0–10)
Vacation choice (horizontal axis: beach, cottage, big city, skiing, camping)

b) Write 2 statements about the bar graph.

e.g., Going to the beach or cottage is more popular than skiing or camping.

Skiing holidays are least popular.

6. A soccer team raised money by selling 100 hamburgers at a tournament. This chart shows the number sold for the 4 meals.

Make a pictograph to show the data.
Choose a scale so that all the data fits in the grid.

Hamburger Sales

Meal	Number of hamburgers sold
Saturday lunch	24
Saturday dinner	40
Sunday lunch	20
Sunday dinner	16

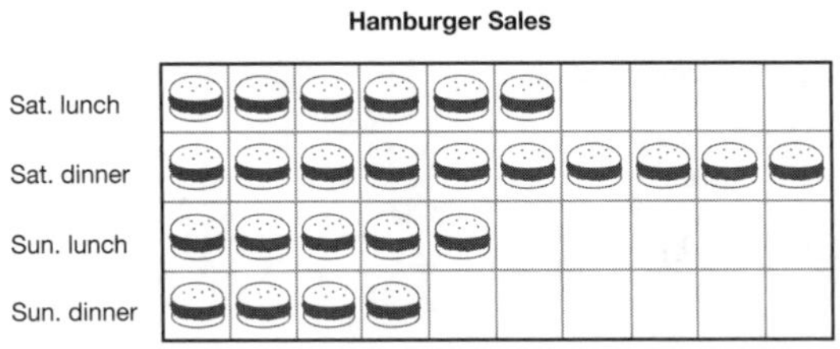

Hamburger Sales

Sat. lunch
Sat. dinner
Sun. lunch
Sun. dinner

Each _____ means __4__ hamburgers.

Pathway 2

Pathway 1

Name:_____ Date:_____

7. Compare the 2 bar graphs.

How We Use Computers

How are the graphs the same? e.g., It looks like the same
information is graphed on both; both are horizontal bar graphs;
both start at 0 and end at 100.

How are the graphs different? e.g., The scales are different; the
scale of the top graph goes up by 10s, and the scale of the bottom
graph goes up by 20s.

Copyright © 2011 by Nelson Education Ltd.   *Leaps and Bounds*   Displaying Data, Diagnostic Tool **223**

Copyright © 2011 by Nelson Education Ltd.   *Leaps and Bounds 3/4*   Data Management: Displaying Data **227**

Data: Many-to-One Correspondence

You will need

- Soccer (BLM 37)
- coloured pencils
- identical stickers or rubber stamps (optional)
- rulers or straightedges (optional)
- grid paper (optional) (BLMs 6, 7)
- Graphing Grid (BLM 36)
- Student Resource pages 218–219

Colour of car	Tally
blue	卌 卌 II
red	卌 卌 卌 I
black	卌 卌 卌 卌 卌 卌 卌 II
grey	卌 卌 卌 卌 卌 卌 III
white	卌 卌 卌 III
yellow	IIII

Open-Ended Intervention

Before Using the Open-Ended Intervention

Display the soccer pictograph (BLM 37). Ask:

▸ How does the symbol help you figure out what the graph might be about? (e.g., *A soccer ball makes sense as the symbol if the graph is about soccer.*)

Discuss the meaning of *scale*—the number of items for each symbol on a graph. Show an example of scale by writing *2 goals* on the blank line. Ask:

▸ How would you label the categories on the left? What title would you use? (e.g., *I could write the names of 4 different teams. The title could be Goals Scored in House League.*)

▸ Suppose that the values for the 4 rows were 10, 25, 5, and 10. What value would each ball represent now? (e.g., *5*)

▸ Why is it necessary to include a scale? (e.g., *You need to know how much a symbol is worth so you can figure out the numbers in each row.*)

Using the Open-Ended Intervention (Student Resource pages 218–219)

Provide extra grid paper (BLMs 6, 7), straightedges, and stickers or stamps if necessary to help students make their pictographs. Together, read through the tasks on the student pages. Students might choose one of the topics shown in the art. If necessary, provide a tally chart for students to use.

Allow students time to work, ideally in pairs.

Observe whether students
- use categories that make sense
- are able to justify the scale they choose
- can create a correct bar graph with an appropriate scale
- can create a correct pictograph with a scale
- can correctly predict how the graph would change with a different scale

Consolidating and Reflecting

Ensure understanding by asking questions based on students' work:

▸ What does each square represent? (e.g., *5 people who picked the same car colour*)

▸ Did the size of the grid affect the scale you used? (e.g., *Yes. When my scale was 2, there weren't enough squares, so I chose a bigger scale of 5.*)

▸ If you select a different scale, would you choose the value of each square or symbol to be greater or less? Why? (e.g., *less, because even though there would be more of them, I don't have to worry about part squares*)

▸ Why did you need to use half symbols for some of your data? (e.g., *because data was left over that wouldn't mean a whole symbol*)

▸ How would you explain to someone why some bar graphs and pictographs need scales? (e.g., *You can't graph high numbers easily using a scale of 1.*)

Data: Many-to-One Correspondence

Guided Intervention

Before Using the Guided Intervention

Display the soccer pictograph (BLM 37). Tell students that it is important to label a graph. Write a title (e.g., Number of Seasons That Players Have Played Soccer). Then write the labels for the categories (e.g., 1st season, 2nd season, 3rd season, 4th season).

Discuss the meaning of *scale*—the number of items for each symbol on a graph. Show an example of a scale by writing *2 players* on the blank line. Ask:

▸ Why is it necessary to include a scale? (e.g., *You need to know how much a symbol is worth so you can figure out the number in each row.*)

▸ Suppose that the values for the 4 categories were 10, 25, 5, and 10. What value would you let each ball represent now? (*5*)

Using the Guided Intervention (Student Resource pages 220–223)

Together, read through the instructional section of the student pages. Guide students as they create a pictograph and a bar graph. They can use graphing grids (BLM 36) and stickers or stamps to make these graphs. Discuss with the students what information they see in the graphs and how each graph was created.

Have students work through the **Try These** questions in pairs or individually. Students may use stickers or stamps to make their pictographs. Provide grid paper for Question 5.

Observe whether students can
- interpret a pictograph (Questions 1, 2)
- interpret a bar graph (Questions 3, 4)
- make a pictograph using a scale of 2, 5, or 10 (Questions 2, 5)
- make a bar graph using a scale of 2, 5, and 10 (Questions 3, 4, 5)

Consolidating and Reflecting

Ensure understanding by asking students the following questions:

▸ How does the tally chart help you make your graph in Question 2? (e.g., *I used the tally chart to help me count by 5s and use a scale of 5.*)

▸ For Question 2, why was it a little easier to show the vanilla data than the chocolate data? (e.g., *Vanilla was 6, so I needed 3 symbols. Chocolate was 11, so I needed 5 symbols and half a symbol.*)

▸ Which do you prefer for displaying data—pictographs or bar graphs? Why? (e.g., *The bar graph is easier for showing the data because you can just count squares to make your bars, and you can see the longest and shortest bars more easily.*)

▸ How would you explain to someone why some bar graphs and pictographs need a scale other than 1? (e.g., *When the data numbers are high, you can't graph it easily using a scale of 1. You would need a lot more graph paper.*)

- Soccer (BLM 37)
- coloured pencils
- identical stickers or rubber stamps (optional)
- Graphing Grid (BLM 36)
- grid paper (BLMs 6, 7)
- Student Resource pages 220–223

Data: One-to-One Correspondence

You will need

- T-Shirts (BLM 38)
- coloured pencils
- identical stickers or rubber stamps (optional)
- grid paper (BLMs 6, 7)
- Graphing Grid (BLM 36)
- straightedges (optional)
- Student Resource pages 224–225

Open-Ended Intervention

Before Using the Open-Ended Intervention

Display the T-shirt pictograph (BLM 38). Ask:

▸ How does the T-shirt symbol help you figure out what the graph might be about? (e.g., *It might be about different colours of T-shirts or about numbers on a baseball team's jerseys.*)

▸ Suppose that each T-shirt represents 1 student's choice of colour. How would you label the categories on the left? (e.g., *red, green, orange, blue*)

▸ Why might it be useful to compare the number of T-shirts in each category? (e.g., *You might want to know what the favourite colour of T-shirt is.*)

▸ Is it necessary to include a scale? (e.g., *No, you can simply count the symbols to get the number in a row.* Or, *yes, you may not know for sure what the T-shirts represent—number of shirts or number of people.*)

Using the Open-Ended Intervention   (Student Resource pages 224–225)

Read through the tasks on the student pages together. Provide grid paper (BLMs 6, 7, 36), straightedges, and stickers or stamps to make their pictographs. Allow students time to work, ideally in pairs.

Observe how students
- relate data to the graph displaying it
- deal with data when 0 is one of the categories
- make reasonable conclusions about what data might represent
- visualize how graphs will look before creating them
- create bar graphs and pictographs
- create and respond to questions about graphs

Consolidating and Reflecting

Ensure understanding by asking questions based on students' work:

▸ How did you decide which data matched the graph on the page? (e.g., *There were 5 categories and one was 0.*)

▸ Is there a bar missing? (*No, there is a place for a bar; that category is 0.*)

▸ How can you tell how many bars there will be in a bar graph by looking at the data? (e.g., *The number of bars is the same as the number of categories.*)

▸ How does a graph help you compare data? (e.g., *You can see which is most or least right away by just looking at it.*)

▸ Why is it important that all the bars start at the same place? (e.g., *to make comparisons easier*)

▸ How are pictographs like bar graphs? How are they different? (e.g., *They both have one symbol for each square. Pictographs are a little harder to draw but are more interesting to look at.*)

Guided Intervention

Before Using the Guided Intervention

Display the T-shirt pictograph (BLM 38).

▸ How does the T-shirt symbol help you figure out what the graph might be about? (e.g., *It might be about different colours of T-Shirts or about numbers on a baseball team's jerseys.*)

▸ What title would you use? (e.g., *Favourite Colours for Our Club's T-Shirt*)

▸ Suppose that each T-shirt represents 1 student's choice of colour. How would you label the categories on the left? (e.g., *red, green, orange, blue*)

▸ Why might it be useful to count the number of T-shirts in each category? (e.g., *to find out the number of people who prefer each colour*)

Using the Guided Intervention   (Student Resource pages 226–229)

Together read through the instructional section of the student pages. Guide students as they create a pictograph and a bar graph. They can use graphing grids (BLMs 6, 7, 36) and straightedges to make these graphs. Ask questions to help students interpret the graph.

Then have them work through the **Try These** questions in pairs or individually. Students may prefer to use stickers or stamps to make their pictographs.

Observe whether students can
- interpret a pictograph (Questions 1, 3)
- make a pictograph using an appropriate symbol (Questions 2, 3)
- make a bar graph (Questions 5, 6)
- can interpret a bar graph (Question 6).

Consolidating and Reflecting

Ensure understanding by asking questions based on students' work:

▸ Is there always more than one way to display your data? (e.g., *Yes, I think you can always make a pictograph and a bar graph for the same set of data.*)

▸ How can the graph you made in Question 3 be used? (e.g., *The favourite breakfast items can be used to plan a meal.*)

▸ You made a vertical bar graph. What would it have looked like if it had been horizontal? (e.g., *The data are the same, but the graph is just turned on its side.*)

▸ Why is a graph a good way to show data? (e.g., *It's easy to compare.*)

▸ How are pictographs like bar graphs? How are they different? (e.g., *They both have one symbol for each square. Pictographs are a little harder to draw but are more interesting to look at.*)

▸ What kinds of questions would you ask about almost any pictograph or bar graph? (e.g., *how much more or less one category is than another*)

You will need

- T-Shirts (BLM 38)
- coloured pencils
- rulers or other straightedges
- identical stickers or rubber stamps (optional)
- grid paper (optional) (BLMs 6, 7)
- Graphing Grid (BLM 36)
- Student Resource pages 226–229

Concrete and Picture Graphs

You will need

- a variety of objects for making concrete graphs (e.g., pattern blocks, buttons, square tiles, linking cubes, paper clips)
- same-sized sticky notes or small cards
- graphing mats (drawn on large chart paper, or use BLM 35)
- Student Resource pages 230–231

Open-Ended Intervention

Before Using the Open-Ended Intervention

Use a graphing mat (BLM 35) or make one using a large sheet of chart paper. Create a concrete graph by placing 3 different types of pattern blocks on the mat.

▶ Is it easy to tell which kind of block we have the most of? Why? (e.g., *yes, because they are lined up and the longest line shows the most blocks*)

▶ Why is it important to line up the blocks so they match? (e.g., *You want to be able to compare the different lines of blocks to each other.*)

▶ Why might it be useful to compare the number of blocks in 2 or more categories? (e.g., *You may want to know which category has the most or the least number of blocks.*)

Using the Open-Ended Intervention (Student Resource pages 230–231)

Read through the tasks on the student pages together. Provide graphing mats and a variety of objects that students can use to make concrete graphs. Also provide sticky notes or small cards that they can use to draw on. Allow students time to work, ideally in pairs.

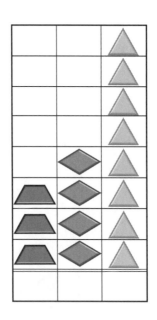

Observe how students

- create concrete graphs using the actual objects or objects that represent the data
- relate data to the graph displaying it
- recognize the need for matching in concrete graphs and picture graphs
- create and respond to questions about graphs
- recognize how to relate a picture graph to a concrete graph

Consolidating and Reflecting

Ensure understanding by asking questions based on students' work:

▶ The lineups of buttons were vertical. How would the graph be the same or different if the lineups had been horizontal? (e.g., *the same number of categories and the same number of objects but the graphing mat is turned sideways*)

▶ How can you tell how many lineups should be in your picture graph or concrete graph by looking at the data? (e.g., *one for each category that is not 0*)

▶ How can you quickly look at the graph to tell which category is greater? (e.g., *the longest line*)

▶ How does a graph help you compare data? (e.g., *You can see which is most or least right away by just looking.*)

▶ What kinds of questions did you ask and answer about your graphs? (e.g., *How many more are there of one thing than another? How many are there altogether?*)

▶ How are picture graphs like concrete graphs? How are they different? (e.g., *There is one picture for each object. In a picture graph, you don't have to use real things.*)

Concrete and Picture Graphs

Guided Intervention

Before Using the Guided Intervention

Make a concrete graph with 3 categories using any objects on the graphing mat (BLM 35) or a larger graphing mat. (See graph in margin.) Ask:

▶ Is it easy to tell which kind of block we have the most of? Why is it easy?
(e.g., *yes, because they are lined up, and the longest line shows the most blocks*)

▶ Why is it important to line up the blocks so they match?
(e.g., *It helps you to compare the different lines of blocks without counting.*)

Using the Guided Intervention (Student Resource pages 232–235)

Provide graphing mats and a variety of objects that students can use to make concrete graphs. Also provide sticky notes or small cards to draw or write on. Guide students as they create concrete graphs and picture graphs to display the data on the student pages. If you have photographs of the students, these could be used to make the picture graphs.

Have students work through the **Try These** questions in pairs or individually.

Observe whether students can
• interpret concrete graphs (Questions 1, 2)
• make a concrete graph using objects as models (Question 2)
• interpret picture graphs (Question 3)
• make a picture graph (Question 4)

Consolidating and Reflecting

Ensure understanding by asking students the following questions:

▶ How do concrete objects like linking cubes help you compare groups?
(e.g., *You can link them together and see easily which group is longest or shortest, and compare how many more or less.*)

▶ How are picture graphs like concrete graphs? How are they different?
(e.g., *There is one picture for each object. In a picture graph, you don't have to use real things.*)

▶ Why is a graph a good way to show data? (e.g., *It's easy to compare.*)

▶ Why do you think we can consider the graph in Question 2 a picture graph, even though it uses words instead of pictures? (e.g., *Each sticky note represents the person who made that choice. Each person probably wrote his or her own name on the sticky note and then placed it on the graphing mat.*)

▶ What kinds of questions could you ask about almost any picture graph or concrete graph? (e.g., *How much more or less is one category than another? Or, how many are there altogether?*)

You will need

• a variety of objects for making concrete graphs (e.g., pattern blocks, buttons, square tiles, linking cubes, paper clips)
• same-sized sticky notes or small cards to draw or write on
• graphing mats (drawn on large chart paper, or use BLM 35)
• Student Resource pages 232–235

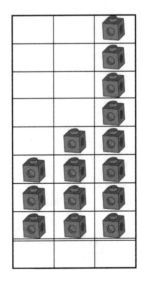

BLM 1: Place Value Chart (Hundreds, Tens, Ones)

Ones	Tens	Hundreds

Copyright © 2011 by Nelson Education Ltd.   *Leaps and Bounds*

Name:_____ Date:_____

BLM 2: Place Value Chart (Tens, Ones)

Ones	
Tens	

Leaps and Bounds   Copyright © 2011 by Nelson Education Ltd.

BLM 3: 10-Frames

Name:_____   Date:_____

BLM 4: Number Lines

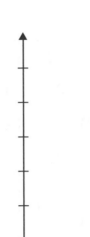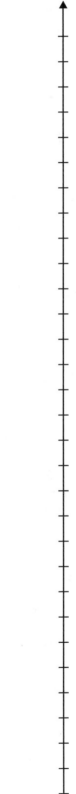

Leaps and Bounds   Copyright © 2011 by Nelson Education Ltd.

BLM 5: 100 Charts

1	2	3	4	5	6	7	8	9	10
11	12	13	14	15	16	17	18	19	20
21	22	23	24	25	26	27	28	29	30
31	32	33	34	35	36	37	38	39	40
41	42	43	44	45	46	47	48	49	50
51	52	53	54	55	56	57	58	59	60
61	62	63	64	65	66	67	68	69	70
71	72	73	74	75	76	77	78	79	80
81	82	83	84	85	86	87	88	89	90
91	92	93	94	95	96	97	98	99	100

1	2	3	4	5	6	7	8	9	10
11	12	13	14	15	16	17	18	19	20
21	22	23	24	25	26	27	28	29	30
31	32	33	34	35	36	37	38	39	40
41	42	43	44	45	46	47	48	49	50
51	52	53	54	55	56	57	58	59	60
61	62	63	64	65	66	67	68	69	70
71	72	73	74	75	76	77	78	79	80
81	82	83	84	85	86	87	88	89	90
91	92	93	94	95	96	97	98	99	100

1	2	3	4	5	6	7	8	9	10
11	12	13	14	15	16	17	18	19	20
21	22	23	24	25	26	27	28	29	30
31	32	33	34	35	36	37	38	39	40
41	42	43	44	45	46	47	48	49	50
51	52	53	54	55	56	57	58	59	60
61	62	63	64	65	66	67	68	69	70
71	72	73	74	75	76	77	78	79	80
81	82	83	84	85	86	87	88	89	90
91	92	93	94	95	96	97	98	99	100

1	2	3	4	5	6	7	8	9	10
11	12	13	14	15	16	17	18	19	20
21	22	23	24	25	26	27	28	29	30
31	32	33	34	35	36	37	38	39	40
41	42	43	44	45	46	47	48	49	50
51	52	53	54	55	56	57	58	59	60
61	62	63	64	65	66	67	68	69	70
71	72	73	74	75	76	77	78	79	80
81	82	83	84	85	86	87	88	89	90
91	92	93	94	95	96	97	98	99	100

Copyright © 2011 by Nelson Education Ltd. *Leaps and Bounds*

Name:_____   Date:_____

BLM 6: 1 cm Square Grid Paper

Leaps and Bounds   Copyright © 2011 by Nelson Education Ltd.

Name:_____ Date:_____

BLM 7: 2 cm Square Grid Paper

Copyright © 2011 by Nelson Education Ltd.   *Leaps and Bounds*

Name:_____   Date:_____

BLM 8: Fraction Circles

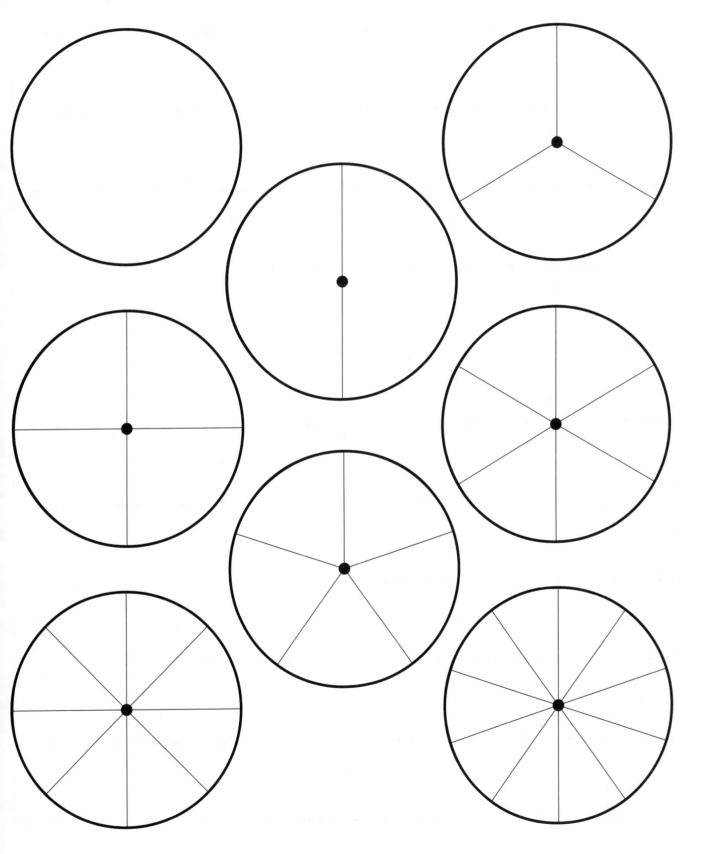

Leaps and Bounds
Copyright © 2011 by Nelson Education Ltd.

Name:_____ Date:_____

BLM 9: Fraction Rectangles

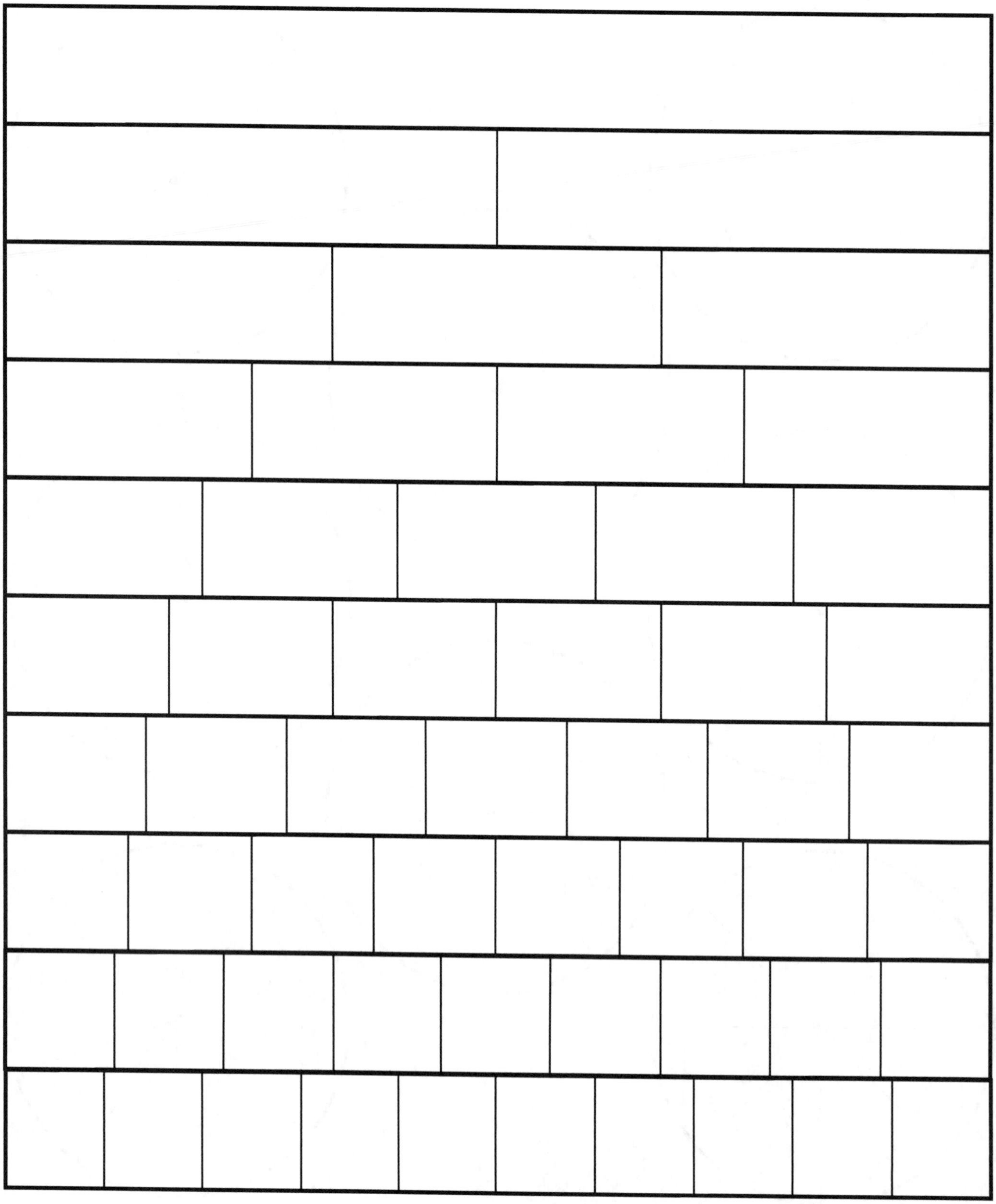

BLM 10: 3-D Shapes

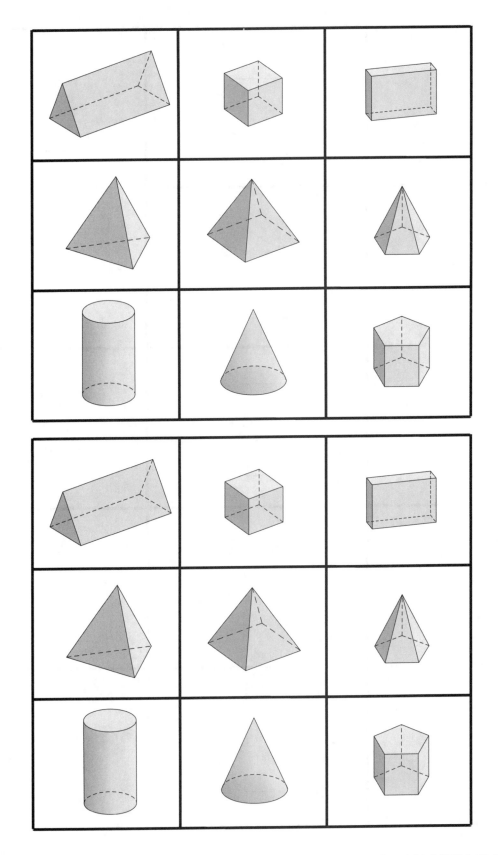

Leaps and Bounds Copyright © 2011 by Nelson Education Ltd.

BLM 11: Polygons

BLM 12: Tangrams

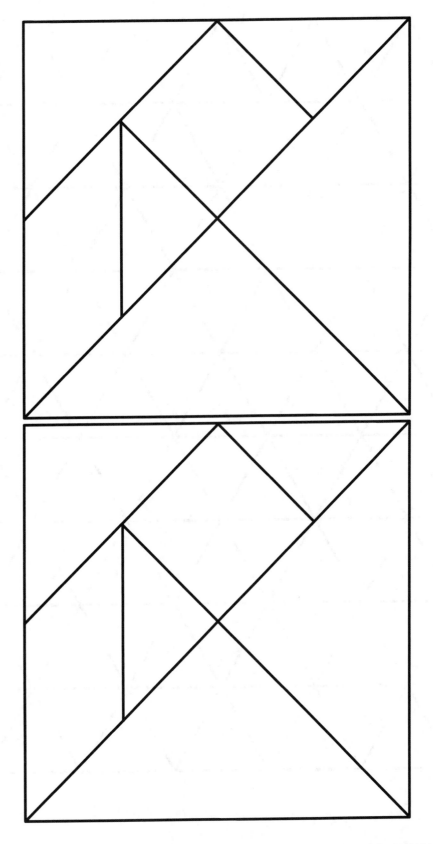

Leaps and Bounds

Copyright © 2011 by Nelson Education Ltd.

BLM 13: Pattern Blocks: Triangle/Grid

Copyright © 2011 by Nelson Education Ltd. *Leaps and Bounds*

BLM 14: Pattern Blocks: Square

Leaps and Bounds Copyright © 2011 by Nelson Education Ltd.

BLM 15: Pattern Blocks: Rhombus A

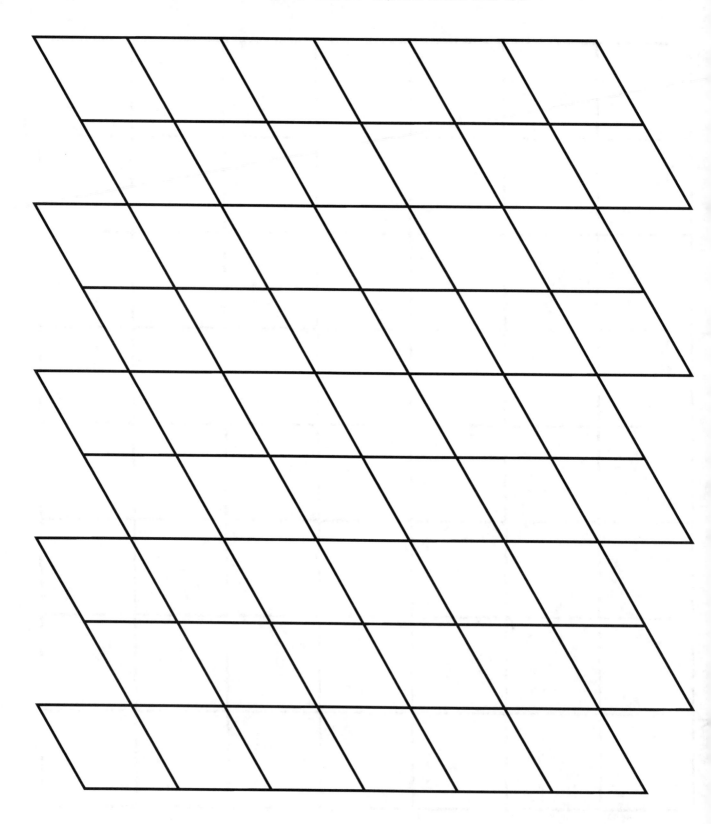

Copyright © 2011 by Nelson Education Ltd. *Leaps and Bounds*

BLM 16: Pattern Blocks: Rhombus B

Leaps and Bounds Copyright © 2011 by Nelson Education Ltd.

BLM 17: Pattern Blocks: Trapezoid

Copyright © 2011 by Nelson Education Ltd. *Leaps and Bounds*

BLM 18: Pattern Blocks: Hexagon

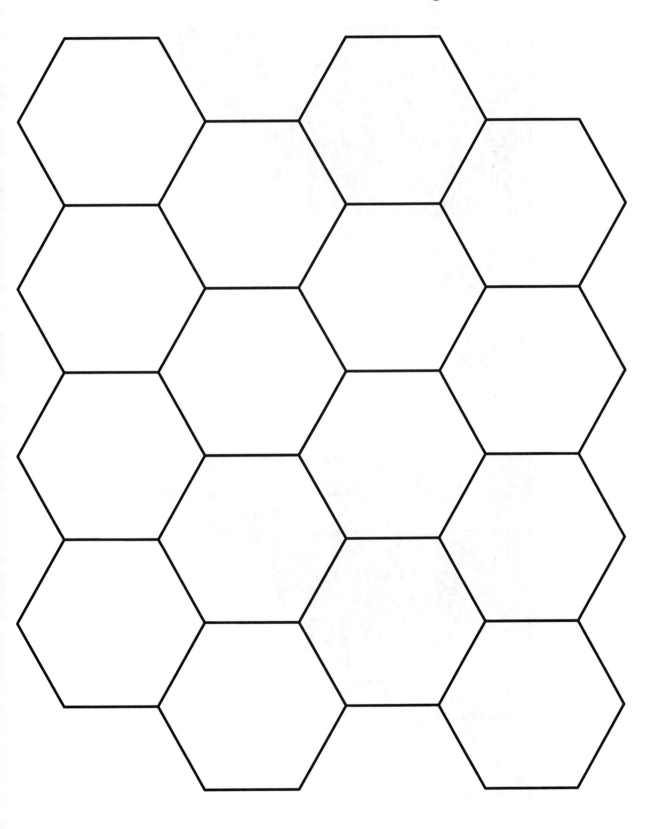

Leaps and Bounds Copyright © 2011 by Nelson Education Ltd.

BLM 19: Coloured Rods

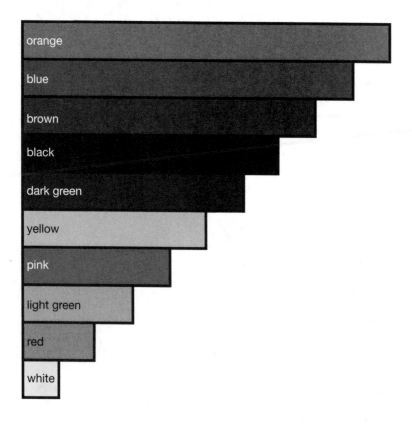

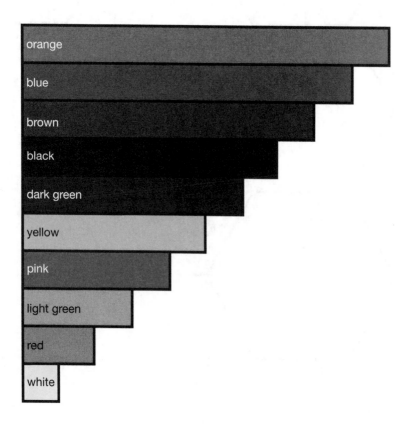

Copyright © 2011 by Nelson Education Ltd. *Leaps and Bounds*

Name:_____   Date:_____

BLM 20: Objects in Grams

Leaps and Bounds   Copyright © 2011 by Nelson Education Ltd.

Name:_____   Date:_____

BLM 21: Objects in Kilograms

Copyright © 2011 by Nelson Education Ltd.   *Leaps and Bounds*

Name:_____   Date:_____

BLM 22: Pizza Shapes

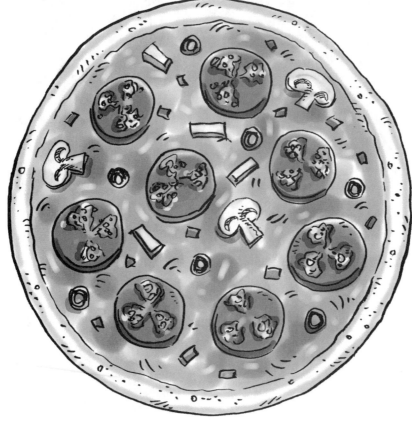

Leaps and Bounds   Copyright © 2011 by Nelson Education Ltd.

Name:_____ Date:_____

BLM 23: Wrapping Paper (Rectangle)

Copyright © 2011 by Nelson Education Ltd. *Leaps and Bounds*

Name:_____ Date:_____

BLM 24: Wrapping Paper (Hexagon)

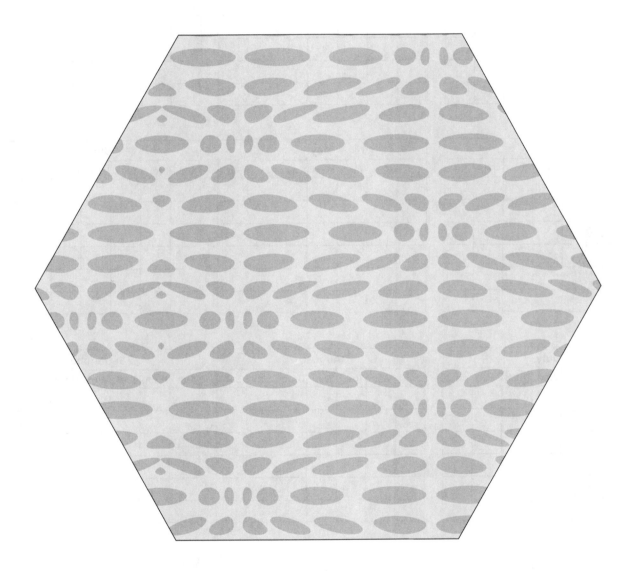

Leaps and Bounds   Copyright © 2011 by Nelson Education Ltd.

Name:_____ Date:_____

BLM 25: Calendar

			January			
Sun.	Mon.	Tues.	Wed.	Thurs.	Fri.	Sat.

			February			
Sun.	Mon.	Tues.	Wed.	Thurs.	Fri.	Sat.

			March			
Sun.	Mon.	Tues.	Wed.	Thurs.	Fri.	Sat.

			April			
Sun.	Mon.	Tues.	Wed.	Thurs.	Fri.	Sat.

			May			
Sun.	Mon.	Tues.	Wed.	Thurs.	Fri.	Sat.

			June			
Sun.	Mon.	Tues.	Wed.	Thurs.	Fri.	Sat.

			July			
Sun.	Mon.	Tues.	Wed.	Thurs.	Fri.	Sat.

			August			
Sun.	Mon.	Tues.	Wed.	Thurs.	Fri.	Sat.

			September			
Sun.	Mon.	Tues.	Wed.	Thurs.	Fri.	Sat.

			October			
Sun.	Mon.	Tues.	Wed.	Thurs.	Fri.	Sat.

			November			
Sun.	Mon.	Tues.	Wed.	Thurs.	Fri.	Sat.

			December			
Sun.	Mon.	Tues.	Wed.	Thurs.	Fri.	Sat.

Copyright © 2011 by Nelson Education Ltd.   *Leaps and Bounds*

BLM 26: Time Line

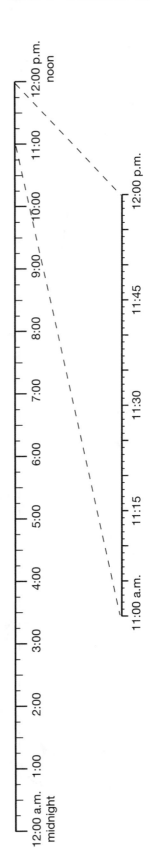

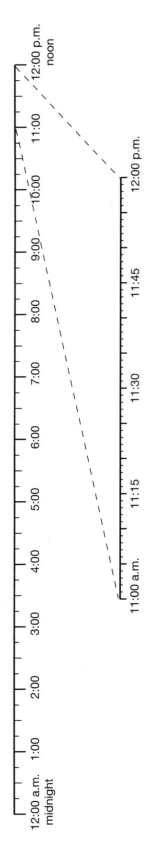

Name:_____ Date:_____

BLM 27: Venn Diagram

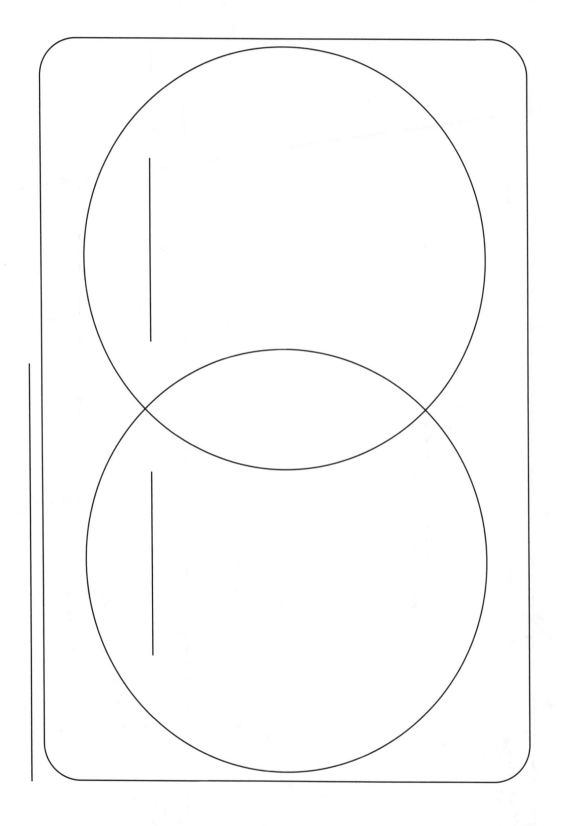

Copyright © 2011 by Nelson Education Ltd.   *Leaps and Bounds*

Name:_____   Date:_____

BLM 28: Sorting Mat

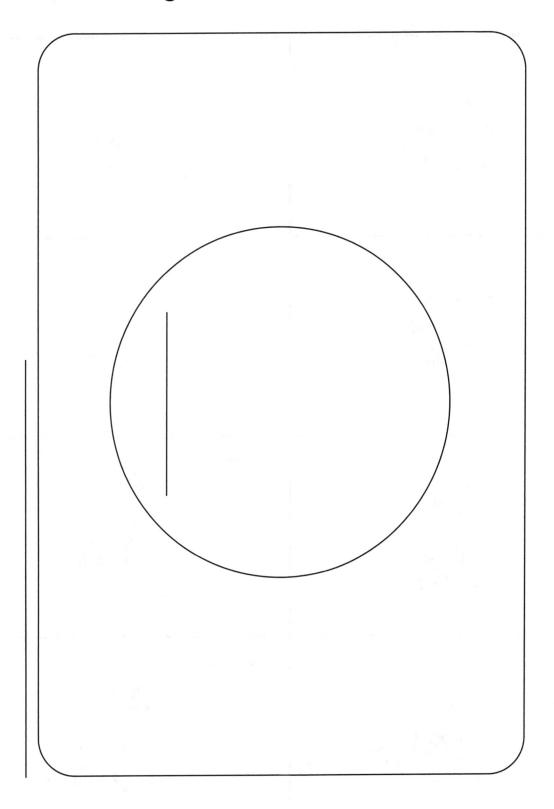

BLM 29: Pet Cards

goldfish	terrier
canary	budgie
hound	parrot
lizard	Siamese cat

BLM 30: Fish Cards

large striped angel fish **A**	small striped angel fish **B**	large spotted guppy **C**
small spotted guppy **D**	large striped guppy **E**	small striped guppy **F**
large striped goldfish **G**	small striped goldfish **H**	small spotted goldfish **I**
large spotted goldfish **J**	large spotted angel fish **K**	small plain angel fish **L**
small plain goldfish **M**	small spotted angel fish **N**	large plain guppy **O**

Leaps and Bounds Copyright © 2011 by Nelson Education Ltd.

BLM 31: Animal Cards

duck D

alligator A

lion L

fish F

crab C

elephant E

monkey M

parrot P

whale W

kangaroo K

Copyright © 2011 by Nelson Education Ltd. *Leaps and Bounds*

BLM 32: Flip Flop Cards

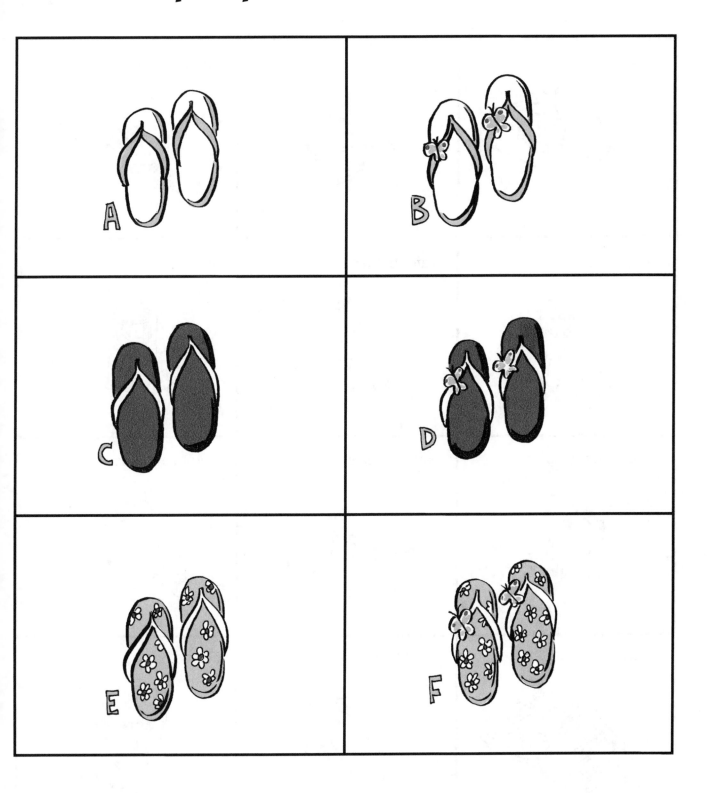

Leaps and Bounds Copyright © 2011 by Nelson Education Ltd.

BLM 33: Waste Cards

tissues T	magazines M	flyers F
apple cores A	water bottles W	drink cans D
toilet paper rolls R	banana peels P	styrofoam cups S
newspapers N	yogurt containers Y	plastic bags B

Copyright © 2011 by Nelson Education Ltd. *Leaps and Bounds*

BLM 34: Food Cards

pork	juice
grapes	hamburger
milk	cheese
ice cream	banana
apple	watermelon

Leaps and Bounds Copyright © 2011 by Nelson Education Ltd.

Name:_____   Date:_____

BLM 35: Graphing Mat

_____

Copyright © 2011 by Nelson Education Ltd.   _Leaps and Bounds_

Name:_____   Date:_____

BLM 36: Graphing Grid

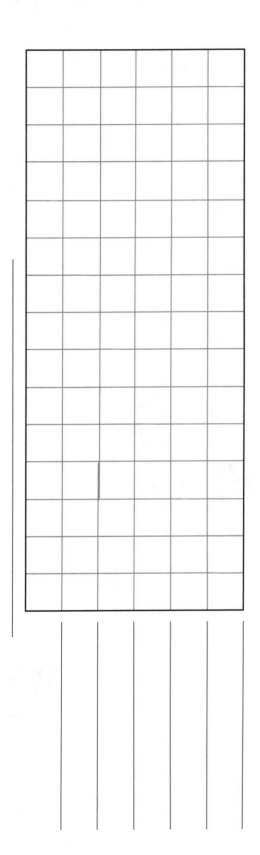

BLM 37: Soccer

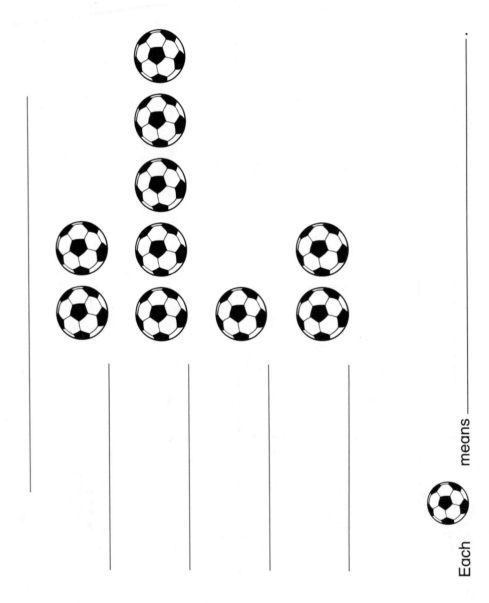

Each ⚽ means _____ .

BLM 38: T-Shirts

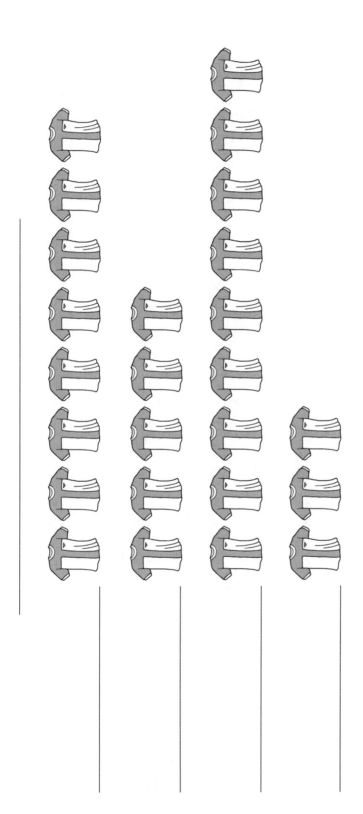

Leaps and Bounds 3/4

Copyright © 2011 by Nelson Education Ltd.

Curriculum Connections   www.nelson.com/leapsandbounds

Student Resource Solutions   www.nelson.com/leapsandbounds
User name: leapsandbounds34
Password: SRsolutions34